TEACHER'S GUIDE

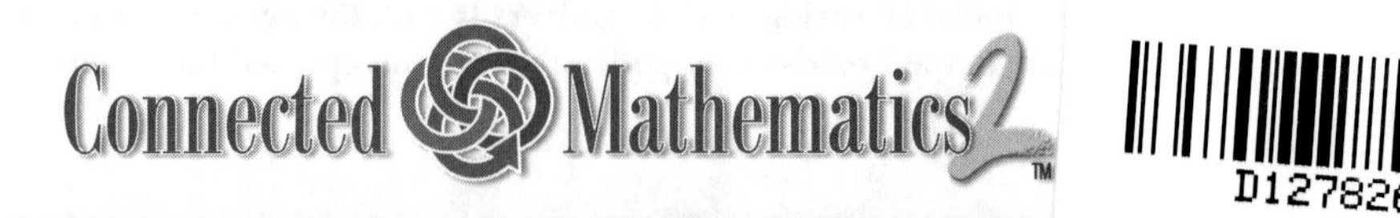

Say It With Symbols

Making Sense of Symbols

Glenda Lappan
James T. Fey
William M. Fitzgerald
Susan N. Friel
Elizabeth Difanis Phillips

Boston, Massachusetts · Glenview, Illinois · Shoreview, Minnesota · Upper Saddle River, New Jersey

Connected Mathematics™ was developed at Michigan State University with financial support from the Michigan State University Office of the Provost, Computing and Technology, and the College of Natural Science.

This material is based upon work supported by the National Science Foundation under Grant No. MDR 9150217 and Grant No. ESI 9986372. Opinions expressed are those of the authors and not necessarily those of the Foundation.

The Michigan State University authors and administration have agreed that all MSU royalties arising from this publication will be devoted to purposes supported by the Department of Mathematics and the MSU Mathematics Enrichment Fund.

Acknowledgments appear on page 146, which constitutes an extension of this copyright page. **Acknowledgments** for the student pages appear on student page 97, which constitutes an extension of this copyright page.

13-digit ISBN 978-0-13-366207-8
10-digit ISBN 0-13-366207-1
1 2 3 4 5 6 7 8 9 10 11 10 09 08

Authors of Connected Mathematics

(from left to right) Glenda Lappan, Betty Phillips, Susan Friel, Bill Fitzgerald, Jim Fey

Glenda Lappan is a University Distinguished Professor in the Department of Mathematics at Michigan State University. Her research and development interests are in the connected areas of students' learning of mathematics and mathematics teachers' professional growth and change related to the development and enactment of K–12 curriculum materials.

James T. Fey is a Professor of Curriculum and Instruction and Mathematics at the University of Maryland. His consistent professional interest has been development and research focused on curriculum materials that engage middle and high school students in problem-based collaborative investigations of mathematical ideas and their applications.

William M. Fitzgerald (*Deceased*) was a Professor in the Department of Mathematics at Michigan State University. His early research was on the use of concrete materials in supporting student learning and led to the development of teaching materials for laboratory environments. Later he helped develop a teaching model to support student experimentation with mathematics.

Susan N. Friel is a Professor of Mathematics Education in the School of Education at the University of North Carolina at Chapel Hill. Her research interests focus on statistics education for middle-grade students and, more broadly, on teachers' professional development and growth in teaching mathematics K–8.

Elizabeth Difanis Phillips is a Senior Academic Specialist in the Mathematics Department of Michigan State University. She is interested in teaching and learning mathematics for both teachers and students. These interests have led to curriculum and professional development projects at the middle school and high school levels, as well as projects related to the teaching and learning of algebra across the grades.

CMP2 Development Staff

Teacher Collaborator in Residence
Yvonne Grant
Michigan State University

Administrative Assistant
Judith Martus Miller
Michigan State University

Production and Field Site Manager
Lisa Keller
Michigan State University

Technical and Editorial Support
Brin Keller, Peter Lappan, Jim Laser, Michael Masterson, Stacey Miceli

Assessment Team
June Bailey and **Debra Sobko** (Apollo Middle School, Rochester, New York), **George Bright** (University of North Carolina, Greensboro), **Gwen Ranzau Campbell** (Sunrise Park Middle School, White Bear Lake, Minnesota), **Holly DeRosia, Kathy Dole,** and **Teri Keusch** (Portland Middle School, Portland, Michigan), **Mary Beth Schmitt** (Traverse City East Junior High School, Traverse City, Michigan), **Genni Steele** (Central Middle School, White Bear Lake, Minnesota), **Jacqueline Stewart** (Okemos, Michigan), **Elizabeth Tye** (Magnolia Junior High School, Magnolia, Arkansas)

Development Assistants
At Lansing Community College *Undergraduate Assistant:* **James Brinegar**

At Michigan State University *Graduate Assistants:* **Dawn Berk, Emily Bouck, Bulent Buyukbozkirli, Kuo-Liang Chang, Christopher Danielson, Srinivasa Dharmavaram, Deb Johanning, Wesley Kretzschmar, Kelly Rivette, Sarah Sword, Tat Ming Sze, Marie Turini, Jeffrey Wanko;** *Undergraduate Assistants:* **Daniel Briggs, Jeffrey Chapin, Jade Corsé, Elisha Hardy, Alisha Harold, Elizabeth Keusch, Julia Letoutchaia, Karen Loeffler, Brian Oliver, Carl Oliver, Evonne Pedawi, Lauren Rebrovich**

At the University of Maryland *Graduate Assistants:* **Kim Harris Bethea, Kara Karch**

At the University of North Carolina (Chapel Hill) *Graduate Assistants:* **Mark Ellis, Trista Stearns;** *Undergraduate Assistant:* **Daniel Smith**

Advisory Board for CMP2

Thomas Banchoff
Professor of Mathematics
Brown University
Providence, Rhode Island

Anne Bartel
Mathematics Coordinator
Minneapolis Public Schools
Minneapolis, Minnesota

Hyman Bass
Professor of Mathematics
University of Michigan
Ann Arbor, Michigan

Joan Ferrini-Mundy
Associate Dean of the College of Natural Science; Professor
Michigan State University
East Lansing, Michigan

James Hiebert
Professor
University of Delaware
Newark, Delaware

Susan Hudson Hull
Charles A. Dana Center
University of Texas
Austin, Texas

Michele Luke
Mathematics Curriculum Coordinator
West Junior High
Minnetonka, Minnesota

Kay McClain
Assistant Professor of Mathematics Education
Vanderbilt University
Nashville, Tennessee

Edward Silver
Professor; Chair of Educational Studies
University of Michigan
Ann Arbor, Michigan

Judith Sowder
Professor Emerita
San Diego State University
San Diego, California

Lisa Usher
Mathematics Resource Teacher
California Academy of Mathematics and Science
San Pedro, California

Field Test Sites for CMP2

During the development of the revised edition of *Connected Mathematics* (CMP2), more than 100 classroom teachers have field-tested materials at 49 school sites in 12 states and the District of Columbia. This classroom testing occurred over three academic years (2001 through 2004), allowing careful study of the effectiveness of each of the 24 units that comprise the program. A special thanks to the students and teachers at these pilot schools.

Arkansas

Magnolia Public Schools
Kittena Bell*, Judith Trowell*; *Central Elementary School:* Maxine Broom, Betty Eddy, Tiffany Fallin, Bonnie Flurry, Carolyn Monk, Elizabeth Tye; *Magnolia Junior High School:* Monique Bryan, Ginger Cook, David Graham, Shelby Lamkin

Colorado

Boulder Public Schools
Nevin Platt Middle School: Judith Koenig

St. Vrain Valley School District, Longmont
Westview Middle School: Colleen Beyer, Kitty Canupp, Ellie Decker*, Peggy McCarthy, Tanya deNobrega, Cindy Payne, Ericka Pilon, Andrew Roberts

District of Columbia

Capitol Hill Day School: Ann Lawrence

Georgia

University of Georgia, Athens
Brad Findell

Madison Public Schools
Morgan County Middle School: Renee Burgdorf, Lynn Harris, Nancy Kurtz, Carolyn Stewart

Maine

Falmouth Public Schools
Falmouth Middle School: Donna Erikson, Joyce Hebert, Paula Hodgkins, Rick Hogan, David Legere, Cynthia Martin, Barbara Stiles, Shawn Towle*

Michigan

Portland Public Schools
Portland Middle School: Mark Braun, Holly DeRosia, Kathy Dole*, Angie Foote, Teri Keusch, Tammi Wardwell

Traverse City Area Public Schools
Bertha Vos Elementary: Kristin Sak; *Central Grade School:* Michelle Clark; Jody Meyers; *Eastern Elementary:* Karrie Tufts; *Interlochen Elementary:* Mary McGee-Cullen; *Long Lake Elementary:* Julie Faulkner*, Charlie Maxbauer, Katherine Sleder; *Norris Elementary:* Hope Slanaker; *Oak Park Elementary:* Jessica Steed; *Traverse Heights Elementary:* Jennifer Wolfert; *Westwoods Elementary:* Nancy Conn; *Old Mission Peninsula School:* Deb Larimer; *Traverse City East Junior High:* Ivanka Berkshire, Ruthanne Kladder, Jan Palkowski, Jane Peterson, Mary Beth Schmitt; *Traverse City West Junior High:* Dan Fouch*, Ray Fouch

Sturgis Public Schools
Sturgis Middle School: Ellen Eisele

Minnesota

Burnsville School District 191
Hidden Valley Elementary: Stephanie Cin, Jane McDevitt

Hopkins School District 270
Alice Smith Elementary: Sandra Cowing, Kathleen Gustafson, Martha Mason, Scott Stillman; *Eisenhower Elementary:* Chad Bellig, Patrick Berger, Nancy Glades, Kye Johnson, Shane Wasserman, Victoria Wilson; *Gatewood Elementary:* Sarah Ham, Julie Kloos, Janine Pung, Larry Wade; *Glen Lake Elementary:* Jacqueline Cramer, Kathy Hering, Cecelia Morris, Robb Trenda; *Katherine Curren Elementary:* Diane Bancroft, Sue DeWit, John Wilson; *L. H. Tanglen Elementary:* Kevin Athmann, Lisa Becker, Mary LaBelle, Kathy Rezac, Roberta Severson; *Meadowbrook Elementary:* Jan Gauger, Hildy Shank, Jessica Zimmerman; *North Junior High:* Laurel Hahn, Kristin Lee, Jodi Markuson, Bruce Mestemacher, Laurel Miller, Bonnie Rinker, Jeannine Salzer, Sarah Shafer, Cam Stottler; *West Junior High:* Alicia Beebe, Kristie Earl, Nobu Fujii, Pam Georgetti, Susan Gilbert, Regina Nelson Johnson, Debra Lindstrom, Michele Luke*, Jon Sorensen

Minneapolis School District 1
Ann Sullivan K–8 School: Bronwyn Collins; Anne Bartel* (Curriculum and Instruction Office)

Wayzata School District 284
Central Middle School: Sarajane Myers, Dan Nielsen, Tanya Ravnholdt

White Bear Lake School District 624
Central Middle School: Amy Jorgenson, Michelle Reich, Brenda Sammon

New York

New York City Public Schools
IS 89: Yelena Aynbinder, Chi-Man Ng, Nina Rapaport, Joel Spengler, Phyllis Tam*, Brent Wyso; *Wagner Middle School:* Jason Appel, Intissar Fernandez, Yee Gee Get, Richard Goldstein, Irving Marcus, Sue Norton, Bernadita Owens, Jennifer Rehn*, Kevin Yuhas

* indicates a Field Test Site Coordinator

Ohio

Talawanda School District, Oxford
Talawanda Middle School: Teresa Abrams, Larry Brock, Heather Brosey, Julie Churchman, Monna Even, Karen Fitch, Bob George, Amanda Klee, Pat Meade, Sandy Montgomery, Barbara Sherman, Lauren Steidl

Miami University
Jeffrey Wanko*

Springfield Public Schools
Rockway School: Jim Mamer

Pennsylvania

Pittsburgh Public Schools
Kenneth Labuskes, Marianne O'Connor, Mary Lynn Raith*; *Arthur J. Rooney Middle School:* David Hairston, Stamatina Mousetis, Alfredo Zangaro; *Frick International Studies Academy:* Suzanne Berry, Janet Falkowski, Constance Finseth, Romika Hodge, Frank Machi; *Reizenstein Middle School:* Jeff Baldwin, James Brautigam, Lorena Burnett, Glen Cobbett, Michael Jordan, Margaret Lazur, Tamar McPherson, Melissa Munnell, Holly Neely, Ingrid Reed, Dennis Reft

Texas

Austin Independent School District
Bedichek Middle School: Lisa Brown, Jennifer Glasscock, Vicki Massey

El Paso Independent School District
Cordova Middle School: Armando Aguirre, Anneliesa Durkes, Sylvia Guzman, Pat Holguin*, William Holguin, Nancy Nava, Laura Orozco, Michelle Peña, Roberta Rosen, Patsy Smith, Jeremy Wolf

Plano Independent School District
Patt Henry, James Wohlgehagen*; *Frankford Middle School:* Mandy Baker, Cheryl Butsch, Amy Dudley, Betsy Eshelman, Janet Greene, Cort Haynes, Kathy Letchworth, Kay Marshall, Kelly McCants, Amy Reck, Judy Scott, Syndy Snyder, Lisa Wang; *Wilson Middle School:* Darcie Bane, Amanda Bedenko, Whitney Evans, Tonelli Hatley, Sarah (Becky) Higgs, Kelly Johnston, Rebecca McElligott, Kay Neuse, Cheri Slocum, Kelli Straight

Washington

Evergreen School District
Shahala Middle School: Nicole Abrahamsen, Terry Coon*, Carey Doyle, Sheryl Drechsler, George Gemma, Gina Helland, Amy Hilario, Darla Lidyard, Sean McCarthy, Tilly Meyer, Willow Nuewelt, Todd Parsons, Brian Pederson, Stan Posey, Shawn Scott, Craig Sjoberg, Lynette Sundstrom, Charles Switzer, Luke Youngblood

Wisconsin

Beaver Dam Unified School District
Beaver Dam Middle School: Jim Braemer, Jeanne Frick, Jessica Greatens, Barbara Link, Dennis McCormick, Karen Michels, Nancy Nichols*, Nancy Palm, Shelly Stelsel, Susan Wiggins

* indicates a Field Test Site Coordinator

Reviews of CMP to Guide Development of CMP2

Before writing for CMP2 began or field tests were conducted, the first edition of *Connected Mathematics* was submitted to the mathematics faculties of school districts from many parts of the country and to 80 individual reviewers for extensive comments.

School District Survey Reviews of CMP

Arizona
Madison School District #38 (Phoenix)

Arkansas
Cabot School District,
Little Rock School District,
Magnolia School District

California
Los Angeles Unified School District

Colorado
St. Vrain Valley School District (Longmont)

Florida
Leon County Schools (Tallahassee)

Illinois
School District #21 (Wheeling)

Indiana
Joseph L. Block Junior High (East Chicago)

Kentucky
Fayette County Public Schools (Lexington)

Maine
Selection of Schools

Massachusetts
Selection of Schools

Michigan
Sparta Area Schools

Minnesota
Hopkins School District

Texas
Austin Independent School District,
The El Paso Collaborative for Academic Excellence,
Plano Independent School District

Wisconsin
Platteville Middle School

Individual Reviewers of CMP

Arkansas
Deborah Cramer; Robby Frizzell *(Taylor)*; Lowell Lynde *(University of Arkansas, Monticello)*; Leigh Manzer *(Norfork)*; Lynne Roberts *(Emerson High School, Emerson)*; Tony Timms *(Cabot Public Schools)*; Judith Trowell *(Arkansas Department of Higher Education)*

California
José Alcantar *(Gilroy)*; Eugenie Belcher *(Gilroy)*; Marian Pasternack *(Lowman M. S. T. Center, North Hollywood)*; Susana Pezoa *(San Jose)*; Todd Rabusin *(Hollister)*; Margaret Siegfried *(Ocala Middle School, San Jose)*; Polly Underwood *(Ocala Middle School, San Jose)*

Colorado
Janeane Golliher *(St. Vrain Valley School District, Longmont)*; Judith Koenig *(Nevin Platt Middle School, Boulder)*

Florida
Paige Loggins *(Swift Creek Middle School, Tallahassee)*

Illinois
Jan Robinson *(School District #21, Wheeling)*

Indiana
Frances Jackson *(Joseph L. Block Junior High, East Chicago)*

Kentucky
Natalee Feese *(Fayette County Public Schools, Lexington)*

Maine
Betsy Berry *(Maine Math & Science Alliance, Augusta)*

Maryland
Joseph Gagnon *(University of Maryland, College Park)*; Paula Maccini *(University of Maryland, College Park)*

Massachusetts
George Cobb *(Mt. Holyoke College, South Hadley)*; Cliff Kanold *(University of Massachusetts, Amherst)*

Michigan
Mary Bouck *(Farwell Area Schools)*; Carol Dorer *(Slauson Middle School, Ann Arbor)*; Carrie Heaney *(Forsythe Middle School, Ann Arbor)*; Ellen Hopkins *(Clague Middle School, Ann Arbor)*; Teri Keusch *(Portland Middle School, Portland)*; Valerie Mills *(Oakland Schools, Waterford)*; Mary Beth Schmitt *(Traverse City East Junior High, Traverse City)*; Jack Smith *(Michigan State University, East Lansing)*; Rebecca Spencer *(Sparta Middle School, Sparta)*; Ann Marie Nicoll Turner *(Tappan Middle School, Ann Arbor)*; Scott Turner *(Scarlett Middle School, Ann Arbor)*

Minnesota
Margarita Alvarez *(Olson Middle School, Minneapolis)*; Jane Amundson *(Nicollet Junior High, Burnsville)*; Anne Bartel *(Minneapolis Public Schools)*; Gwen Ranzau Campbell *(Sunrise Park Middle School, White Bear Lake)*; Stephanie Cin *(Hidden Valley Elementary, Burnsville)*; Joan Garfield *(University of Minnesota, Minneapolis)*; Gretchen Hall *(Richfield Middle School, Richfield)*; Jennifer Larson *(Olson Middle School, Minneapolis)*; Michele Luke *(West Junior High, Minnetonka)*; Jeni Meyer *(Richfield Junior High, Richfield)*; Judy Pfingsten *(Inver Grove Heights Middle School, Inver Grove Heights)*; Sarah Shafer *(North Junior High, Minnetonka)*; Genni Steele *(Central Middle School, White Bear Lake)*; Victoria Wilson *(Eisenhower Elementary, Hopkins)*; Paul Zorn *(St. Olaf College, Northfield)*

New York
Debra Altenau-Bartolino *(Greenwich Village Middle School, New York)*; Doug Clements *(University of Buffalo)*; Francis Curcio *(New York University, New York)*; Christine Dorosh *(Clinton School for Writers, Brooklyn)*; Jennifer Rehn *(East Side Middle School, New York)*; Phyllis Tam *(IS 89 Lab School, New York)*; Marie Turini *(Louis Armstrong Middle School, New York)*; Lucy West *(Community School District 2, New York)*; Monica Witt *(Simon Baruch Intermediate School 104, New York)*

Pennsylvania
Robert Aglietti *(Pittsburgh)*; Sharon Mihalich *(Freeport)*; Jennifer Plumb *(South Hills Middle School, Pittsburgh)*; Mary Lynn Raith *(Pittsburgh Public Schools)*

Texas
Michelle Bittick *(Austin Independent School District)*; Margaret Cregg *(Plano Independent School District)*; Sheila Cunningham *(Klein Independent School District)*; Judy Hill *(Austin Independent School District)*; Patricia Holguin *(El Paso Independent School District)*; Bonnie McNemar *(Arlington)*; Kay Neuse *(Plano Independent School District)*; Joyce Polanco *(Austin Independent School District)*; Marge Ramirez *(University of Texas at El Paso)*; Pat Rossman *(Baker Campus, Austin)*; Cindy Schimek *(Houston)*; Cynthia Schneider *(Charles A. Dana Center, University of Texas at Austin)*; Uri Treisman *(Charles A. Dana Center, University of Texas at Austin)*; Jacqueline Weilmuenster *(Grapevine-Colleyville Independent School District)*; LuAnn Weynand *(San Antonio)*; Carmen Whitman *(Austin Independent School District)*; James Wohlgehagen *(Plano Independent School District)*

Washington
Ramesh Gangolli *(University of Washington, Seattle)*

Wisconsin
Susan Lamon *(Marquette University, Hales Corner)*; Steve Reinhart *(retired, Chippewa Falls Middle School, Eau Claire)*

Say It With Symbols

Contents

The Student Edition pages for the Unit Opener follow page 18.

Unit Introduction

Say It With Symbols

Making Sense of Symbols

Goals of the Unit

- Model situations with symbolic statements
- Write equivalent expressions
- Determine if different symbolic expressions are mathematically equivalent
- Interpret the information equivalent expressions represent in a given context
- Determine which equivalent expression to use to answer particular questions
- Solve linear equations involving parentheses
- Solve quadratic equations by factoring
- Use equations to make predictions and decisions
- Analyze equations to determine the patterns of change in the tables and graphs that the equation represents
- Understand how and when to use symbols to display relationships, generalizations, and proofs

Developing Students' Mathematical Habits

As students work on the problems in this unit, ask them questions about problem situations that involve symbolic expressions and equations.

- *What expression or equation represents the pattern or relationship in a context?*
- *What information do you get from an equivalent expression for a quantity?*
- *What information do you get by combining two or more expressions?*
- *How can you tell if two or more expressions are equivalent?*
- *What operations can transform a given equation or expression into an equivalent form that can be used to answer a question?*
- *What patterns of change do the equation or expression represent?*
- *How can symbolic reasoning help confirm a conjecture?*

Mathematics of the Unit

Overview

Algebra is the centerpiece of most standard secondary school mathematics curricula, and more and more schools are teaching a course called Algebra I in the eighth grade. Traditionally, the goal of algebra instruction has been the development of students' proficiency in working with symbolic expressions and equations, usually tasks that involve simplifying, factoring, expanding, evaluating, or solving. In addition to these traditional roles of symbols, students in *Connected Mathematics* learn to use symbolic expressions to represent and reason about relationships and to manipulate symbolic expressions into equivalent forms to access new information about a given context. Access to graphing calculators and computers and the organization of the curriculum around problems provide a natural focus on functions and their use in modeling patterns of quantitative change. In *Connected Mathematics*, there is more emphasis on multiple representations such as graphic, tabular, and symbolic representations.

The algebra strand in *Connected Mathematics* reflects this approach to algebraic instruction. Beginning in grade 6, students learn to examine multiple representations (equations, graphs, tables, diagrams, and verbal descriptions) to help them understand mathematical relationships and to represent them in a variety of ways. In the sixth grade, students develop formulas for the area and perimeter of two-dimensional shapes by looking at the relationship between the dimensions of a shape and its perimeter or area. They study geometric relationships such as the relationship between the sides and angles of two-dimensional shapes and numerical relationships such as finding a missing factor or addend in a number sentence.

In the seventh grade, students are introduced to the basic language, concepts, and representations of algebra in *Variables and Patterns*. They examine linear models in detail in *Moving Straight Ahead*.

In the eighth grade, *Thinking With Mathematical Models* continues the study of linear relationships, but shifts the focus to linear and non-linear models, in particular, inverse relationships. *Looking For Pythagoras* provides a geometric interpretation of the Pythagorean relationship and of parallel and perpendicular lines. Questions about variables, relationships, patterns of change, and representations raised in *Moving Straight Ahead* are applied to exponential relationships in *Growing, Growing, Growing* and quadratic relationships in *Frogs, Fleas, and Painted Cubes*.

Representing and reasoning about patterns of change has been the main focus up to this point in the development of algebra. Students have used tables, graphs, and symbols to represent relationships and to solve equations to find information or make predictions. The properties of real numbers such as the Commutative and Distributive properties were first introduced in *Accentuate the Negative* and then used again in *Moving Straight Ahead* and *Growing, Growing, Growing*. The Distributive Property was expanded in *Frogs, Fleas, and Painted Cubes* to include multiplication of two binomials.

In this unit, *Say It With Symbols*, the emphasis shifts to using the properties of numbers to look at equivalent expressions and the information each expression represents in a given context, and to interpret underlying patterns that a symbolic equation or statement represents. Students look critically at each part of an expression and how each part relates to the original expression. They examine the graph and table of an expression as well as the context the expression models. The properties of equality and numbers are used extensively in this unit as students write and interpret equivalent expressions, combine expressions to form new expressions, predict patterns of change represented by an equation or expression, and solve equations. Collectively, the algebra units and, in particular, this unit help to develop what we call "symbol sense."

Summary of Investigations

Investigation 1

Equivalent Expressions

Students have an opportunity to generate and justify, in their own ways, the equivalence of two or more symbolic expressions for the same situation. They are encouraged to think about problems in a variety of ways, leading to different, yet equivalent, expressions. Equivalency is discussed in terms of graphs and tables and the validity of the reasoning each expression or equation represents. In addition, the structures of the problems make it inevitable that important properties of numbers will be articulated and used, especially the Distributive Property. By the conclusion of the investigation, students will have developed a strong sense of the Distributive Property independent of a specific context.

Investigation 2

Combining Expressions

In this investigation, students combine expressions to write new expressions either by adding or subtracting expressions or by substituting an equivalent expression for a given quantity in an expression or equation. They use the properties of real numbers to write equivalent expressions as they continue to connect symbolic expressions with real-world contexts.

Investigation 3

Solving Equations

In the previous two investigations, students have been using the Distributive and Commutative properties to write equivalent expressions. In this investigation, they continue to use these properties as well as the properties of equalities to solve linear equations with parentheses and to solve quadratic equations by factoring.

Investigation 4

Looking Back at Functions

In this investigation, students describe the underlying pattern of change represented by a symbolic statement. They also write symbolic equations to represent specific patterns of change and to find answers to specific questions. This investigation pulls many of the algebraic ideas from the algebra strand together.

Investigation 5

Reasoning With Symbols

Another important aspect of understanding symbols and writing equivalent expressions is their role in confirming or proving a conjecture. Sometimes, as we have seen in writing equivalent expressions, the symbolic statements can reveal additional patterns in the context. In this investigation, students explore why number puzzles work. They also explore algebraic expressions that represent even and odd integers and the patterns that emerge from squaring an odd number and then subtracting one.

Mathematics Background

Students come to this unit with considerable experience in working with symbolic expressions, tables, and graphs that arise out of problem situations. This unit develops students' facility in reasoning with purely symbolic expressions. At the same time students observe how these symbolic expressions are used in real problem situations. This unit provides meaningful settings for using conventional algebraic notation and techniques. Thinking with symbolic expressions in situations that use mathematics as a context, and others that use real problems as a context, plays a significant role in developing students' "symbolic sense" (facility with symbolic statements).

The unit is organized around five aspects of symbolic expressions: generating and interpreting equivalent expressions, combining expressions, solving equations, observing patterns of change, and reasoning with symbols. Throughout all of the investigations, the problems require students to write symbolic statements to model a problem situation, interpret symbolic statements, write equivalent symbolic expressions, and make predictions using symbolic statements.

Equivalent Expressions

In *Variables and Patterns* and *Moving Straight Ahead*, students explored ways in which relationships can be expressed in tables, graphs, and equations. The contextual clues or the patterns in tables or graphs were usually so influential in the construction of the equation that only one version of the equation emerged. In this unit, students are deliberately presented with situations in which contextual clues can be interpreted in several ways to produce different but equivalent equations. For example:

> Find the number of 1-foot-square tiles N needed to make a border around a square pool with sides of length s feet.

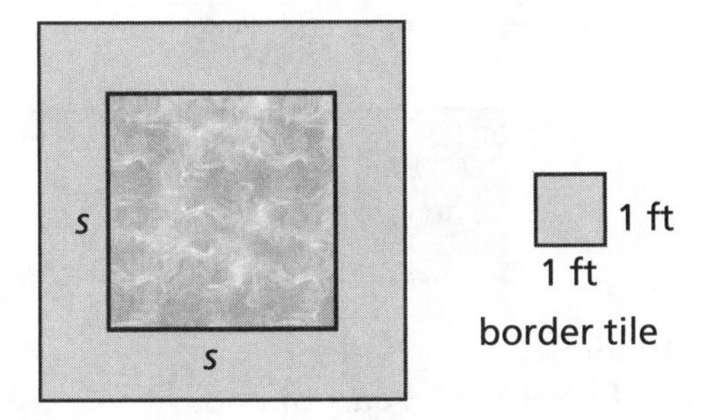

Different conceptualizations of the situation can lead to different but equivalent expressions for the number of tiles: $N = 4(s + 1)$, $N = 4(s + 2) - 4$, or $N = (s + 2)^2 - s^2$ among others.

Verifying Equivalence

At this stage of development, students may consider the reasonableness of the geometric reasoning represented by each equation. For example, the equation $N = 4(s + 1)$ represents the following geometric pattern:

> The border is divided into four rectangles with dimensions $s + 1$ and 1, resulting in the equation $N = 4(s + 1)$.

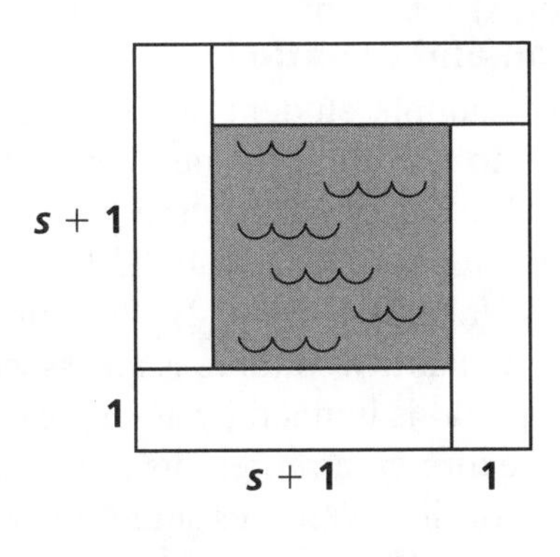

For the equation $N = 4(s + 2) - 4$, students might have used the following geometric pattern:

> Add the four long strips along the sides and then subtract the four corner tiles that are counted twice, resulting in the equation $N = 4(s + 2) - 4$.

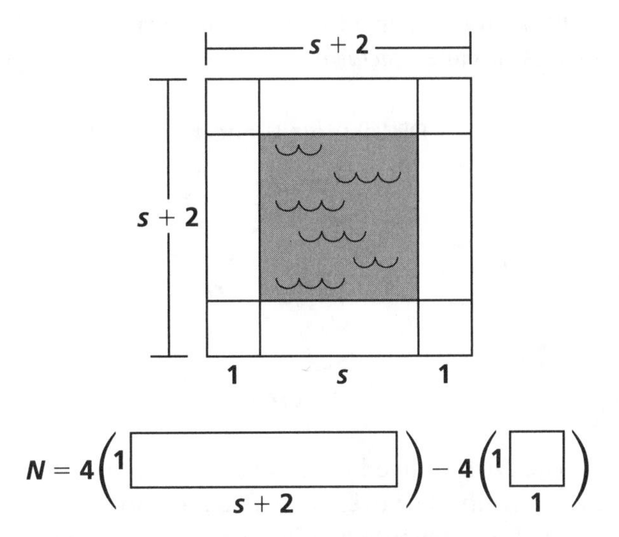

Students may also generate a table or graph to show the equivalence of the set of expressions for the number of border tiles. Some students may note that the table and graph represent a linear relationship. They find that the constant rate of change is 4 and y-intercept is 4 and write $N = 4s + 4$.

Students also verify the equivalence of the expressions for the number of border tiles using the Distributive and Commutative properties. Students may raise questions about the expression for the number of border tiles, $(s + 2)^2 - s^2$, because it seems to be quadratic. Using the Distributive and Commutative properties, they verify that it is equivalent to $4s + 4$.

Notes on the Distributive Property

The Distributive Property was first introduced in *Accentuate the Negative* and then used in several units in seventh and eighth grade in the linear form, $a(b + c) = ab + ac$. In a preceding unit, *Frogs, Fleas, and Painted Cubes*, the Distributive Property was extended to include two binomials, $(a + b)(c + d)$. In each case, an area model was used to show the relationship between the expanded and factored form of an expression. In general, the Distributive Property states that for any three real numbers, r, s, and t,

$$r(s + t) = rs + rt$$

If an expression is written as a factor multiplied by a sum of two or more terms, the Distributive Property can be applied to *multiply* the factor by each term in the sum. If an expression is written as a sum of terms, and the terms have a common factor, the Distributive Property can be applied to rewrite the expression as the common factor multiplied by a sum of two or more terms. This process is called *factoring*.

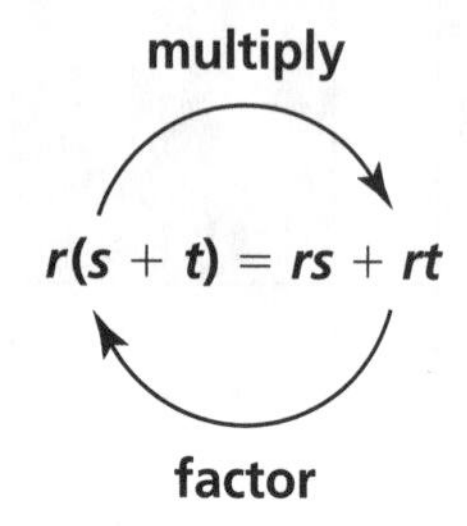

The Distributive Property allows students to group symbols or to expand an expression as needed. The Distributive Property is one of the most important properties for writing equivalent expressions.

Realistic problems can also suggest a rule for *distributing a negative sign*. Distributing a negative sign is introduced in Investigation 3. The following example provides some informal understanding for the general idea that $a - (b + c) = a - b - c$.

> Suppose a checking account contains $100 at the start of the week. Two checks are written during the week, one for $22 and one for $50. Students may find the balance in the account at the end of the week in two ways:
>
> $100 - (22 + 50) = 28$ or $100 - 22 - 50 = 28$

Mathematically, $a - (b + c) = a + (-1)(b + c) = a + (-1)b + (-1)c = a - b - c$.

Practice with multiplying binomials and factoring simple quadratic expressions is provided throughout the unit as students write equivalent quadratic expressions or solve quadratic equations by factoring.

Interpreting Expressions

Interpreting information that is represented by expressions occurs throughout all of the problems. In the first example, students interpret the geometric patterns that each student's equation represents about the relationship between the number of border tiles and the dimensions of the square pool.

Another example where students need to interpret a symbolic expression has the added complexity of being a quadratic expression.

> A community center is building a pool, part indoors and part outdoors. A diagram of the indoor part of the pool is shown. The indoor shape is made from a half-circle and a rectangle. The diagram does not show the shape of the outdoor part of the pool. The exact dimensions of the pool are not available, but the area A of the whole pool is given by the equation:
>
> $$A = \frac{\pi x^2}{2} + x^2 + 8x^2 + \frac{\pi x^2}{4}$$

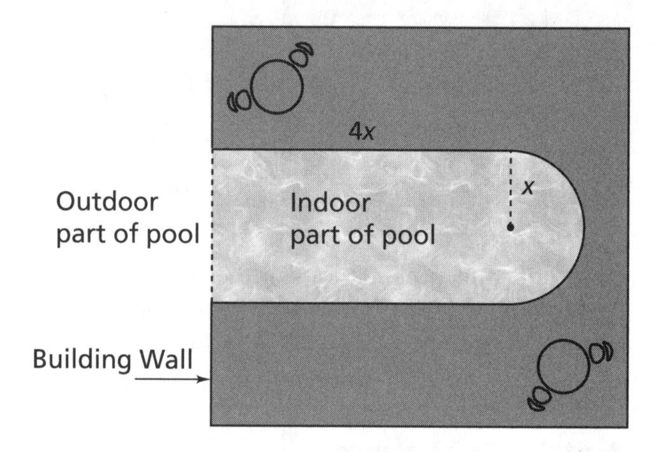

Students identify the part of the expression that represents the area of the indoor part $(\frac{\pi x^2}{2} + 8x^2)$ and also the part of the expression that represents the outdoor part $(x^2 + \frac{\pi x^2}{4})$. They then sketch a shape for the outdoor part of the pool, for which there are many different possibilities.

A Note on the Use of Expression and Equation

In the first example, students are writing expressions to represent the number of border tiles needed to surround a square pool. Some of these expressions are $4s + 4$, $4(s + 1)$, $2(s + 2) - 4$, and $2s + 2(s + 2)$. An expression represents a quantity, so there is an associated relationship that is implied by an expression. Here, each expression represents the quantity or the number of tiles N. In this situation, we can say $N =$ expression. The expression could be any one of the expressions listed above or any other equivalent expression. The implied relationship that is represented by the equation in this example is linear. That is, the relationship between the number of tiles N and the length of the square pool s is a linear relationship.

Combining Expressions

In Investigation 2, students combine expressions to write new expressions either by adding or subtracting expressions or by substituting an equivalent expression for a given quantity in another expression that contains the quantity.

Adding Expressions

Problem 2.1 revisits a walkathon from *Moving Straight Ahead*. It provides students an opportunity to apply the Distributive and Commutative properties to write equivalent expressions for the total amount of money raised by the students in a walkathon.

> Leanne, Gilberto, and Alana enter a walkathon as a team. This means that each person will walk the same number of kilometers. The walkathon organizers offer a prize to the three-person team that raises the most money.

Students first write three equations to represent the total amount of money raised by each student.

$M_{\text{Leanne}} = 160$
$M_{\text{Gilberto}} = 7(2x)$
$M_{\text{Alana}} = 11(5 + 0.5x)$

They can use these equations to find the total by using them to calculate the money raised by each student, or they can combine (add) the three expressions to form one equation that represents the total amount money M_{total} raised by all three students if each walks x kilometers.

$$M_{\text{total}} = 160 + 7(2x) + 11(5 + 0.5x)$$

Students then find an equivalent expression for the total amount of money. They interpret the information the variables and numbers represent in the new expression and discuss the advantages or disadvantages of each equation.

Creating New Expressions by Substitution

The next example involves writing one linear equation that will predict the profit P for an amusement park based on the probability of rain R by substituting into the profit equation an equivalent expression for the number of visitors.

> The manager of the Water City amusement park uses data collected over the past several years to write equations that will help her make predictions about the daily operations of the park.
>
> The daily concession-stand profit in dollars P depends on the number of visitors V. The manager writes the equation below to model this relationship:
>
> $P = 2.50V - 500$
>
> She uses the equation below to predict the number of visitors V based on the probability of rain R.
>
> $V = 600 - 500R$
>
> Write an equation that can be used to predict the profit based on the probability of rain.

This requires students to replace V in the first equation with $600 - 500R$, the equivalent expression for the number of visitors from the second equation.

$$P = 2.50(600 - 500R) - 500.$$

Students then write an equivalent expression for profit and compare the information each expression represents in this situation.

Solving Equations

One aspect of developing students' facility with symbols is to use equations to make predictions or answer specific questions. This sometimes requires solving equations for a specific variable.

Solving Linear Equations

Students are quite comfortable with using tables or graphs to solve equations. They can solve simple linear equations of the form $y = mx + b$ or $mx + b = nx + c$ and simple equations with parentheses, such as $y = a(x + b)$. In Investigation 3, students solve more complicated equations like that in the following example.

> A school choir is selling boxes of greeting cards to raise money for a trip. The equation for the profit in dollars P in terms of the number of boxes sold s is $P = 5s - (100 + 2s)$.

- *What information do the expressions* $5s$ *and* $100 + 2s$ *represent?* ($5s$ represents the income for selling s boxes at \$5 a box. $(100 + 2s)$ represents the cost of selling the boxes; it costs \$2 per box to buy the boxes and there is \$100 fixed cost for miscellaneous expenses such as advertising and postage.)

- *How many boxes must the choir sell to make a $200 profit? Explain.* (Students might use a calculator or they could substitute several values for s. Some may be ready to try to solve this using the properties of equality and the Distributive Property.)
- *What is the break-even point?* (Students may recognize that income must equal cost to break even and then set $5s = 100 + 2s$ and solve for s. Some may use tables or graphs.)
- *Write an equivalent expression for profit. What new information does this expression represent?*
- *One of the choir members wrote the following expression for profit: $5s - 2(50 + s)$. Explain whether this expression is equivalent to the original expression for profit.*
- *Describe how to solve an equation that has parentheses without using a table or graph.*

The first few questions are similar to those that have been asked early in the unit or in previous units, but this equation involves more work with the use of parentheses. Students use the Distributive Property to show that the two expressions for profit, $5s - (100 + 2s)$ and $5s - 2(50 + s)$, are equivalent. However, the focus in this problem is on developing techniques for solving equations symbolically without the use of tables and graphs. The last question pushes students to think about using their knowledge of solving linear equations and properties of equality and numbers to solve this equation. Next they apply these strategies to equations like $y = 5 + 2(3 + 4x)$ or $y = 5 - 2(3 - 4x)$.

Solving Quadratic Equations

To solve quadratic equations like $0 = 2x^2 + 8$ or $0 = x^2 + 5x + 6$, students recognize that these equations are specific cases of the equations, $y = 2x^2 + 8$ or $y = x^2 + 5x + 6$. Finding x when $y = 0$ is the same as finding the x-intercepts of the graphs of these equations. So in some sense students have already had experience solving quadratic equations in *Frogs, Fleas, and Painted Cubes*. In Investigation 3, the connection between solving quadratic equations for x when $y = 0$ and finding x-intercepts is made. Students are introduced to solving quadratic equations by factoring.

Quadratic equations of the form $y = ax(x + b)$, $y = x^2 + bx$, or those of the form $y = ax^2 + bx + c$ that are easily factored into the product of two binomials, are solved for x when $y = 0$.

If $y = 2x^2 + 8x$, find the values of x when $y = 0$.

Students need to recognize that the expression $2x^2 + 8x$ can be rewritten in the equivalent form of $2x(x + 4)$. Next, the students must recognize that this product can only be zero if one of the factors, $2x$ or $x + 4$, is equal to zero. Thus, $2x = 0$ or $x + 4 = 0$. Solving each of these linear equations gives $x = 0$ or $x = -4$.

It is important that students understand that finding x when $y = 0$ is the same as finding the x-intercepts of the graph of $y = 2x^2 + 8x$. Important steps are factoring the quadratic expression and applying the fact that for any two real numbers, a and b, if $ab = 0$, then either $a = 0$ or $b = 0$.

If $y = x^2 + 5x + 6$, find the values of x when $y = 0$.

Students write $x^2 + 5x + 6$ in factored form $(x + 2)(x + 3)$ and then solve $0 = (x + 2)(x + 3)$. Thus, $x + 2 = 0$, which means $x = -2$, or $x + 3 = 0$, which means $x = -3$.

Students are asked to check their solutions when solving equations. Frequently, they are also asked to connect the solutions to a quadratic equation to its graph.

A Note on Factoring

Before quadratic equations are solved, students spend some time factoring quadratic expressions in Problem 3.3. It is important to note that factoring is mostly trial and error using clues from the coefficients of x, x^2 and the constant term. Also, it is unlikely that, given any three real numbers for a, b, and c in $ax^2 + bx + c$, the expression is easily factorable, even if we pick whole nmbers between 1 and 10 for a, b, and c. Over a number of years, mathematicians developed the quadratic formula that can be applied to any quadratic equation. It states if $0 = ax^2 + bx + c$, then $x = \dfrac{-b \pm \sqrt{b^2 - 4ac}}{2a}$.

What is important is that students understand that quadratic expressions can be written in two equivalent forms, expanded form and factored form, and that these two expressions represent different pieces of information about the underlying quadratic function or the context that it models. Students should be able to factor simple quadratic expressions and understand how factoring quadratic expressions uses the Distributive Property.

Predicting the Underlying Patterns of Change

Prior to this unit, the focus of the algebra strand has been the study of patterns of change between two variables. Students represented these relationships using tables, graphs and symbolic statements. They used these representations to study the special patterns of change associated with linear, exponential, and quadratic functions and to solve equations. For linear situations, the statements were in the form of $y = mx + b$; for exponential situations, the statements have been of the form $y = a(b)^x$, and for quadratic situations, $y = ax^2 + bx + c$ or $y = (x + p)(x + q)$. Students used contexts or representations to determine whether a situation is linear, exponential, quadratic, or none of these and to write an equation to model the situation. The following discussion reviews the patterns of change associated with linear, exponential, and quadratic functions.

Patterns of Change

In the linear equation $y = 70 - 5x$, students can interpret the coefficient of x (–5) as the constant rate of change for the linear relationship represented by this equation. The coefficient of x is the slope of the line represented by this equation. The constant term (70) is the y-intercept. If the equation represents a "real" situation, then they can relate parts of the equation to the situation. For example, a club may have $70 to spend on a trip. If the trip costs $5 per person, then y or $70 - 5x$ represents the amount of money left if x people go on the trip.

For an exponential situation, $y = 3(2)^x$, the 3 is the y-intercept and 2 is the growth factor. As x increases by 1, y changes by a factor of 2. Again students should be able to relate the equation to a situation. Suppose the Queen of Montarek offers a peasant 3 rubas at the start and then doubles the amount of money each day. Then the equation $y = 3(2)^x$ represents the amount of money y on day x. The constant growth factor is 2.

x	0	1	2	3	4	5
y	3	6	12	24	48	96
Constant Factor	×2	×2	×2	×2	×2	

Quadratic situations are fairly easy for students to recognize by looking at second differences of successive values of y (the dependent variable). Writing an equation is a bit more challenging. In quadratic situations, the y-value grows as the square of the x-value. In the equation $y = x(x + 1)$, or equivalently, $y = x^2 + x$, the y-value is x^2 plus x. For large values of x, x^2 is much larger than x. The equation is also characterized by a constant second difference, which is 2. If students go on to calculus, they will learn that this difference is the second derivative of the function.

x	0	1	2	3	4	5
y	0	2	6	12	20	30
First Difference	2	4	6	8	10	
Second Difference	2	2	2	2		

Students also recognize that the graph of $y = x(x + 1)$ has a minimum point at $(-\frac{1}{2}, -\frac{1}{4})$, and its x-intercepts are (0, 0) and $(-1, 0)$. This equation could represent the number of handshakes that take place between two teams, one with x members and one with $x + 1$ members. For quadratic equations, the expression for y can be written in expanded or factored form. Which form to use depends on the information that is requested. The expression $x^2 + x$ is easy to predict the y-intercept and patterns of change. The expression $x(x + 1)$ is easier to use to predict the x-intercepts, line of symmetry, and the maximum or minimum points.

Even though the first three investigations of this unit focus on equivalent expressions and solving equations, students are frequently asked to describe the patterns of change that a situation or equation represented. Predicting patterns of change and interpreting the special features of a function is the focus of Investigation 4. This investigation provides some contexts that involve more complex equations, including some that involve all three functions. Finally, it serves as a cumulative review for the algebra strand up to this point.

Predicting Linear Patterns of Change

Every winter, Magnolia Middle School empties their school pool for cleaning. Ms. Theodora's math class decides to collect data on the amount of water in the pool and how long it takes to empty it. They write an equation to represent the amount of water w (in gallons) in the pool after t hours.

$$w = -450(2t - 7)$$

- *How many gallons of water are pumped out each hour?*
- *How long will it take to empty the pool?*
- *How many gallons of water are in the pool at the start?*
- *Write an expression for the amount of water w. What information does this expression represent? Which expression is more useful in this situation? Explain.*
- *Without graphing the equation, describe the shape of the graph.*

This linear situation contains parentheses that students have briefly encountered in *Moving Straight Ahead* and *Thinking With Mathematical Models*. To find the rate at which water is being pumped out per hour, students may use a variety of strategies such as making a table and noting that as t increases by 1, the water decreases by 900 gallons. They may also substitute values into the equations and note the difference between two consecutive hours. They may apply the Distributive Property and write $w = -900t - 3{,}150$ and then recognize that the coefficient of t is the constant rate of change for a linear relationship. The amount of water at the start of the pumping is the y-intercept, which students may read from an equivalent expression for the amount of water in the tank, or they can use a table or graph. Similarly, to find how long it will take to empty the pool, they may solve the equation for $w = 0$, or use a table or graph. Some students may note that the expression is in factored form and if the amount of water w is 0, then one of the factors must be 0. So $2t - 7 = 0$ or $t = 3.5$. Students also describe the graph of the relationship without making a table or graph.

These questions are similar to questions asked in previous units except that the expression for the amount of water contains parentheses. This is an example of interpreting symbolic statements to find specific information about the situation and describing the underlying relationship that the equation represents.

The next problem asks students to make a table of values for linear, exponential, and quadratic equations given the same two points for each relationship.

Writing Equations for Linear, Exponential, and Quadratic Functions Given Two Points

The first two entries in a table of numbers are given below.

x	Linear y	Exponential y	Quadratic y
1	1	1	1
2	4	4	4
3	■	■	■
4	■	■	■
5	■	■	■
6	■	■	■

Write four more numbers in each column to write a linear, exponential, and quadratic relationship. Explain why the relationship in each column works. Write an equation for each relationship. Explain what information the variables and numbers represent. Compare your equations with your classmates. Do you all have the same equations? Explain.

There is exactly one relationship for each of the linear and exponential relationship. There are infinitely many for quadratic relationships for the quadratic pattern. This problem shows students' understanding of the underlying pattern of change for each function.

Finally, this investigation ends with a problem in which students sort several functions by types of relationships. Then within each relationship, they must decide which, if any, two equations represent the same function and provide particular information about each function such as the pattern of change, x- and y-intercepts, maximum or minimum points, and lines of reflection.

Reasoning With Symbols

In Investigation 5, the central idea is to use symbolic statements, together with appropriate mathematical properties, to confirm conjectures.

In *Prime Time*, students conjecture that the sum of two odd numbers and the sum of two even numbers are even. They try many examples that confirm their conjecture, and they use geometric arrangements of square tiles to validate their conjecture. They arrange rectangular arrays whose dimensions are 2 and n, (where n is a whole number) to represent even numbers. The arrays for odd numbers are the same as those for even except they have one extra piece added to the rectangle.

Some students argue that even numbers have a factor of 2, so the sum of two even numbers will have a factor of 2. For odd numbers they argue that when you add two odd numbers you are combining the two extra 1's so that you end up with an even number. Using symbolic statements adds a level of confirmation to these intuitive arguments.

Using Symbolic Statements to Confirm a Conjecture

If n is any integer, then $2n$ represents an even number and $2n + 1$ represents an odd number.

Let $2m$ and $2n$ represent any two even numbers. Then $2n + 2m = 2(n + m)$.

The number $2(n + m)$ is even, so the sum of two even numbers is even.

$$2n + 1 + 2m + 1 = 2n + 2m + 2$$
$$= 2(n + m + 1)$$

$2(n + m + 1)$ is an even number, so the sum of two odd numbers is even.

Similar arguments can be used for the sum of an odd and an even number and for the product of odd and even numbers. The symbolic arguments offer a very precise and convincing argument that covers all integers.

In the next example, students look for patterns in a quadratic relationship, and then find a way to confirm their conjectures about the patterns.

Perform the following operations on the first eight odd numbers. Record your information in a table.

- Pick an odd number.
- Square it.
- Subtract 1.

- *What patterns do you see in the resulting numbers?*
- *Make conjectures about these numbers. Explain why your conjectures are true for any odd number.*

If students try this procedure for the first few odd numbers, they quickly see that the numbers are multiples of 8. If they rewrite each number as a product of 8, they also see that each of these numbers is 8 times a triangular number. The nth triangular number is represented by $\frac{n(n + 1)}{2}$.

n	1	3	5	7
$n^2 - 1$	0	8	24	48
Pattern	8×0	8×1	8×3	8×6

To prove this, students might provide the following argument:

Let $2n + 1$ represent an odd number.

$$(2n + 1)^2 - 1 = 4n^2 + 4n + 1 - 1$$
$$= 4n^2 + 4n$$
$$= 4n(n + 1)$$ This is 4 times a number that is twice a triangular number.
$$= \frac{8n(n + 1)}{2}$$ Multiply the numerator and denominator by 2.

We have shown that squaring an odd number and subtracting 1 yields a number that is 8 times a triangular number. The first part of this problem, which involves observing patterns and making conjectures, is accessible to all students. Whether you want to help students develop a symbolic argument at this time is a decision you can make based on your students' needs.

In this unit, students

- Write symbolic expressions to represent the dependent variable in a situation
- Write equivalent expressions to reveal new information about a situation

- Interpret expressions, use expressions and equations to make decisions
- Solve equations and predict patterns of change that are represented by symbolic statements
- Use symbolic statements and properties of numbers to provide arguments for conjectures

Much of the work involved in this unit could be thought of as developing traditional algebra skills, but an important difference is that students are learning these skills in a purposeful way. Not only are they using properties of numbers to write equivalent expressions, they are using expressions and equations to make important decisions about a problem situation or a function.

Content Connections to Other Units

Big Idea	Prior Work	Future Work
Interpreting symbolic expressions and statements	Using the appropriate order of operations in evaluating expressions and writing symbolic sentences; using parentheses and properties of real numbers to communicate effectively (*Accentuate the Negative; Variables and Patterns; Moving Straight Ahead; Filling and Wrapping; Thinking With Mathematical Models; Growing, Growing, Growing; Frogs, Fleas, and Painted Cubes*); making sense of linear, quadratic, exponential, and other symbolic expressions (*Variables and Patterns; Moving Straight Ahead; Thinking With Mathematical Models; Growing, Growing, Growing; Frogs, Fleas, and Painted Cube*); evaluating and making sense of symbolic expressions *(Variables and Patterns; Moving Straight Ahead; Thinking With Mathematical Models; Growing, Growing, Growing; Frogs, Fleas, and Painted Cubes*)	Making sense of linear relationships of the form $ax + by = c$ and linear inequalities (*The Shapes of Algebra*); making sense of polynomial, logarithmic, trigonometric, and rational symbolic expressions and functions (high school)
Writing and interpreting equivalent expressions; combining expressions to form new expressions	Writing and interpreting symbolic sentences (*Variables and Patterns; Moving Straight Ahead; Thinking With Mathematical Models; Growing, Growing, Growing; Frogs, Fleas, and Painted Cubes*)	Writing equivalent linear relationships, systems of linear equations and linear inequalities (*The Shapes of Algebra*); writing equivalent expressions involving polynomial, logarithmic, trigonometric, and rational expressions that communicate reasoning using the properties of real numbers (*high school*)
Reasoning with equivalent expressions and equations	Reasoning with equivalent expressions (*Bits and Pieces I; Bits and Pieces II; Variables and Patterns; Moving Straight Ahead; Thinking With Mathematical Models; Growing, Growing, Growing; Frogs, Fleas, and Painted Cubes*); predicting patterns of change (*Variables and Patterns; Moving Straight Ahead; Thinking With Mathematical Models; Growing, Growing, Growing; Frogs, Fleas, and Painted Cubes*)	Reasoning with linear relationships and inequalities (*The Shapes of Algebra*); reasoning with equivalent expressions to solve problems that can be modeled by polynomial, logarithmic, trigonometric, and rational functions (*high school*)
Solving linear and quadratic equations	Solving linear and quadratic equations using tables, graphs, and simple symbolic rules (*Variables and Patterns; Moving Straight Ahead; Thinking With Mathematical Models; Growing, Growing, Growing; Frogs, Fleas, and Painted Cubes*); modeling and solving problems (*Variables and Patterns; Moving Straight Ahead; Thinking With Mathematical Models; Growing, Growing, Growing; Frogs, Fleas, and Painted Cubes*)	Solving linear inequalities and systems of linear equations (*The Shapes of Algebra*); developing a deeper understanding of solving linear and quadratic equations and applying and extending the techniques to solving polynomial and rational equations (*high school*)
Modeling and using symbolic reasoning to prove conjectures	Modeling and solving problems (*Variables and Patterns; Moving Straight Ahead; Thinking With Mathematical Models; Growing, Growing, Growing; Frogs, Fleas, and Painted Cubes*)	Modeling and solving problems using polynomial, logarithmic, and trigonometric functions (*high school*)

Planning for the Unit

Pacing Suggestions and Materials

Investigations and Assessments	Pacing 45–50 min. classes	Materials for Students	Materials for Teachers
1 Equivalent Expressions	4 days	Grid paper, square tiles (optional), Labsheets 1.1, 1.3	Transparencies 1.1, 1.2A, 1.2B, 1.3, 1.4
Mathematical Reflections	$\frac{1}{2}$ day		
Assessment: Check Up 1	$\frac{1}{2}$ day		
2 Combining Expressions	3 days		
Mathematical Reflections	$\frac{1}{2}$ day		
Assessment: Partner Quiz	1 day		
3 Solving Equations	5 days		Graphing calculator (optional), overhead graphing calculator display (optional), Transparencies 3.1, 3.3A, 3.3B, 3.4
Mathematical Reflections	$\frac{1}{2}$ day		
Assessment: Check Up 2	$\frac{1}{2}$ day		
4 Looking Back at Functions	3 days		Transparency 4.3
Mathematical Reflections	$\frac{1}{2}$ day		
5 Reasoning With Symbols	3 days		Transparencies 5.2, 5.3A, 5.3B
Mathematical Reflections	$\frac{1}{2}$ day		
Looking Back and Looking Ahead	$\frac{1}{2}$ day		
Assessment: Self Assessment	Take Home		
Assessment: Unit Test	1 day		
Assessment: Unit Project	optional		
Total Time	**24 days**		

Materials for Use in All Investigations	
Graphing calculators (optional), poster paper, or blank transparencies and transparency markers (optional), student notebooks	Blank transparencies and transparency markers (optional)

For detailed pacing for Problems within each Investigation, see the Suggested Pacing at the beginning of each Investigation.

For pacing with block scheduling, see next page.

Pacing for Block Scheduling (90-minute class periods)

Investigation	Suggested Pacing	Investigation	Suggested Pacing	Investigation	Suggested Pacing
Investigation 1	**$2\frac{1}{2}$ days**	**Investigation 3**	**$2\frac{1}{2}$ days**	**Investigation 5**	**2 days**
Problem 1.1	$\frac{1}{2}$ day	Problem 3.1	$\frac{1}{2}$ day	Problem 5.1	$\frac{1}{2}$ day
Problem 1.2	$\frac{1}{2}$ day	Problem 3.2	$\frac{1}{2}$ day	Problem 5.2	$\frac{1}{2}$ day
Problem 1.3	$\frac{1}{2}$ day	Problem 3.3	$\frac{1}{2}$ day	Problem 5.3	$\frac{1}{2}$ day
Problem 1.4	$\frac{1}{2}$ day	Problem 3.4	$\frac{1}{2}$ day	Math Reflections	$\frac{1}{2}$ day
Math Reflections	$\frac{1}{2}$ day	Math Reflections	$\frac{1}{2}$ day		
Investigation 2	**2 days**	**Investigation 4**	**2 days**		
Problem 2.1	$\frac{1}{2}$ day	Problem 4.1	$\frac{1}{2}$ day		
Problem 2.2	$\frac{1}{2}$ day	Problem 4.2	$\frac{1}{2}$ day		
Problem 2.3	$\frac{1}{2}$ day	Problem 4.3	$\frac{1}{2}$ day		
Math Reflections	$\frac{1}{2}$ day	Math Reflections	$\frac{1}{2}$ day		

Vocabulary

Essential Terms Developed in This Unit	Useful Terms Referenced in This Unit	Terms Developed in Previous Units	
equivalent expressions	roots	algebraic expression	order of operations
		Commutative Property of Addition	parabola
		Commutative Property of Multiplication	patterns of change
		Distributive Property	quadratic relationship
		even numbers	solutions to equations
		expanded form	solving equations
		exponential relationship	surface area
		factored form	term
		function	*x*-intercept
		linear relationship	*y*-intercept
		odd numbers	

Program Resources

For: Teacher Resources
Web Code: apk-5500

Components

Use the chart below to quickly see which components are available for each Investigation.

Investigation	Labsheets	Additional Practice	Transparencies		Formal Assessment		Assessment Options	
			Problem	Summary	Check Up	Partner Quiz	Multiple-Choice	Question Bank
1	1.1, 1.3	✔	1.1, 1.3, 1.4	1.2A, 1.2B	✔		✔	✔
2		✔				✔	✔	✔
3		✔	3.1, 3.4		✔		✔	✔
4		✔	4.3				✔	✔
5		✔	5.2	5.3A, 5.3B			✔	✔
Unit Project								
For the Unit		*ExamView* CD-ROM, Web site	LBLA		Unit Test, Notebook Check, Self Assessment		Multiple Choice, Question Bank, *ExamView* CD-ROM	

Also Available For Use With This Unit

- Parent Guide: take-home brochure for the unit
- Implementing CMP
- Spanish Assessment Resources
- Additional online and technology resources

Technology

The Use of Calculators

Connected Mathematics was developed with the belief that calculators should be available and that students should learn when their use is appropriate. For this reason, we do not designate specific problems as "calculator problems." If you choose, students can use graphing calculators for much of their work in this unit. Occasionally, students will be asked not to use their calculators to encourage them to think about how they must perform mathematical operations to solve equations or write equivalent expressions.

Student Interactivity CD-ROM

Includes interactive activities to enhance the learning in the Problems within Investigations.

PHSchool.com

For Students Multiple-choice practice with instant feedback, updated data sources, data sets for Tinkerplots data software.

For Teachers Professional development, curriculum support, downloadable forms and more.

See also www.math.msu.edu/cmp for more resources for both teachers and students.

ExamView™ **Test Generator**

Create multiple versions of practice sheets and tests for course objectives and standardized tests. Includes dynamic questions, online testing, student reports, and all test and practice items in Spanish. Also includes all items in the *Assessment Resources* and *Additional Practice*.

Teacher Express CD-ROM

Includes a lesson planning tool, the Teacher's Guide pages, and all the teaching resources.

LessonLab Online Courses

LessonLab offers comprehensive, facilitated professional development designed to help teachers implement CMP and improve student achievement. To learn more, please visit PHSchool.com/cmp2.

Assessment Summary

Ongoing Informal Assessment

Embedded in the Student Unit

Problems Use students' work from the Problems to check student understanding.

ACE exercises Use ACE exercises for homework assignments to assess student understanding.

Mathematical Reflections Have students summarize their learning at the end of each Investigation.

Looking Back and Looking Ahead At the end of the unit, use the first two sections to allow students to show what they know about the unit.

Additional Resources

Teacher's Guide Use the Check for Understanding feature of some Summaries and the probing questions that appear in the *Launch, Explore,* or *Summarize* sections of all Investigations to check student understanding.

Summary Transparencies Use these transparencies to focus class attention on a summary check for understanding.

Self Assessment

Notebook Check Students use this tool to organize and check their notebooks before giving them to their teacher. Located in *Assessment Resources*.

Self Assessment At the end of the unit, students reflect on and provide examples of what they learned. Located in *Assessment Resources*.

Formal Assessment

Choose the assessment materials that are appropriate for your students.

Assessment	For Use After	Focus	Student Work
Check Up 1	Invest. 1	Skills	Individual
Partner Quiz	Invest. 2	Rich problems	Pairs
Check Up 2	Invest. 3	Skills	Individual
Unit Test	The Unit	Skills, rich problems	Individual
Unit Project	The Unit	Rich problems	Individual or Group

Additional Resources

Multiple-Choice Items Use these items for homework, review, a quiz, or add them to the Unit Test.

Question Bank Choose from these questions for homework, review, or replacements for Quiz, Check Up, or Unit Test questions.

Additional Practice Choose practice exercises for each investigation for homework, review, or formal assessments.

***ExamView* Test Generator** Create practice sheets, review quizzes, and tests with this dynamic software. Give online tests and receive student progress reports. (All test items are also available in Spanish.)

Spanish Assessment Resources

Includes Partner Quizzes, Check Ups, Unit Test, Multiple-Choice Items, Question Bank, Notebook Check, and Self-Assessment. Plus, the *ExamView* CD-ROM has all test items in Spanish.

Correlation to Standardized Tests

Investigation	NAEP	Terra Nova		ITBS	SAT10	Local Test
		CAT6	CTBS			
1 Equivalent Expressions	A3b, A3a	✔	✔	✔	✔	
2 Combining Expressions	A2a, A3b	✔	✔	✔	✔	
3 Solving Equations	A2b, A4b	✔	✔	✔	✔	
4 Looking Back at Functions	A2g, A1e		✔		✔	
5 Reasoning With Symbols	A1b, A1e	✔	✔	✔	✔	

NAEP National Assessment of Educational Progress
CAT6/Terra Nova California Achievement Test, 6th Ed.
CTBS/Terra Nova Comprehensive Test of Basic Skills
ITBS Iowa Test of Basic Skills, Form M
SAT10 Stanford Achievement Test, 10th Ed.

Launching the Unit

Introducing Your Students to *Say It With Symbols*

To begin the unit, ask the class to give some examples of symbolic expressions or equations that were used to represent exponential, linear, and quadratic relationships in the problems they investigated in previous units. You can post these examples in the classroom. Ask:

- What information do the numbers and symbols represent in the problem?
- If you know the value of one variable, explain how you could find the value of the other variable.
- Describe the shape of the graph.
- Describe a context or problem that could be represented by this expression or equation.

Using the Unit Opener

The questions posed on the opening page of the Student Edition are designed to start students thinking about the kinds of questions and mathematics in the unit. Do not look for "correct" answers at this time. Do, however, present an opportunity for the class to discuss the questions and to start to think about what is needed to answer them. Listen as students share their ideas about each example and ask yourself the following questions.

- *Can they evaluate expressions for a given value of one of the independent variables?*
- *Do they recognize the patterns of change associated with each relationship?*
- *Can they relate parts of the symbolic expression or equation for the relationship to the table and graph of the equation?*

This introduction will raise issues related to reading, interpreting, and evaluating symbolic expressions and to finding equivalent expressions.

You may want to revisit these questions as students learn the mathematical ideas and techniques necessary to find the answers.

Problems in contexts are used to help students informally reason about the mathematics of the unit. The problems are deliberately sequenced to develop understanding of concepts and skills.

Using the Mathematical Highlights

The Mathematical Highlights page in the Student Edition provides information to students, parents, and other family members. It gives students a preview of the mathematics and some of the overarching questions that they should ask themselves while studying *Say It With Symbols*.

As they work through the unit, students can refer back to the Mathematical Highlights page to review what they have learned and to preview what is still to come. This page also tells students' families what mathematical ideas and activities will be covered as the class works through *Say It With Symbols*.

Using the Unit Project

The Unit Project can be used as a final assessment of *Say It With Symbols* in which students can apply what they have learned about equivalent expressions and equations. Throughout this unit, students communicate their ideas using mathematical symbols; this will help them express their thinking and recognize the algebraic patterns that arise during their exploration in this project.

Students will find the volume and surface area of stacks of rods. The surface area is linear, and the volume is quadratic in terms of the number of rods used. Students will find that different but equivalent expressions can be used to model the data.

See the Guide to the Unit Project section on page 133 for more information about assigning and assessing the project. There you will find a rubric and samples of student projects. Each example is followed by a teacher's comments about assessing the project.

Say It With Symbols

Making Sense of Symbols

Glenda Lappan
James T. Fey
William M. Fitzgerald
Susan N. Friel
Elizabeth Difanis Phillips

Boston, Massachusetts · Glenview, Illinois · Shoreview, Minnesota · Upper Saddle River, New Jersey

STUDENT PAGE

STUDENT PAGE

Notes

Say It With Symbols

Making Sense of Symbols

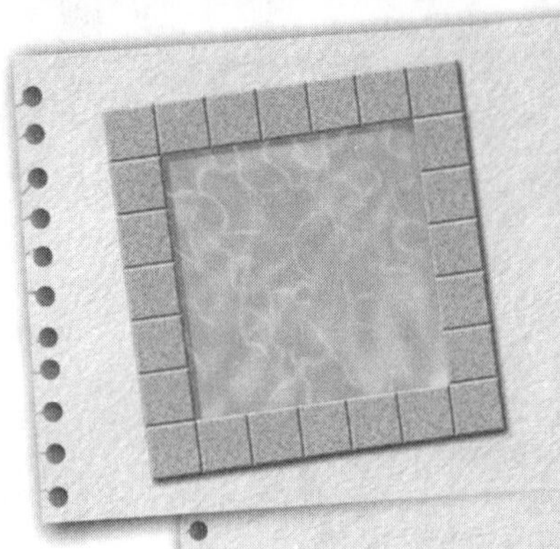

In-ground swimming pools are often surrounded by borders of tiles. How many border tiles N do you need to surround the square pool in the figure at the left?

The school choir is selling boxes of greeting cards to raise money for a trip. How many boxes must the choir sell to make a $200 profit?

Perform the following operations on the first eight odd numbers.

- Pick an odd whole number.
- Square it.
- Subtract 1.

What patterns do you see in the resulting numbers?

Notes

You have used many powerful tools, including graphs, tables, and equations, to represent relationships among variables. Graphs allow you to see the shape of a relationship. They also help you identify intercepts and maximum and minimum points. Tables help you observe patterns of change in the values of the variables. Equations give you an efficient way to generalize relationships.

In *Say It With Symbols*, you will concentrate on symbolic expressions and equations. You will see that different ways of reasoning about a situation can lead to different but equivalent expressions. You will use mathematical properties to rewrite expressions, and you may discover that an equivalent expression allows you to think about a problem in a new way. And, you will learn new ways to solve equations. Pools are used as a context throughout this unit to introduce these ideas.

As you work through the unit, you will solve problems similar to those on the previous page.

Notes

Mathematical Highlights

Making Sense of Symbols

Algebra provides ideas and symbols for expressing information about quantitative variables and relationships. In *Say It With Symbols*, you will solve problems designed to develop your understanding and skill in using symbolic expressions and equations in algebra.

You will learn how to

- Represent patterns and relationships in symbolic forms
- Determine when different symbolic expressions are mathematically equivalent
- Write algebraic expressions in useful equivalent forms
- Combine symbolic expressions using algebraic operations
- Analyze expressions or equations to determine the patterns of change in the tables and graphs that the equation represents
- Solve linear and quadratic equations using symbolic reasoning
- Use algebraic reasoning to validate generalizations and conjectures

As you work on problems in this unit, ask yourself questions about situations that involve symbolic expressions and equations.

What expression or equation represents the pattern or relationship in a context?

Can you write an equivalent expression for a given expression to provide new information about a relationship?

What operations can transform a given equation or expression into an equivalent form that can be used to answer a question?

How can symbolic reasoning help confirm a conjecture?

Notes

Investigation 1 Equivalent Expressions

Mathematical and Problem-Solving Goals

- Model situations with symbolic statements
- Interpret expressions in a given context
- Interpret the information equivalent expressions represent in a given context
- Review the Distributive Property
- Write equivalent expressions using the Distributive Property
- Determine if two or more expressions are equivalent in a variety of ways including using the Distributive Property and other properties of real numbers

Summary of Problems

Problem 1.1 Tiling Pools

Students write equations to represent the number of unit tiles N that surround a square pool of side length s. They justify the equivalence of two or more symbolic expressions for the same situation.

Problem 1.2 Thinking in Different Ways

This problem serves as a summary for Problem 1.1. It provides several equations that students have used to represent the relationships between the number of unit border tiles and the side length of a square pool. Students use the logic underlying each equation or tables and graphs to show equivalence.

Problem 1.3 The Community Pool Problem

Students interpret a symbolic expression, $A = \frac{\pi x^2}{2} + x^2 + 8x^2 + \frac{\pi x^2}{4}$ that represents the surface area of a community center pool, part of which is inside and part of which is outside the community center.

Problem 1.4 Diving In

This problem revisits the area model for the Distributive Property and then applies the Distributive Property to write equivalent expressions with or without parentheses and to show that two or more expressions are equivalent.

Mathematics Background

For background on equivalent expressions, see pages 4–7.

	Suggested Pacing	Materials for Students	Materials for Teachers	ACE Assignments
All	$4\frac{1}{2}$ days	Graphing calculators (optional), grid paper (optional), large poster paper of blank transparencies and transparency markers (optional), student notebooks		
1.1	1 day	Square tiles (optional); Labsheet 1.1 (optional)	Transparency 1.1	1, 2, 18–24
1.2	1 day		Transparency 1.2A, 1.2B	3, 4, 25–32, 57, 58
1.3	1 day	Labsheet 1.3	Transparency 1.3	5, 6, 33–50
1.4	1 day		Transparency 1.4	7–17, 51–56, 59
MR	$\frac{1}{2}$ day			

1.1 Tiling Pools

Goals

- Model situations with symbolic statements
- Interpret the information equivalent expressions represent in a given context
- Determine if two or more expressions are equivalent

In *Moving Straight Ahead, Thinking With Mathematical Models, Growing, Growing, Growing*, and *Frogs, Fleas, and Painted Cubes,* students explored ways in which relationships can be expressed in tables, graphs, and equations. The contextual clues or the patterns in the tables or graphs were so influential in the construction of the symbolic rule that only one version of the rule appeared. In this problem, students are deliberately presented with a situation in which contextual clues can be interpreted in several ways to produce different equivalent symbolic expressions. Students are asked to justify, in informal ways, the equivalence of these expressions.

Launch 1.1

Talk with the class about the Getting Ready questions on the opening page of Investigation 1. Ask students to justify why both expressions for the rectangle's perimeter, $2(L + W)$ and $2L + 2W$, are correct and why Jim used parentheses in his equation. Students may offer examples or talk generally about the dimensions and perimeter of any rectangle.

Suggested Questions If necessary, direct the conversation to focus on the method each expression represents.

- *Describe the method each student is using to compute the perimeter.* [Mika notes that the perimeter is the length of all four sides, $L + W + W + L$ or $2L + 2W$. Jim notes that if you add $L + W$ as you go around the rectangle, you are halfway around, so all you need to do is multiply by 2 to get $2(L + W)$.]
- *Could Jim have written $2L + W$?* (No, because you would only be counting length twice and width once. The parentheses are needed to show that you must add length and width, which means you are halfway around. Then you multiply the sum by 2.)
- *Are $3(x + 5)$ and $3x + 5$ equivalent? Why?* (No, because the Distributive Property states that $3(x + 5) = 3x + 15$ and $3x + 15 \neq 3x + 5$.)

To introduce Problem 1.1, construct a model of a square pool with sides of length s units using transparent square tiles, draw a square pool on the board, or use Transparency 1.1.

- *This pool has sides of length s feet. You want to make a border around the pool from 1-foot-square tiles.*

Put some tiles around the pool. Try to keep this problem open. That is, do not illustrate the problem for specific values of s. This may send students down the path of making tables. Our experience with this problem is that if the problem is kept open, students will use interesting geometric patterns in the border and pool to write several different expressions for the number of tiles. During the Explore, if a student or pair is struggling you can suggest trying specific cases for the size of the pool.

Suggested Questions Consider asking:

- *Is there an efficient way to calculate the number of border tiles needed for a square pool, no matter what the lengths of the sides of the pool are?*

Distribute grid paper, and make square tiles available for students who want to use them to model pools and borders.

Have students work in pairs on the problem.

Explore 1.1

Having students articulate how they visualize the situation will help them to make the transition to interpreting the reasoning represented by the symbols. Different ways of reasoning about the problem lead to different strategies, which in turn result in different equations. Encourage students to find more than one way to reason about the situation. (Problem 1.2 presents several ways of thinking about this situation, some of which your students will discover.)

Some students may need help using parentheses in their equations. If you see students who cannot communicate their ideas in writing, you might talk with them about the use of parentheses. Students will work more with this idea in Problem 1.4. The primary objective of this problem is that students be able to justify to their classmates that the expressions they develop to represent the number of tiles are equivalent. It is essential that students articulate their reasoning.

Look for interesting ways students are thinking about the problem. Have them put their work with pictures on large poster paper for the summary. Also look for interesting ways that they use to show that two expressions for the number of tiles are equivalent.

Have each pair of students explain to another pair or to their class how they thought about the problem in order to write their equations. This can be done in the summary. Asking them to explain their thinking in writing would also be helpful.

Summarize 1.1

Have the class examine the posters and allow them time to ask questions about each piece of work.

Suggested Questions For each equation, ask:

- *Can you explain the reasoning that was used to arrive at this equation?*
- *How do the parts of the equation relate to the elements of the problem?*

For any equations that the class cannot decipher, ask the students who wrote them to use diagrams to explain their thinking and how the parts of the equation relate to the elements of the problem. Students' explanations might be noted on the board where they can be amended if necessary. Students may be reasoning from numerical examples or from a geometric sketch. Verbal and graphical arguments are sufficient at this stage. Students' equations may include some of the following:

- $N = 4s + 4$
- $N = s + s + s + s + 4$
- $N = 2s + 2(s + 2)$
- $N = 4(s + 2) - 4$
- $N = (s + 2)^2 - s^2$
- $N = 4(s + 1)$
- $N = 8 + 4(s - 1)$

Don't try to get all of these equations at this time. This question is revisited in Problem 1.2, where students are asked to draw pictures that represent the thinking captured in several different expressions, to show that the expressions are equivalent.

Following are some of the ways students may have reasoned about the number of border tiles. It is acceptable if students do not offer all these ideas. They will explore several methods in the next problem.

- They may have considered the four sides first and then added the corner tiles, resulting in the equation $N = 4s + 4$.

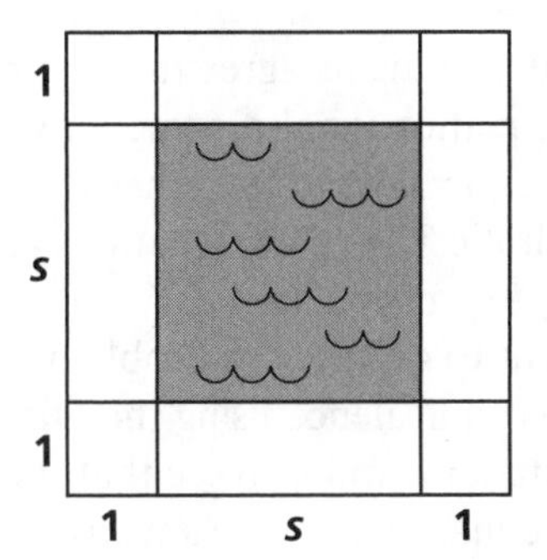

N = 4(1 [s]) + 4(1 [1])

- They may have thought about adding the four long strips along the sides and then subtracting the four corner tiles that are counted twice, resulting in the equation $N = 4(s + 2) - 4$.

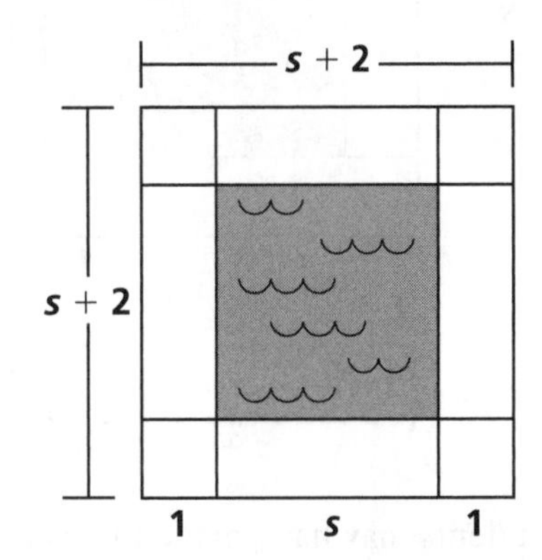

N = 4(1 [s + 2]) − 4(1 [1])

- They may have reasoned that the number of border tiles is equal to the difference between the areas of the two squares, resulting in the equation $N = (s + 2)^2 - s^2$.

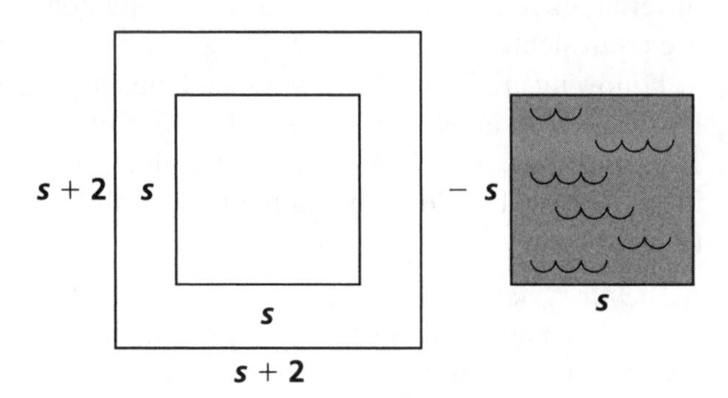

Even though students agree that the reasoning behind this equation is valid, some may question whether it is equivalent to the other equations since it looks quadratic. The other equations are all linear. In fact, if the expression, $(s + 2)^2 - s^2$ is simplified, it is equivalent to $4s + 4$. (In Problem 1.4, students will show this equivalence using the Distributive Property.). Students will also see that the graph and table of this equation are the same as for the other equations.

- They may have divided the border into four rectangles with dimensions $s + 1$ and 1, resulting in the equation $N = 4(s + 1)$.

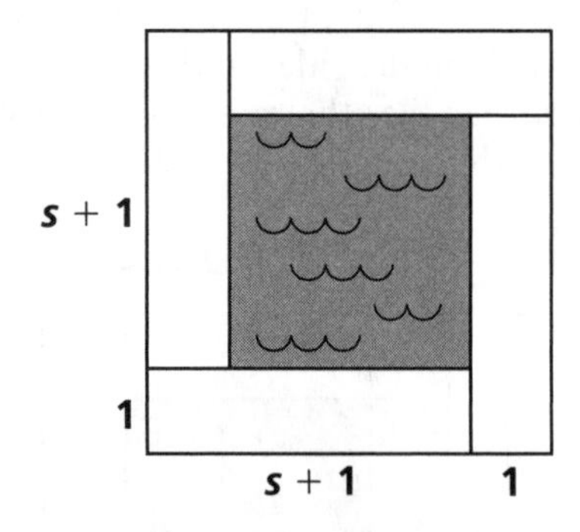

$N = 4($ 1 $s + 1$ $)$

- Some students may have made tables and seen the following pattern in their table: To find the number of border tiles, add 1 to the side length and then multiply by 4, or $N = 4(s + 1)$.

s	1	2	3	4	5	6	7	8	9
N	8	12	16	20	24	28	32	36	40

- Other students may use a table to arrive at the equation $N = 4s + 4$ by noting that the table represents a linear relationship whose slope is 4. Students may reason backward in the table to find the y-intercept, which is 4, and then write the equation $N = 4s + 4$.
- Some students may observe this pattern in the table: For $s = 1, N = 8$. For $s = 2, N = 8 + 4$. For $s = 3, N = 8 + 4 + 4$. For $s = 4, N = 8 + 4 + 4 + 4$. Thus, for any s, N is equal to 8 plus $(s - 1)$ fours, or $N = 8 + 4(s - 1)$. In other words, they used 8 as a starting point and successively added 4. The number of 4's added to get N for any value of s is one less than s.

Be sure to look at tables and graphs for the equations that are generated in class.

Suggested Questions

- *If the graphs and tables are the same, are the equations equivalent?* (Students may be surprised that equations that appear quite different can have identical graphs and tables. Making graphs for different, but equivalent, equations reinforces what students have learned about equivalent representations. You might ask students how they could predict the shape of the graph from the equations or the tables. See pages 4–7 in the Mathematics Background for more information about equivalent expressions.)

The summary of this problem can lead into the Launch of Problem 1.2.

- *Are there other ways to show that these expressions for the number of tiles are equivalent, without using tables or graphs?* (Some students may suggest checking the equivalence for a few values of s and argue that if two answers are correct, the expressions must be equivalent. This is discussed in the next problem.)

Discuss whether the equations are linear, quadratic, or exponential. Use a few of the equations to make the connection between the numbers and variables in the equation and how they relate to various components of the table and graph.

1.1 Tiling Pools

At a Glance

PACING 1 day

Mathematical Goals

- Model situations with symbolic statements
- Interpret the information equivalent expressions represent in a given context
- Determine if two or more expressions are equivalent

Launch

Talk with the class about the Getting Ready questions. Ask students why Jim used parentheses in his equation.

- *Describe the method each student is using to compute the perimeter.*
- *Could Jim have written $2L + W$?*

Construct a model of a square pool with sides of length s units, using transparent square tiles, draw a square pool on the board, or use Transparency 1.1.

- *This pool has sides of length s feet. You want to make a border around the pool from 1-foot-square tiles.*

Put some tiles around the pool. Do not illustrate the problem for specific values of s. Consider asking:

- *Is there an efficient way to calculate the number of border tiles needed for a square pool, no matter what the lengths of the sides of the pool are?*

Distribute grid paper, and make square tiles available for students who want to use them to model pools and borders.

Have students work in pairs on the problem.

Materials

- Grid paper (optional)
- Square tiles (optional)
- Labsheet 1.1 (optional)
- Transparency 1.1

Vocabulary

- equivalent expressions

Explore

Have students articulate how they visualize the situation. Encourage them to find more than one way to reason.

Some students may need help using parentheses in their equations. They will work more with this idea in Problem 1.4.

Have students justify to their classmates that the expressions they develop are equivalent. Have them put their work on large poster paper for the summary.

Materials

- Large poster paper or transparency paper (optional)

Summarize

Have the class examine the posters. For each equation, ask the class:

- *Can you explain the reasoning that was used to arrive at this equation?*
- *How do the parts of the equation relate to the elements of the problem?*

Materials

- Student notebooks

continued on next page

Summarize

continued

Students may be reasoning from numerical examples or from a geometric sketch. Verbal and graphical arguments are sufficient at this stage. See the extended version of Teacher's Guide for examples of student reasoning and equations. Discuss the tables and graphs for each of these equations.

- *If the graphs and tables are the same, are the equations equivalent?*
- *Are there other ways to show that these expressions for the number of tiles are equivalent, without using tables or graphs?*

Discuss whether the equations are linear, quadratic, or exponential.

ACE Assignment Guide for Problem 1.1

Core 1, 2, 18–20
Other *Connections* 21–24

Adapted For suggestions about adapting ACE exercises, see the CMP *Special Needs Handbook.*
Connecting to Prior Units 18–23: *Frogs, Fleas, and Painted Cubes*; 24: *Covering and Surrounding*

Answers to Problem 1.1

A. 1. One possible answer: You could add the number of tiles needed for each side to the four tiles in the corner. One possible expression: $s + s + s + s + 4$. See the summary for more examples.

2. One possible answer: You could double the number of tiles needed for a side plus two corner tiles, and add that answer to the number of tiles needed for the two remaining sides. One possible expression: $s + 2 + s + 2 + s + s$

3. One possible answer: These expressions are equivalent because they both represent the same number of side and corner tiles.

B. 1. A table for $N = s + s + s + s + 4$ and for $N = s + 2 + s + 2 + s + s$ is shown. The graphs and tables will be the same for all equations (except for graph scales and specific table entries).

2. Because the table and the graph are the same for each equation, it appears that the expressions are equivalent.

s	1	2	3	4	5	6	7	8	9
N	8	12	16	20	24	28	32	36	40

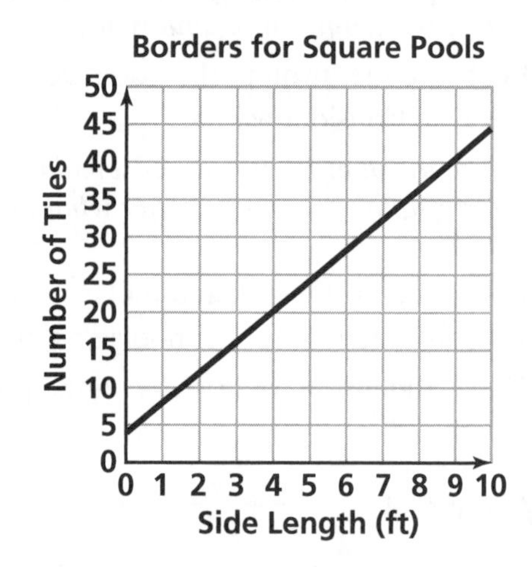

C. One possible answer: The relationship between the side length of the pool and the border tiles is linear because the graph is a straight line, and in the table you can see that the side length of the pool and the number of tiles increase at a constant rate.

1.2 Thinking in Different Ways

Goals

- Interpret the information equivalent expressions represent in a given context
- Determine if two or more expressions are equivalent

Launch 1.2

Some of this problem may have been discussed in the summary of Problem 1.1. If so, have students use the equations for the number of border tiles from ACE Exercise 4, or direct the students to Question B of this problem.

Suggested Question Ask:

- *If a pair of values for (s, N) such as (4, 20) satisfies two different expressions, are the expressions equivalent?*

If your students didn't discuss the equations in Question A, ask them about Takashi's picture of $N = 4s + 4$.

- *Does Takashi's equation represent the picture he drew to explain how he was thinking about the problem?*

Explain to students that they will be drawing pictures to illustrate how other students may have been thinking about the border of the pool.

Let the class work in pairs on this problem.

Explore 1.2

Encourage students to think about whether or not checking one value of s for two expressions is sufficient to show equivalence.

- *How many values do you need to try before you are convinced that the two expressions are equivalent?*

NOTE: Only three of the expressions in Question A are equivalent. Hank's is not equivalent. Students may reason geometrically that Hank forgot to remove the four corner pieces, or they may see that after substituting a value for s into Hank's and Takashi's that the number of tiles is not the same. For the other three expressions, even though the value of 10 produces the same value for N in each expression, it doesn't mean that the expressions are equivalent. This discussion should come out in the summary.

Some students may try to find other expressions. Keep these in mind and use them during the summary to test various conjectures that occur.

Summarize 1.2

Suggested Questions

- *Is one value enough to check in order to prove that two expressions are equivalent?* (You can use Summary Transparencies 1.2A, 1.2B or ask the following questions.)

If students say yes, then write the equations $N = 2s + 1$ and $N = s + 2$ on the board.

- *Find N if $s = 1$.* ($N = 3$ in each case.)
- *Find N if $s = 3$.* ($N = 7$ in the first equation, and $N = 5$ in the second equation. So the two expressions $2s + 1$ and $s + 2$ are not equivalent.)

Write two more equations on the board: $N = 4(s + 2) - 4$ and $N = 4(s + 1)$.

- *Suppose you try two values of s, and the N-value is the same in both cases. Is this sufficient to show that two expressions are equivalent? Suppose you try $s = 1$ and $s = 2$.* (The answer is yes, but this may be a bit subtle for students. If so, ask the next two questions.)
- *What kind of relationship does each equation in this problem represent?* (They are all linear.)
- *So if you know that two distinct points, (1, 8) and (2, 12), lie on the graph of two linear equations, what can you say about the graphs?* (Some students may know that two points determine exactly one straight line. If two points lie on the graph of two linear equations, then the graphs of the linear equations are the same line, so the equations must be equivalent.)

INVESTIGATION 1

It is also valuable to use the unique rate of change for a linear situation. Ask:

- *How else could you show that checking two points is sufficient for showing that two linear expressions are equivalent?* [If you know that an expression represents a linear situation, then it only takes two points to determine its rate of change. For the two points above, the rate of change is 4, so in the table below, the next value of N is $12 + 4$, and the next value is $12 + 4 + 4$. Since (1, 8) and (2, 12) lie on the lines that represent the expressions 1, 2, and 4 from Question A, no matter which equation you pick, the rate and the set of points generated are the same. Since the rate of change is the same, each equation will generate the same set of values for (s, N).]

s	1	2	3	4
N	8	12	12 + 4	12 + 4 + 4

For any complicated expressions that students come up with for the number of border tiles, you may want to come back to them after Problem 1.4 to see if they can use the Distributive and Commutative properties as a way to justify equivalence. For example, students may have found the expressions in ACE Exercise 4. After Problem 1.4, this ACE exercise could be revisited in class.

Summary Transparency

1. *Are $2s + 2(s + 2)$ and $4s + 4$ equivalent?* [Yes, $2s + 2(s + 2)$ and $4s + 4$ are equivalent. Both of these expressions represent a linear relationship. The graph of each relationship is a straight line. Substitute two different values for s into each expression. If $s = 3$, then N, or the value of each expression, equals 16. Similarly, if $s = 5$, then $N = 24$. This means that the points (3, 16) and (5, 24) lie on both lines. And since two points determine exactly one line, the two expressions must be the same.]
2. *What are other ways of showing that the two expressions are equivalent?* (You can use tables, graphs, or valid reasoning behind the symbols.)

At a Glance

PACING 1 day

1.2 Thinking in Different Ways

Mathematical Goals

- Interpret the information equivalent expressions represent in a given context
- Determine if two more expressions are equivalent

Launch

Some of this problem may have been discussed in the summary of Problem 1.1. If so, have students use the equations for the number of border tiles from ACE Exercise 4, or direct the students to Question B of this problem.

- *If a pair of values for (s, N) satisfies two different expressions, are the expressions equivalent?*

If your students didn't discuss the equations in Question A, ask students about Takashi's picture of $N = 4s + 4$.

- *Does Takashi's equation represent the picture he drew to explain how he was thinking about the problem?*

Explain to students that they will be drawing pictures to illustrate how students may have been thinking about the border of the pool.

Let the class work in pairs on this problem.

Explore

Encourage students to think about:

- *How many values do you need to try before you are convinced that the two expressions are equivalent?*

Keep in mind any other expressions students find and use them during the summary.

Summarize

Notice that Hank's expression is not equivalent to Takashi's.

- *Is one value enough to check in order to prove that two expressions are equivalent?*

Use Summary Transparency 1.2, or ask the following questions.

If students say yes, then write the equations $N = 2s + 1$ and $N = s + 2$ on the board. Ask students to:

- *Find N if $s = 1$. Find N if $s = 3$.*

The expressions are not equivalent since they produce different values for 3.

Write the equations $N = 4(s + 2) - 4$ and $N = 4(s + 1)$ on the board.

- *Suppose you try two values of s, and N is the same in both cases. Is this sufficient to show that two expressions are equivalent? Suppose you try $s = 1$ and $s = 2$.*

Materials

- Student notebooks
- Summary transparencies 1.2A, 1.2B

continued on next page

Summarize
continued

- *What kind of relationship does each equation in this problem represent?*
- *So if you know that two distinct points, (1, 8) and (2, 12), lie on the graph of two linear equations, what can you say about the graphs?*

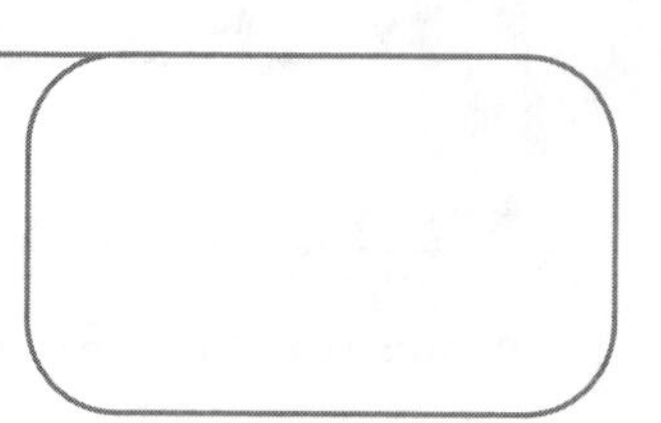

ACE Assignment Guide for Problem 1.2

Core 3, 4, 25, 26
Other *Connections* 27–32; Extensions 57, 58; unassigned choices from previous problems

Adapted For suggestions about adapting Exercise 3 and other ACE exercises, see the CMP *Special Needs Handbook.*
Connecting to Prior Units 25: *Moving Straight Ahead*; 26: *Accentuate the Negative*; 27–32: *Frogs, Fleas, and Painted Cubes*

Answers to Problem 1.2

NOTE: Students' illustrations and ideas will vary. If all or most of these expressions arose in the discussion of Problem 1.1, you may want to encourage students to use their intuitive sense of the Distributive Property to show that the expressions are equivalent.

A. **1.** See the diagram on p. 5 of the Mathematics Background.

2. See the diagram in the Student Edition.

3. See Takashi's pool. This equation is not correct since the corner tiles are all counted twice.

4.

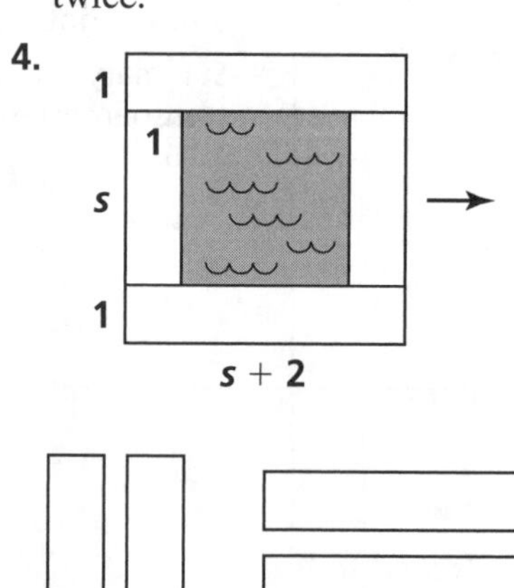

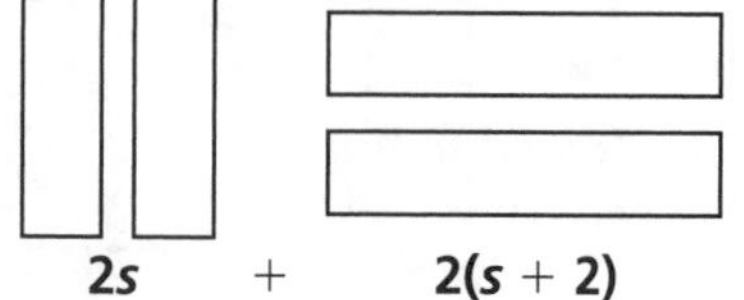

B. Stella's, Jeri's, and Sal's expressions yield the same result of 44 for $s = 10$. It is possible that the expressions are all equivalent, but we can't conclude this from checking one value. (See discussion above in Summary). Hank's expression is not equivalent to the other three because it yields a result of 48 for $s = 10$.

C. Students may use geometric reasoning and say that Stella's, Jeri's, and Sal's expressions are equivalent to Takashi's expression because the expressions all represent the 4 sides of the pool and the 4 corner tiles. Hank's is not equivalent because he double-counted all of the corners. Students may also use tables, graphs, or symbol manipulation to explain their ideas about the equivalences. The graphs and tables of Stella's, Jeri's, and Sal's expressions are the same, which supports the idea that the expressions are all equivalent.

s	1	2	3	4	5
N	8	12	16	20	24

s	6	7	8	9	10
N	28	32	36	40	44

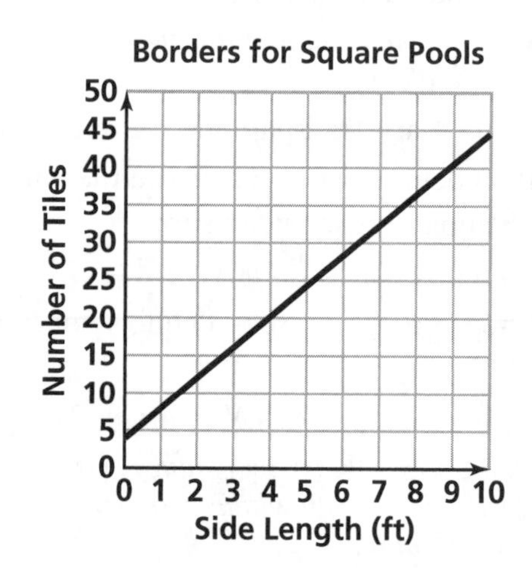

1.3 The Community Pool Problem

Goals

- Interpret expressions in a given context

In this situation, students are working with a quadratic expression.

Launch 1.3

Display Transparency 1.3. Try to keep the problem open enough that a variety of interesting strategies emerge. You might ask students to describe the shape of the indoor part of the pool. Be sure that they know that the outdoor part of the pool is not shown. Distribute Labsheet 1.3.

Let the class work in pairs on this problem.

Explore 1.3

Students generally come out of CMP sixth- and seventh-grade classes quite comfortable with the area of a circle. If a student is unsure, ask another student for the formula for the area of a circle. You may also ask someone in the class to describe why this formula works. Students who have developed the area of a circle in *Covering and Surrounding* and then used it in later units, particularly *Filling and Wrapping,* usually remember the formula or can quickly recall it with a little prompting.

Suggested Questions Students may need some prompting to find the part of the expression that describes the area of the rectangle.

- *What are the dimensions of the rectangle?* ($4x$ and something else)
- *What is the something else? How can you find it? Draw the missing dimension.* (Students may now make the connection that the missing dimension is the diameter of a circle whose radius is x. So the missing dimension is $2x$. The area of the pool is $2x$ times $4x$ or $8x^2$.)

For Question C, if students are struggling with the interpretation, ask:

- *How are* $\frac{\pi x^2}{8}$ *and* $\frac{\pi x^2}{4}$ *related?* (One is half the other, since $\frac{\pi x^2}{8}$ can be represented by an eighth of a circle and $\frac{\pi x^2}{4}$ can be represented by a quarter of a circle.)

You might want students to put their drawings on poster paper or transparency paper to use during the summary.

Summarize 1.3

Go over Questions A and B. Students will be intrigued at all the ways that the outdoor pool can be drawn. Some might represent x^2 as a square, and some might represent it as a rectangle with dimensions $\frac{x}{2}$ and $2x$. This rectangle will match one side of the rectangle. Some will add a quarter of a circle to the square or rectangle. Some may split the quarter circle into two equal eighths of a circle.

Suggested Question Ask students to:

- *Describe how each shape might be useful for different water activities.*

For Question C, allow students time to discuss why certain expressions are equivalent for the outside of the pool and introduce two ways of thinking about the outside pool design, which may or may not have come out in the class already. If no one brings up using the Distributive Property, you may want to wait to ask the following questions until after Problem 1.4. If your students are ready, ask:

- *How can we use the Distributive and Commutative properties to show that the expressions are equivalent?*

INVESTIGATION 1

- *How might Stella and Jeri have drawn the outside of the pool? How do you know that their expressions are equivalent to the original expression for the outside of the pool?* (At this time, students may use geometric reasoning and say that they are all equivalent because the expressions represent the same surface area of the outside of the pool. They may also make a table or a graph. Some students may reason symbolically by matching up parts of the expression and comparing parts of the expression. If students check two values for x in the expressions, you will want to come back to this idea after Question D. You may want to see whether students think two points are enough to check for equivalence of quadratics. It is not, but leave the question open for now. This idea comes up in Investigation 4, Problem 4.2.

For Question D, you could ask:

- *Describe the shape of the graph of the equation* $A = \frac{\pi x^2}{4} + x^2 + 8x^2 + \frac{\pi x^2}{4}$ *or* $A = (\frac{3\pi}{4} + 9)x^2$. [It is a parabola whose minimum point is on the y-axis at $(0, 0)$. The coefficient $(\frac{3\pi}{4} + 9)$ is a number approximately equal to 11.35. This fits between the parabolas of $y = 11x^2$ and $y = 12x^2$. The line of symmetry is the y-axis and the x-intercept is $(0, 0)$.]

1.3 The Pool Problem

At a Glance

PACING 1 day

Mathematical Goals

- Interpret expressions in a given context

Launch

Materials
- Transparency 1.3
- Labsheet 1.3

Display Transparency 1.3. Ask students to describe the shape of the indoor part of the pool. Be sure that they know that the outdoor part of the pool is not shown. Distribute Labsheet 1.3.

Let the class work in pairs on this problem.

Explore

Materials
- Poster paper or transparency paper (optional)

Students should be comfortable with the formula for the area of a circle. If not, ask another student for the formula and why this formula works.

- *What are the dimensions of the rectangle?*

For Question C, if students are struggling with the interpretation, ask:

- *How are $\frac{\pi x^2}{8}$ and $\frac{\pi x^2}{4}$ related?*

You might want students to put their drawings on poster paper or transparency paper to use during the summary.

Summarize

Materials
- Student notebooks

Go over Questions A and B. For the outdoor pool, some will represent x^2 as a square, and some will represent it as a rectangle with dimensions $\frac{x}{2}$ and $2x$. Some will add a quarter of a circle to the square or rectangle. Some may split the quarter circle into two equal eighths of a circle.

- *Describe how each shape might be useful for different water activities.*

For Question C, allow students to discuss why certain expressions are equivalent for the outside of the pool. If no one brings up using the Distributive Property, you may want to wait to ask the following questions until after Problem 1.4.

- *How can you use the Distributive and Commutative properties to show that the expressions are equivalent?*
- *How might Stella and Jeri have drawn the outside of the pool? How do you know that their expressions are equivalent to the original expression for the outside of the pool?*

ACE Assignment Guide for Problem 1.3

Differentiated Instruction
Solutions for All Learners

Core 5, 6
Other *Connections* 33–50; unassigned choices from previous problems

Adapted For suggestions about adapting ACE exercises, see the CMP *Special Needs Handbook.*
Connecting to Prior Units 33–36: *Bits and Pieces II*; 37–45: *Accentuate the Negative*; 46–49: *Prime Time*; 50: *Covering and Surrounding*

Answers to Problem 1.3

A. 1. Area of indoor part: $\frac{\pi x^2}{2} + 8x^2$. The area of the indoor part is the area of a half circle with radius x plus a rectangle with length $4x$ and width $x + x = 2x$ (since the diameter of the circle is the width of the rectangle). So the area of the indoor pool is $\frac{1}{2}(\pi x^2) + (4x)(2x) = \frac{\pi x^2}{2} + 8x^2$.

2. Area of outdoor part: $x^2 + \frac{\pi x^2}{4}$. The area of the outside part is just what is left over when you subtract the indoor parts.

B. 1. Answers will vary. Here are some possible students' pictures for the entire pool:

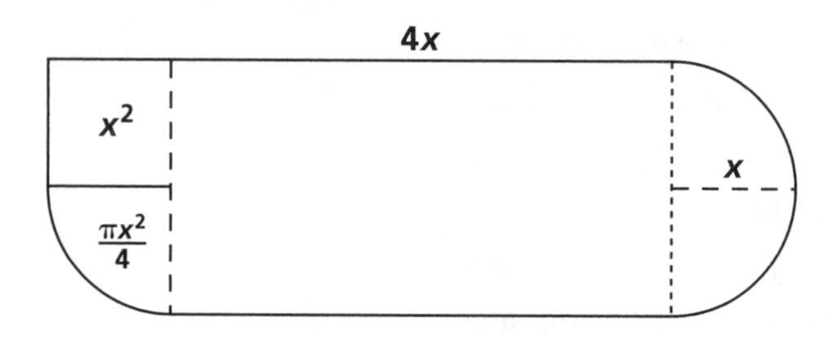

Another possibility: In the diagram above, move the quarter of a circle to the left of the square.

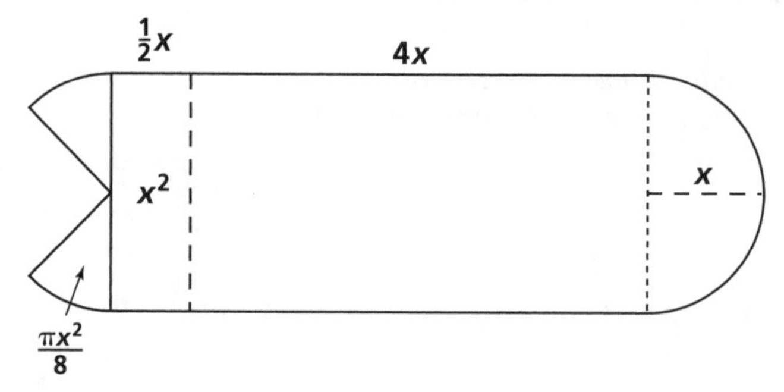

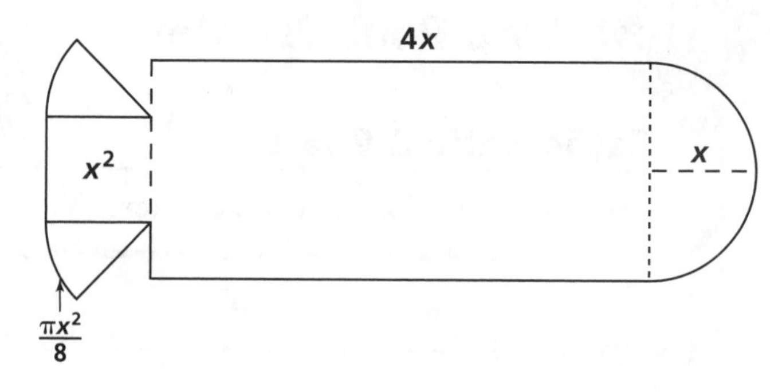

2. Answers will vary. Some students may think that their drawing in part (1) is the only one. Some may think that there is another one but can't draw it. For possible student pictures see part (1).

C. 1. Stella probably had a square piece with a side length of x and two eighths of a circle pieces for the outside of the pool, since the outside of the pool is represented by $A = x^2 + \frac{\pi x^2}{4}$, which is the original equation. Stella may have pictured the fourth pool in Question B part (1). Jeri may have been picturing a pool similar to the third pool in Question B part (1). However this pool combines the two eighths shown in the third pool into a quarter circle to account for the $\frac{\pi x^2}{4}$ part of the expression and the $(\frac{1}{2}x)(2x)$ representing a rectangle with width and length $(\frac{1}{2}x)$ and $2x$.

2. The expressions are equivalent. Students may use a table or graphing calculator to show that they are equivalent. If students check points to show equivalence, they must check three points in each expression. This is because the expressions are quadratic and three points determine a unique quadratic equation. This is discussed more in the Teacher's Guide for Investigation 4. Students also may reason using the picture since the expressions both represent the same area or symbolically by giving reasoning like $\frac{\pi x^2}{8}$ plus $\frac{\pi x^2}{8}$ is $\frac{2\pi x^2}{8}$ which is equal to $\frac{\pi x^2}{4}$.

D. Quadratic; the area of the pool represents a quadratic relationship because the equation for area has the highest power of x appearing as 2.

1.4 Diving In

Goals

- Review the Distributive Property
- Write equivalent expressions using the Distributive Property
- Determine if two or more expressions are equivalent by using the Distributive Property and other properties of the real numbers

Launch 1.4

Display Transparency 1.4. This is a review from previous units.

Suggested Questions

- *Find two equivalent expressions for the area of each rectangle.* [Pool 1: $30(x + 10)$ and $30x + 300$; Pool 2: $25x + x^2$ and $x(25 + x)$; Pool 3: $(x + 2)(x + 3)$ and $x^2 + 2x + 3x + 6 = x^2 + 5x + 6$; Pool 4: $ab + ac$ or $a(b + c)$]
- *Explain how these illustrate the Distributive Property.* [At this time, write an expression like $30(x + 10)$ or $(x + 2)(x + 3)$ on the board.]

$$30(x + 10) = 30x + 300$$

$$(x + 2)(x + 3) = (x + 2)x + (x + 2)3 =$$

$$(x + 2)x + (x + 2)3 = x^2 + 2x + 3x + 6 = x^2 + 5x + 6$$

You may want to write the Distributive Property and the Commutative Property for Addition and Multiplication on the board. Ask the class to give examples of each. Tell the class that they will be using the Distributive Property to write equivalent expressions.

Let the class work in pairs.

Explore 1.4

Look for students who may be struggling. This is an opportunity for you to assess how well your students understand the Distributive Property.

After Questions A and B, discuss as a class some strategies for using the Distributive Property. It is important that throughout this unit you continue to make sure that students are using the Distributive Property correctly in the Explore. Have students work on the rest of the problem.

Suggested Question For Question C, ask:

- *What is an equivalent expression for* $(s + 2)^2$? [Students may need help recognizing that $(s + 2)^2$ can be written as $(s + 2)(s + 2)$.]

Question C is a good time to ask students about the order of operations. Ask class to describe the order of operations. For Sal's expression $2s + 2(s + 2)$, you first perform the multiplication using the Distributive Property. Then you can combine $2s + 2s$ getting a final expression of $4s + 4$.

Make sure that students understand what Question E is asking them to do. They are to place a set of parentheses in the equations, so that the expression on the right side is equivalent to the expression on the left side.

Summarize 1.4

Go over Questions C–E. For Question C, you could include other equations that occurred in your class for the Problem 1.1 as a check on their understanding.

Suggested Questions For Question D, if students do not use linearity in their answer, ask:

- *Suppose y = expression. What relationship does each equation (or expression) represent?* (The relationship associated with the expression is a linear relationship.)

- *What must be true about equivalent linear expressions?* (Each expression represents a quantity that is the dependent variable. They have identical graphs. The rate of change between the independent variable and implied dependent variable or slope of the line for each equation must be the same.)
- *How could you use this information to show which expression is not equivalent?* (The expression that does not have the same slope as the other three is not equivalent. Its graph and table will also be different.)

After the class has shared their reasoning for Question E, challenge the class to find another way to write an expression like $6p + 2 - 2p$ using parentheses and to give the resulting expression. The rest of the class can guess how the student placed the parentheses. For example, a student may give $12 - 6p$. For this to happen the parentheses would have to occur as follows: $6(p + 2 - 2p)$.

1.4 Diving In

At a Glance

PACING 1 day

Mathematical Goals

- Review the Distributive Property
- Write equivalent expressions using the Distributive Property
- Determine if two or more expressions are equivalent by using the Distributive Property and other properties of the real numbers

Launch

Materials

- Transparency 1.4

Vocabulary

- Distributive Property

Display Transparency 1.4.

- *Find two equivalent expressions for the area of each rectangle.*
- *Explain how these illustrate the Distributive Property.*

Write an expression such as $30(x + 10)$ or $(x + 2)(x + 3)$ on the board.

$$30(x + 10) = 30x + 300$$

$$(x + 2)(x + 3) = (x + 2)x + (x + 2)3 =$$

$$(x + 2)x + (x + 2)3 = x^2 + 2x + 3x + 6 = x^2 + 5x + 6$$

Write the Distributive Property and the Commutative Property for Addition and Multiplication on the board. Have students give examples of each.

Let the class work in pairs.

Explore

After Questions A and B, discuss as a class some strategies for using the Distributive Property. It is important that throughout this unit you continue to make sure that students are using the Distributive Property correctly in the Explore.

Have students work on the rest of the problem. For Question C, ask:

- *What is an equivalent expression for $(s + 2)^2$?*

For Question C, ask students about the order of operations.

- *Describe how you can use the order of operations on Sal's expression $2x + 2(x + 2)$.*

Explain that for Question E, they must place a set of parentheses in the equations so that the expression on the right side is equivalent to the expression on the left side.

continued on next page

Summarize

Go over Questions C–E. For Question C, include other equations that occurred in your class for Problem 1.1 as a check for understanding. For Question D, if students do not use linearity in their answer, ask:

- *What relationship does each expression represent?*
- *What must be true about equivalent linear expressions?*
- *How could you use this information to show which expression is not equivalent?*

After Question E, challenge students to find another way to write the expression $6p + 2 - 2p$ using parentheses and to give the resulting expression.

Materials

- Student notebooks

ACE Assignment Guide for Problem 1.4

Core 8, 9, 12–14, 51

Other *Applications* 7, 10, 11, 15–17; *Connections* 52–56, *Extensions* 59; unassigned choices from previous problems

Adapted For suggestions about adapting ACE exercises, see the CMP *Special Needs Handbook*.

Connecting to Prior Units 52–54: *Moving Straight Ahead*; 55: *Filling and Wrapping*; 56: *Accentuate the Negative*

Answers to Problem 1.4

A. **1.** $3x + 15$

2. $6x - 20$

3. $2x^2 + 10x$

4. $x^2 + 2x + 5x + 10$ or $x^2 + 7x + 10$

B. **1.** $12(1 + 2x)$

2. $3(x + 2)$; since $x + x + x + 6 = x(1 + 1 + 1) + 6 = 3x + 6$, the factored form is $3(x + 2)$

3. $x(x + 3)$

4. $(x + 3)(x + 1)$

C. $4(s + 1) = 4s + 4$

$s + s + s + s + 4 = 1s + 1s + 1s + 1s + 4 = s(1 + 1 + 1 + 1) + 4 = s(4) + 4 = 4s + 4$

For this, you many have to remind students that $s = 1s$. Students may also reason that $s + s + s + s$ is the same as taking s four times or $4 \times s$.

$2s + 2(s + 2) = 2s + 2s + 4 = (2 + 2)s + 4 = 4s + 4$

$4(s + 2) - 4 = 4s + 8 - 4 = 4s + 4$

$(s + 2)^2 - s^2 = s^2 + 4s + 4 - s^2 = 4s + 4$

D. Expression 2; $(12 - 2)x + 10 = 10x + 10$, which is not equivalent to the other three. For the other expressions, using the Commutative and Distributive properties, we find that they all are equivalent to $10 - 10x$:

$2x - 12x + 10 = (2 - 12)x + 10 = -10x + 10 = 10 - 10x$ and $10(1 - x) = 10 - 10x$

Explanations may vary. You could graph all the equations and see if they make the same graph. You could make a table and see if the entries are different. Since all the expressions are linear, you could test two values in each expression. If the values of the expressions are different for either of the two values, then the expressions are not equivalent.

E. **1.** $6(p + 2) - 2p = 4p + 12$

2. $6p + (2 - 2)p = 6p$

Investigation 1

Equivalent Expressions

When you want to communicate an idea in words, you can usually express it in many ways. All the statements below communicate the same information about Mika and Jim.

- Jim is older than Mika.
- Mika is younger than Jim.
- Jim was born before Mika.
- Mika was born after Jim.

Can you think of other ways to express the same idea?

Symbolic expressions, formulas, and equations are valuable tools in mathematics. The formula $P = 2L + 2W$ gives directions for calculating the perimeter of any rectangle with length L and width W.

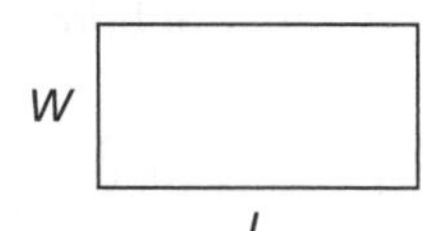

Since you can usually think about a situation in more than one way, you can often express the situation in symbols in more than one way.

Getting Ready for Problem  1.1

Jim says the perimeter of the rectangle above is $P = 2(L + W)$. Mika says the perimeter is $P = 2L + 2W$.

- Why do you think Jim used parentheses in his equation?
- Are the expressions $2L + 2W$ and $2(L + W)$ *equivalent*? Do they produce the same perimeter for any given pair of lengths and widths? Explain your reasoning.

Notes

Since $2(L + W)$ and $2L + 2W$ represent the same quantity (the perimeter of a rectangle), they are **equivalent expressions.** This investigation explores situations in which a quantity is described with several different, but equivalent, expressions. The question is:

How can we determine if two expressions are equivalent?

1.1 Tiling Pools

In-ground pools are often surrounded by borders of tiles. The Custom Pool Company gets orders for square pools of different sizes. For example, the pool at the right has side lengths of 5 feet and is surrounded by square border tiles. All Custom Pool border tiles measure 1 foot on each side.

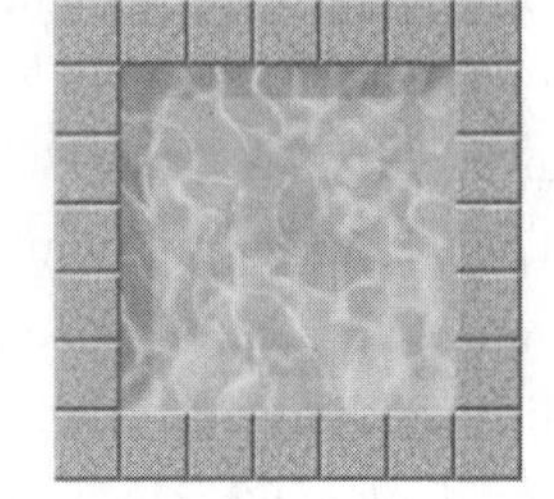

- How many border tiles do you need to surround a square pool?

Problem 1.1 Writing Equivalent Expressions

In order to calculate the number of tiles needed for a project, the Custom Pool manager wants an equation relating the number of border tiles to the size of the pool.

A. 1. Write an expression for the number of border tiles N based on the side length s of a square pool.

2. Write a different but equivalent expression for the number of tiles N needed to surround such a square pool.

3. Explain why your two expressions for the number of border tiles are equivalent.

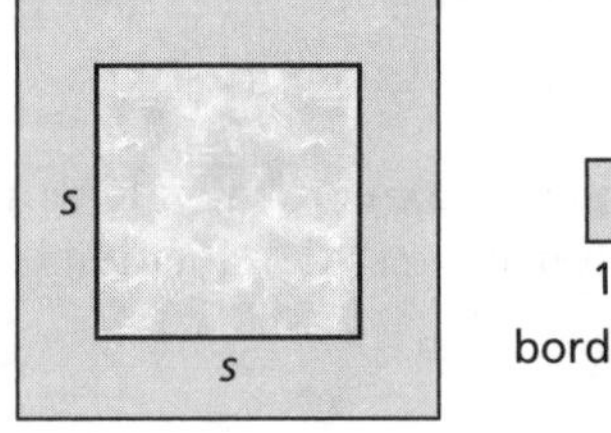

B. 1. Use each expression in Question A to write an equation for the number of border tiles N. Make a table and a graph for each equation.

2. Based on your table and graph, are the two expressions for the number of border tiles in Question A equivalent? Explain.

C. Is the relationship between the side length of the pool and the number of border tiles linear, exponential, quadratic, or none of these? Explain.

ACE Homework starts on page 12.

Notes

1.2 Thinking in Different Ways

When Takashi reported his ideas about an equation relating N and s in Problem 1.1, he made the following sketch.

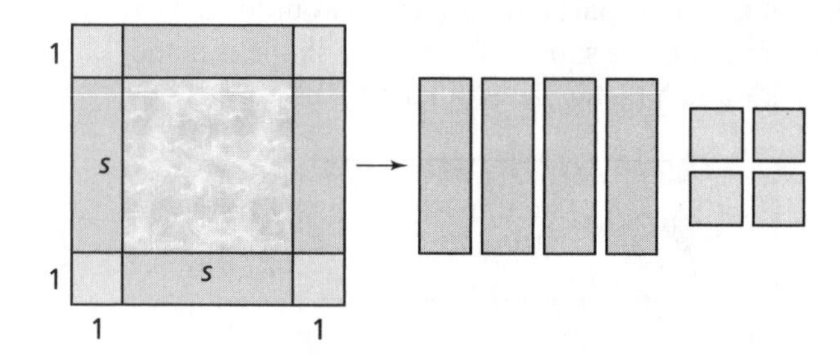

- What equation do you think Takashi wrote to relate N and s?

Problem 1.2 Determining Equivalence

A. Four students in Takashi's class came up with different equations for counting the number of border tiles. For each equation, make a sketch that shows how the student might have been thinking about the border of the pool.

1. Stella's equation: $N = 4(s + 1)$
2. Jeri's equation: $N = s + s + s + s + 4$
3. Hank's equation: $N = 4(s + 2)$
4. Sal's equation: $N = 2s + 2(s + 2)$

B. Use each equation in Question A to find the number of border tiles needed for a square pool with a side length of 10 feet. Can you conclude from your results that all the expressions for the number of tiles are equivalent? Explain your reasoning.

C. Which of the expressions for the number of border tiles in Question A are equivalent to Takashi's expression? Explain.

ACE Homework starts on page 12.

For: Algebra Tools Activity
Visit: PHSchool.com
Web Code: apd-6102

Notes

The Community Pool Problem

In this problem, we will interpret symbolic statements and use them to make predictions.

A community center is building a pool, part indoor and part outdoor. A diagram of the indoor part of the pool is shown. The indoor shape is made from a half-circle with radius x and a rectangle with length $4x$.

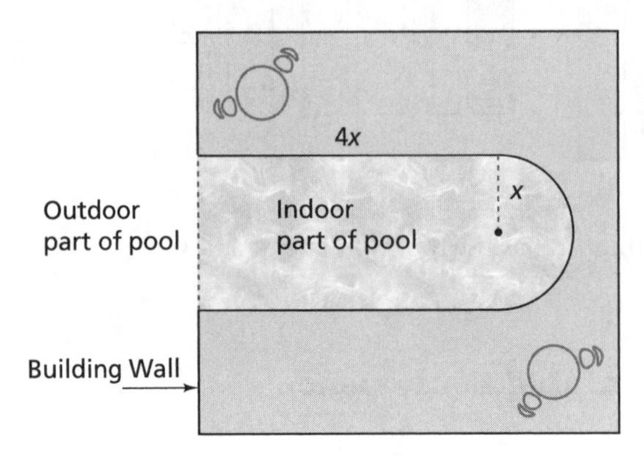

Problem 1.3 Interpreting Expressions

The exact dimensions of the community center pool are not available, but the area A of the whole pool is given by the equation:

$$A = x^2 + \frac{\pi x^2}{2} + 8x^2 + \frac{\pi x^2}{4}$$

A. Which part of the expression for area represents

1. the area of the indoor part of the pool? Explain.
2. the area of the outdoor part of the pool? Explain.

B. 1. Make a sketch of the outdoor part. Label the dimensions.

2. If possible, draw another shape for the outdoor part of the pool. If not, explain why not.

STUDENT PAGE

Notes

C. Stella and Jeri each rewrote the expression for the area of the outdoor part of the pool to help them make a sketch.

$$\text{Stella: } x^2 + \frac{\pi x^2}{8} + \frac{\pi x^2}{8}$$

$$\text{Jeri: } \left(\tfrac{1}{2}x\right)\left(2x\right) + \frac{\pi x^2}{4}$$

1. Explain the reasoning each person may have used to write their expression.
2. Decide if these expressions are equivalent to the original expression in Question A, part (2). Explain your reasoning.

D. Does the equation for the area of the pool represent a linear, exponential, or quadratic relationship, or none of these? Explain.

ACE **Homework starts on page 12.**

1.4 Diving In

In the pool tile problems, you found patterns that could be represented by several different but equivalent symbolic expressions, such as:

$$4s + 4$$
$$4(s + 1)$$
$$s + s + s + s + 4$$
$$2s + 2(s + 2)$$

The equivalence of these expressions can be shown with arrangements of tiles. Equivalence also follows from properties of numbers and operations.

An important property is the **Distributive Property:**

For any real numbers a, b, and c:

$$a(b + c) = ab + ac \text{ and } a(b - c) = ab - ac$$

For example, this property guarantees that $4(s + 1) = 4s + 4$ for any s.

We say that $a(b + c)$ and $4(s + 1)$ are in *factored form* and $ab + ac$ and $4s + 4$ are in *expanded form*.

The next problem reviews the Distributive Property.

Notes

Getting Ready for Problem 1.4

Swimming pools are sometimes divided into sections that are used for different purposes. A pool may have a section for swimming laps and a section for diving, or a section for experienced swimmers and a section for small children.

Below are diagrams of pools with swimming and diving sections. The dimensions are in meters.

1.

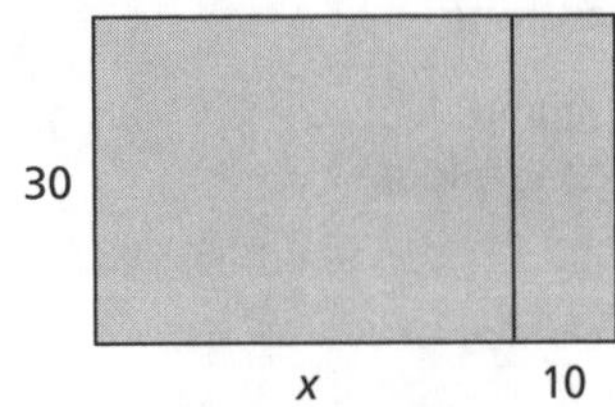

2.

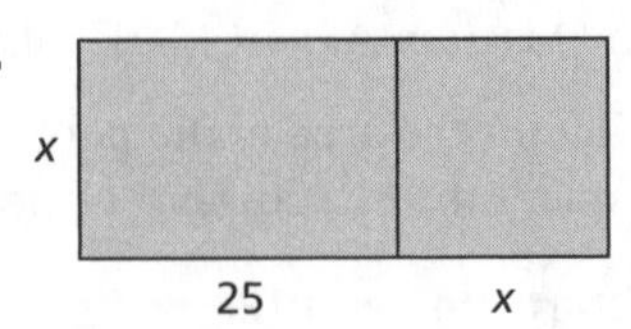

3.

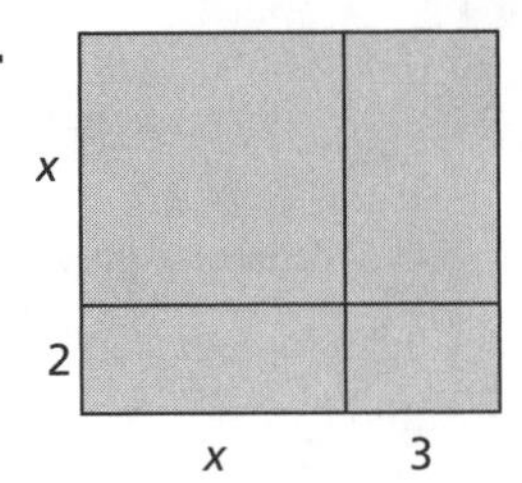

4.

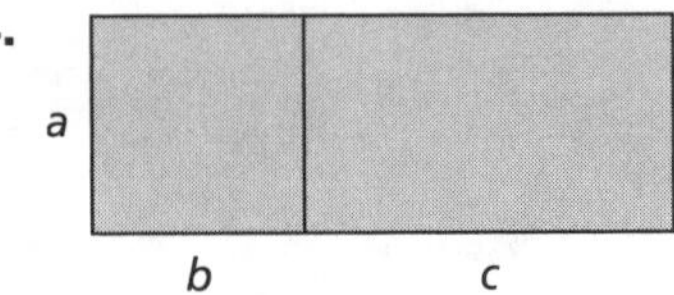

- For each pool, write two different but equivalent expressions for the total area.
- Explain how these diagrams and expressions illustrate the Distributive Property.

Notes

The Distributive Property, as well as the Commutative Property and other properties for numbers, are useful for writing equivalent expressions. The Commutative Property states that $a + b = b + a$ and $ab = ba$, where a and b are real numbers. These properties were discussed in previous units.

Problem 1.4 Revisiting the Distributive Property

A. Write each expression in expanded form.

1. $3(x + 5)$ **2.** $2(3x - 10)$

3. $2x(x + 5)$ **4.** $(x + 2)(x + 5)$

B. Write each expression in factored form.

1. $12 + 24x$ **2.** $x + x + x + 6$

3. $x^2 + 3x$ **4.** $x^2 + 4x + 3$

C. The following expressions all represent the number of border tiles N for a square pool with side length s.

$$4(s + 1)$$
$$s + s + s + s + 4$$
$$2s + 2(s + 2)$$
$$4(s + 2) - 4$$
$$(s + 2)^2 - s^2$$

Use the Distributive and Commutative properties to show that these expressions are equivalent.

D. Three of the following expressions are equivalent. Explain which expression is not equivalent to the other three.

1. $2x - 12x + 10$ **2.** $12x - 2x + 10$

3. $10 - 10x$ **4.** $10(1 - x)$

E. Copy each equation. Insert one set of parentheses in the expression to the left of the equal sign so that it is equivalent to the expression to the right of the equal sign.

1. $6p + 2 - 2p = 4p + 12$

2. $6p + 2 - 2p = 6p$

ACE **Homework starts on page 12.**

STUDENT PAGE

Notes

Applications

1. a. How many 1-foot-square border tiles do you need to surround a pool that is 10 feet long and 5 feet wide?

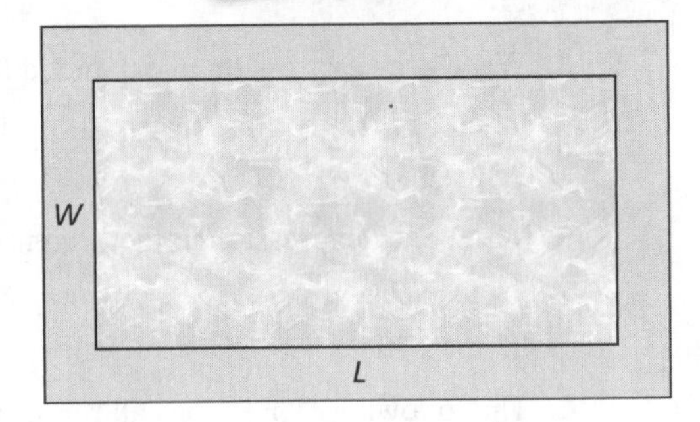

   b. Write an equation for the number of border tiles needed to surround a pool L feet long and W feet wide.

   c. Write a different but equivalent equation for the number of tiles needed in part (b). Explain why your equations are equivalent.

2. A square hot tub has sides of length s feet. A tiler creates a border by placing 1-foot-square tiles along the edges of the tub and triangular tiles at the corners, as shown. The tiler makes the triangular tiles by cutting the square tiles in half along a diagonal.

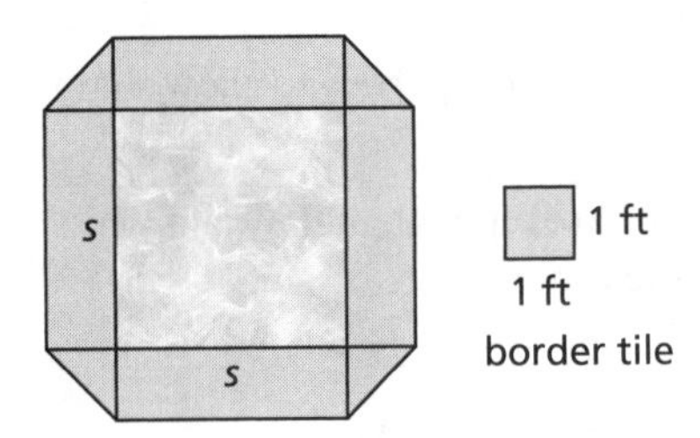

   a. Suppose the hot tub has sides of length 7 feet. How many square tiles does the tiler need for the border?

   b. Write an expression for the number of square tiles N needed to build this border for a square tub with sides of length s feet.

   c. Write a different but equivalent expression for the number of tiles N. Explain why your expressions for the number of border tiles are equivalent.

   d. Is the relationship between the number of tiles and side length linear, exponential, quadratic, or none of these? Explain.

Notes

3. A rectangular pool is L feet long and W feet wide. A tiler creates a border by placing 1-foot-square tiles along the edges of the pool and triangular tiles on the corners, as shown. The tiler makes the triangular tiles by cutting the square tiles in half along a diagonal.

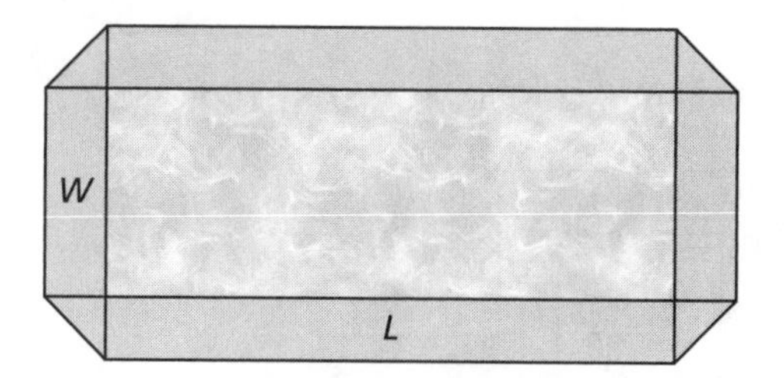

For: Help with Exercise 3
Web Code: ape-6103

a. Suppose the pool is 30 feet long and 20 feet wide. How many square tiles does the tiler need for the border?

b. Write two equations for the number of square tiles N needed to make this border for a pool L feet long and W feet wide.

c. Explain why your two equations are equivalent.

4. Below are three more expressions students wrote for the number of border tiles needed to surround the square pool in Problem 1.2.

$4\left(\frac{s}{2} + \frac{s}{4}\right) + 4$ $\quad$ $2\left(s + 0.5\right) + 2\left(s + 1.5\right)$ $\quad$ $4\left[\frac{s + (s + 2)}{2}\right]$

a. Use each expression to find the number of border tiles N if $s = 0$.

b. Do you think the expressions are equivalent? Explain.

c. Use each expression to find the number of border tiles if $s = 12$. Has your answer to part (b) changed? Explain.

d. What can you say about testing specific values as a method for determining whether two or more expressions are equivalent?

Notes

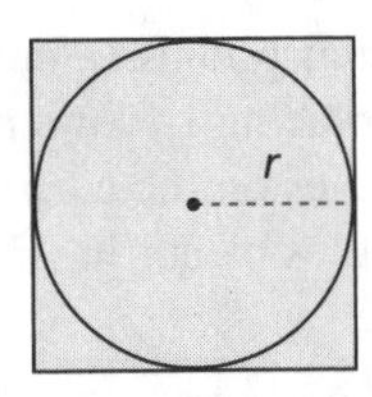

5. A square surrounds a circle with a radius r. Each expression represents the area of part of this figure. Describe the shape or region each area represents.

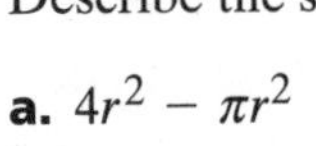

a. $4r^2 - \pi r^2$ **b.** $4r^2 - \frac{\pi r^2}{4}$

6. The dimensions of a pool are shown below.

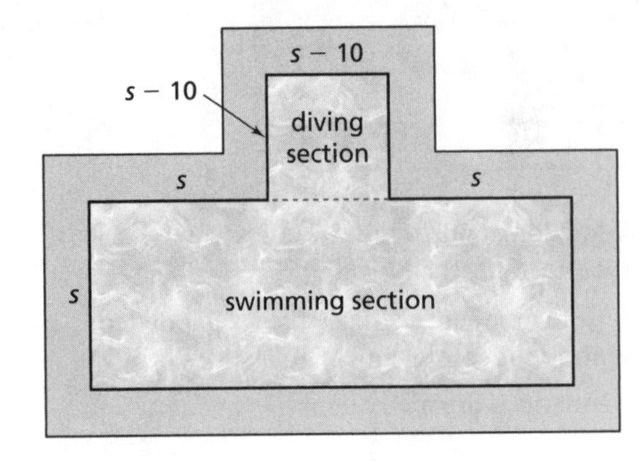

Each expression represents the surface area for part of the pool.

i. $s(3s - 10)$ **ii.** $(s - 10)^2$

iii. $2s^2 + s(s - 10)$ **iv.** $s^2 - 20s + 100$

a. Which expression(s) could represent the surface area of the diving section?

b. Which expression(s) could represent the surface area of the swimming section?

c. If you chose more than one expression for parts (a) and (b), show that they are equivalent.

d. Write an equation that represents the total surface area A of the pool.

e. What kind of relationship does the equation in part (d) represent?

Notes ______________________________

For Exercises 7–9, complete parts (a)–(c).

a. For each expression, write an equation of the form $y =$ *expression.* Make a table and a graph of the two equations. Show x values from -5 to 5 on the graph.

b. Based on your table and graph, tell whether you think the two expressions are equivalent.

c. If you think the expressions are equivalent, use the properties you have learned in this investigation to verify their equivalence. If you think they are not equivalent, explain why.

7. $-3x + 6 + 5x$ and $6 + 2x$

8. $10 - 5x$ and $5x - 10$

9. $(3x + 4) + (2x - 3)$ and $5x + 1$

10. Use the Distributive Property to write each expression in expanded form.

a. $3(x + 7)$ **b.** $5(5 - x)$ **c.** $2(4x - 8)$ **d.** $(x + 4)(x + 2)$

11. Use the Distributive Property to write each expression in factored form.

a. $2x - 10x$ **b.** $2x + 6$ **c.** $14 - 7x$

12. Use the Distributive and Commutative properties to determine whether each pair of expressions is equivalent for all values of x.

a. $3x + 7x$ and $10x$ **b.** $5x$ and $5x - 10x$

c. $4(1 + 2x) - 3x$ and $5x + 4$ **d.** $5 - 3(2 - 4x)$ and $-1 + 12x$

13. Here is one way you might prove that $2(s + 2) + 2s$ is equivalent to $4s + 4$:

(1) $2(s + 2) + 2s = 2s + 4 + 2s$

(2) $= 2s + 2s + 4$

(3) $= (2 + 2)s + 4$

(4) $= 4s + 4$

What properties of numbers and operations justify each step?

14. Find three equivalent expressions for $6x + 3$.

For Exercises 15–17, copy the statement. Insert parentheses on the left side of the equation, if necessary, to make the statement true for all values of *p*.

15. $7 + 5p - p = 11p$

16. $7 + 5p - p = 7$

17. $7 + 5p - p = 7 + 4p$

Notes

Connections

In Exercises 18–23, each expression represents the area of a rectangle. Draw a divided rectangle for each expression. Label the lengths and areas. For Exercises 18–20, write an equivalent expression in expanded form. For Exercises 21–23, write an equivalent expression in factored form.

18. $x(x + 6)$ **19.** $x(x - 6)$ **20.** $x(5 + 1)$

21. $x^2 + 4x$ **22.** $x^2 - 2x$ **23.** $3x + 4x$

24. A circular pool with a radius of 4 feet has a 1-foot border.

a. What is the surface area of the circular pool?

b. What is the surface area of the border?

c. Write an expression for the surface area of a circular pool with a radius of r feet.

d. Write an expression for the area of a 1-foot border around a circular pool with a radius of r feet.

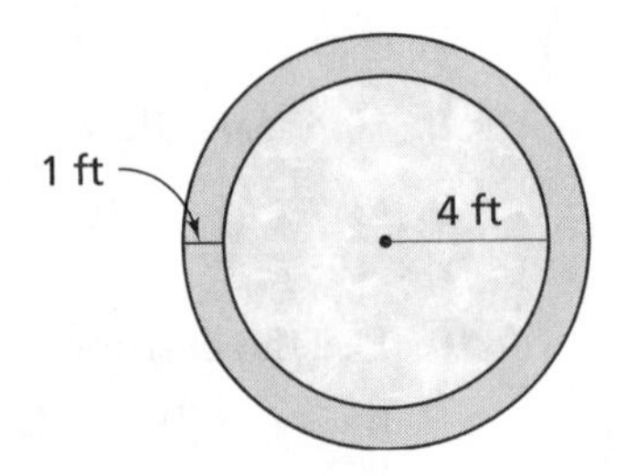

25. Multiple Choice Which of the following expressions is equivalent to $m + m + m + m + m$?

A. $m + 5$ **B.** $5m$ **C.** m^5 **D.** $5(m + 1)$

26. Multiple Choice Which of the following expressions is equivalent to $a - b$, where a and b are any numbers?

F. $b - a$ **G.** $a + b$ **H.** $-a + b$ **J.** $-b + a$

For Exercises 27–32, draw and label a rectangle whose area is represented by the expression. For Exercises 27–29, write an equivalent expression in expanded form. For Exercises 30–32, write an equivalent expression in factored form.

27. $(x + 1)(x + 4)$ **28.** $(x + 5)(x + 6)$ **29.** $3x(5 + 2)$

30. $x^2 + x + 2x + 2$ **31.** $x^2 + 7x + 10$ **32.** $x^2 + 14x + 49$

Find each sum or difference.

33. $\frac{5}{7} - \frac{1}{3}$ **34.** $\frac{5}{2} + \frac{1}{3}$

35. $\frac{1}{2}x + \frac{1}{2}x$ **36.** $\frac{2}{3}x - \frac{1}{2}x$

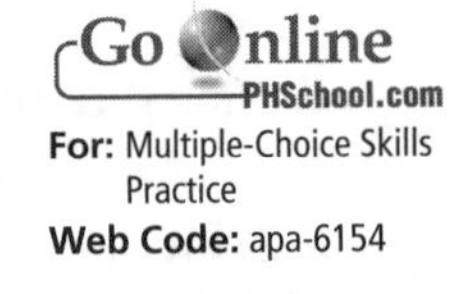

For: Multiple-Choice Skills Practice
Web Code: apa-6154

Notes

Find each sum, difference, product, or quotient.

37. 2×14

38. $-2 - (-14)$

39. $-2 \div (-14)$

40. $-6 \times (-11)$

41. $-6 + 11$

42. $6 - 11$

43. $-18(3x)$

44. $\frac{-24x}{-8}$

45. $-18x \div 3$

Find the greatest common factor for each pair of numbers.

46. 35 and 40

47. 36 and 12

48. 100 and 25

49. 42 and 9

50. Below is a diagram of Otter Middle School's outdoor track. The shape of the interior region (shaded green) is a rectangle with two half circles at each end.

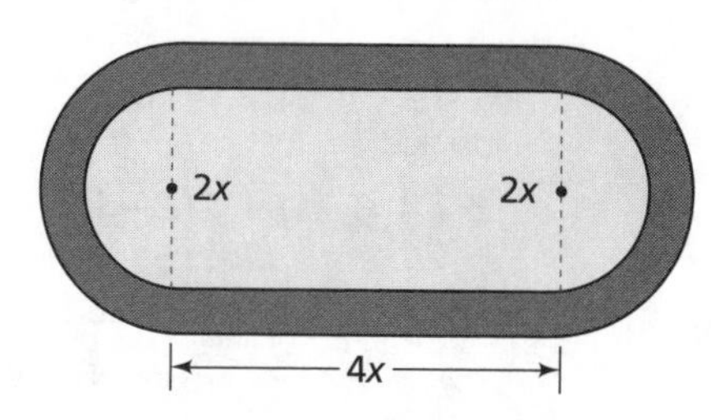

a. Find an expression that represents the area of the interior region.

b. Find the perimeter of the interior region as if you wanted to put a fence around it. Explain how you found your answer.

c. Write an expression equivalent to the one in part (b).

Connections

STUDENT PAGE

STUDENT PAGE

Notes

51. For Problem 1.2, Percy wrote the expression $8 + 4(s - 1)$ to represent the number of border tiles needed to surround a square pool with side length s.

a. Is this expression equivalent to the other expressions? Explain.

b. Four students used Percy's expression to calculate the number of border tiles needed for a pool with a side length of 6 feet. Which student performed the calculations correctly?

Stella

$8 + 4(6 - 1) = 8 + 24 - 1$
$= 31$ tiles

Hank

$8 + 4(6 - 1) = 8 + 4(5)$
$= 8 + 20$
$= 28$ tiles

Takashi

$8 + 4(6 - 1) = 12 + (6 - 1)$
$= 12 + 5$
$= 17$ tiles

Jackie

$8 + 4(6 - 1) = 12(6 - 1)$
$= 12(5)$
$= 60$ tiles

52. Lily invests D dollars in a money-market account that earns 10% interest per year. She does not plan on taking money out during the year. She writes the expression $D + 0.10D$ to represent the amount of money in the account at the end of one year.

a. Explain why this expression is correct.

b. Write an equivalent expression in factored form.

c. Suppose Lily invested $1,500. How much money will she have in her account at the end of one year?

STUDENT PAGE

Notes

For Exercises 53 and 54, use this information: The ski club is planning a trip for winter break. They write the equation $C = 200 + 10N$ to estimate the cost in dollars C of the trip for N students.

53. Duncan and Corey both use the equation to estimate the cost for 50 students. Duncan says the cost is $10,500, and Corey says it is $700.

a. Whose estimate is correct? Show your work.

b. How do you think Duncan and Corey found such different estimates if they both used the same equation?

54. a. Suppose 20 students go on the trip. What is the cost per student?

b. Write an equation for the cost per student S when N students go on the trip.

c. Use your equation to find the cost per student when 40 students go on the trip.

55. The pyramid and rectangular prism have the same base and height.

a. Find the volume of the pyramid.

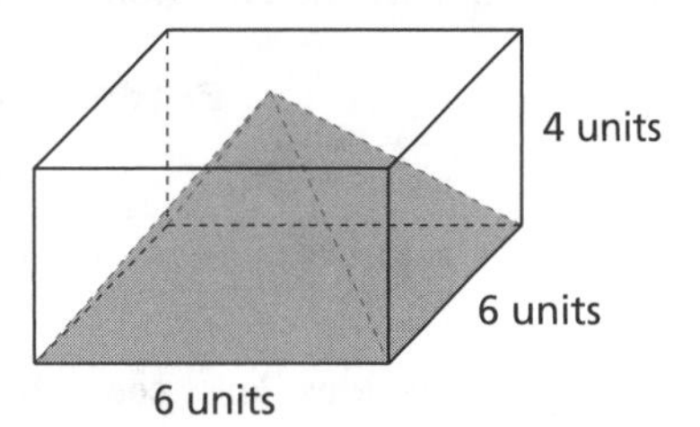

b. Draw a pyramid with a volume of $\left(\frac{1}{3}\right)(8)$ cubic units.

Hint: You might find it easier to draw the related prism first.

c. Draw a pyramid with a volume of $\left(\frac{1}{3}\right)(27)$ cubic units.

d. Find a possible height of a pyramid whose volume is $9x^3$ cubic units.

Connections

STUDENT PAGE

Notes

56. Below are two students' calculations for writing an equivalent expression for $10 - 4(x - 1) + 11 \times 3$.

a. Which student performed the calculations correctly?

b. What mistakes did the other student make?

Sarah

$$\begin{aligned} 10 - 4(x-1) + 11 \times 3 &= 10 - 4x + 4 + 11 \times 3 \\ &= 10 - 4x + 4 + 33 \\ &= 10 - 4x + 37 \\ &= 10 + 37 - 4x \\ &= 47 - 4x \end{aligned}$$

Emily

$$\begin{aligned} 10 - 4(x-1) + 11 \times 3 &= 10 - 4x + 4 + 11 \times 3 \\ &= 10 - 4x + 15 \times 3 \\ &= 25 - 4x \times 3 \\ &= 25 - 12x \end{aligned}$$

Extensions

57. Percy wants to write an equation for the number of tiles needed to surround a square pool with sides of length s feet. He makes a table for pools with sides of length 1, 2, 3, 4, and 5 feet. Then he uses the patterns in his table to write the equation $N = 8 + 4(s - 1)$.

Border Tiles

Side Length	1	2	3	4	5
Number of Tiles	8	12	16	20	24

a. What patterns does Percy see in his table?

b. Is Percy's expression for the number of tiles equivalent to $4(s + 1)$, Stella's expression in Problem 1.2? Explain.

STUDENT PAGE

Notes

58. Two expressions for the number of border tiles for the pool at the right are given.

$2(s + 0.5) + 2(s + 1.5)$

$4\left[\frac{s + (s + 2)}{2}\right]$

Sketch a picture that illustrates each expression.

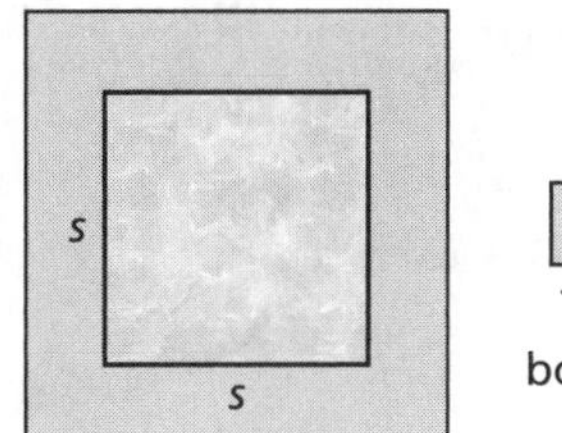

1 ft
1 ft
border tile

59. The *Expression Puzzles* below all start with the original expression $2n - 3 + 4n + 6n + 1$. Each one ends with a different expression.

a. Solve each puzzle by inserting one set of parentheses in the original expression so that it is equivalent to the desired result.

b. Show that your expression is equivalent to the desired result. Justify each step.

Expression Puzzles

Puzzle	Original Expression	Desired Result
1	$2n - 3 + 4n + 6n + 1$	$12n - 5$
2	$2n - 3 + 4n + 6n + 1$	$12n + 3$
3	$2n - 3 + 4n + 6n + 1$	$12n - 2$
4	$2n - 3 + 4n + 6n + 1$	$n + 1$

Connections Extensions

STUDENT PAGE

STUDENT PAGE

Notes

Mathematical Reflections 1

In this investigation, you found different but equivalent expressions to represent a quantity in a relationship. These questions will help you summarize what you have learned.

Think about your answers to these questions. Discuss your ideas with other students and your teacher. Then write a summary of your findings in your notebook.

1. What does it mean to say that two expressions are equivalent?
2. Explain how the Distributive and Commutative properties can be used to write equivalent expressions.
3. Explain how the Distributive and Commutative properties can be used to show that two or more expressions are equivalent.

STUDENT PAGE

Notes

Investigation 1

ACE Assignment Choices

Problem 1.1

Core 1, 2, 18–20
Other *Connections* 21–24

Problem 1.2

Core 3, 4, 25, 26
Other *Connections* 27–32; *Extensions* 57, 58; unassigned choices from previous problems

Problem 1.3

Core 5, 6
Other *Connections* 33–50; unassigned choices from previous problems

Problem 1.4

Core 8, 9, 12–14, 51
Other *Applications* 7, 10, 11, 15–17; *Connections* 52–56, *Extensions* 59; unassigned choices from previous problems

Adapted For suggestions about adapting Exercise 3 and other ACE exercises, see the CMP *Special Needs Handbook.*
Connecting to Prior Units 18–23, 27–32: *Frogs, Fleas, and Painted Cubes*; 24, 50: *Covering and Surrounding*; 25, 52–54: *Moving Straight Ahead*; 26, 37–45, 56: *Accentuate the Negative*; 33–36: *Bits and Pieces II*; 46–49: *Prime Time*; 55: *Filling and Wrapping*

Applications

1. a. $2(10) + 2(5) + 4 = 34$ tiles

   b. Possible equations:
   $N = 2L + 2W + 4$
   $N = 2(L + 1) + 2(W + 1)$
   $N = 2(L + 2) + 2W$
   $N = 2L + 2(W + 2)$

   c. See part (b) for some equations; explanations will vary. Students might draw sketches. For example:

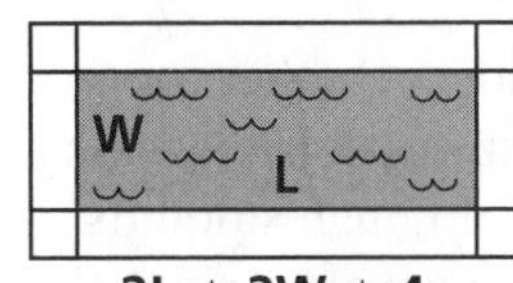

2L + 2W + 4

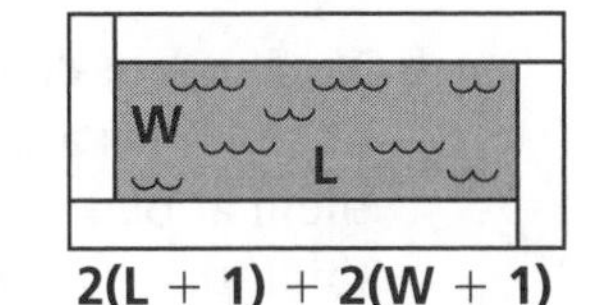

2(L + 1) + 2(W + 1)

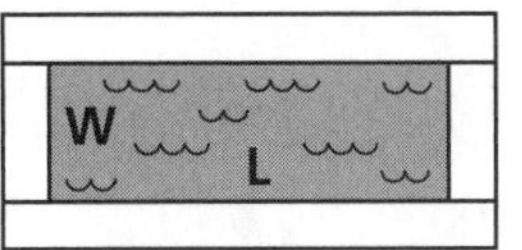

2(L + 2) + 2W

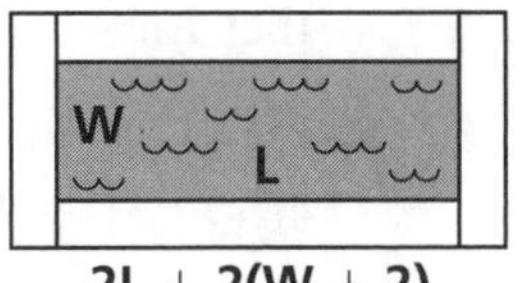

2L + 2(W + 2)

   They might substitute values for L and W in the equations; for example, when $W = 2$ and $L = 3$:
   $N = 2L + 2W + 4 = 2(3) + 2(2) + 4 = 14$
   $N = 2(L + 1) + 2(W + 1) = 2(4) + 2(3) = 14$
   $N = 2(L + 2) + 2W = 2(5) + 2(2) = 14$
   $N = 2L + 2(W + 2) = 2(3) + 2(4) = 14$

2. a. $4(7) + 4(0.5) = 30$ tiles

   b. Possible answers:
   $N = 4s + 2$
   $N = 4(s + 0.5)$
   $N = 2s + 2(s + 1)$

   c. See equations in part (b). Students might substitute values for s [in this case 2 values (s, N) are sufficient because these are linear relationships], generate tables for both equations, or make a geometric argument to show that the two equations are equivalent. They may also graph each equation.

   d. The relationship is linear; students may say that this is because the graphs are straight lines; the table increases by a constant value of 4 for every increase of 1 ft in the side length.

3. a. $2(30) + 2(20) + 2 = 102$ tiles

   b. Possible answers:
   $N = 2L + 2W + 2$
   $N = 2(L + 0.5) + 2(W + 0.5)$
   $N = 2(W + 1) + 2L$

c. Students might substitute values for L and W, create tables or graphs, or make geometric arguments to show that their two equations are equivalent.

4. a. First equation: $4(\frac{0}{2}+\frac{0}{4}) + 4 = 4(0) + 4 = 4$;

Second equation: $2(0 + 0.5) + 2(0 + 1.5) = 2(0.5) + 2(1.5) = 1 + 3 = 4$;

Third equation: $4\left[\frac{0 + (0 + 2)}{2}\right] = 4(\frac{2}{2}) = 4$

b. You cannot determine whether the expressions are equivalent by checking them at one point, although students may think that they are equivalent since these expressions produced the same number of tiles for $s = 0$.

c. First equation: $4(\frac{12}{2} + \frac{12}{4}) + 4 = 4(6 + 3) + 4 = 40$;

Second equation: $2(12 + 0.5) + 2(12 + 1.5) = 2(12.5) + 2(13.5) = 52$;

Third equation: $4\left[\frac{12 + (12 + 2)}{2}\right] = 4(\frac{26}{2}) = 4(13) = 52$

d. Since you can determine non-equivalency of linear equations by checking one point, the first expression is not equal to the second and the third expressions because they did not produce the same number of tiles when you checked using the same side value.

In general, it is not enough to show that two expressions are equivalent when they have the same value at two different points, because you need to check all points, which is impossible. However, for linear equations such as those in this problem, checking only two values would be enough because only one line can pass through the two points. So linear expressions which agree on two values (two points) contain the same two points. So, the lines that they represent must be the same. Students will either need to check all points, which is impossible, or know that two points uniquely determine a line. (This topic was addressed on the Summary Transparency for Problem 1.2.)

5. a. The shape is the area between the circle and the square.

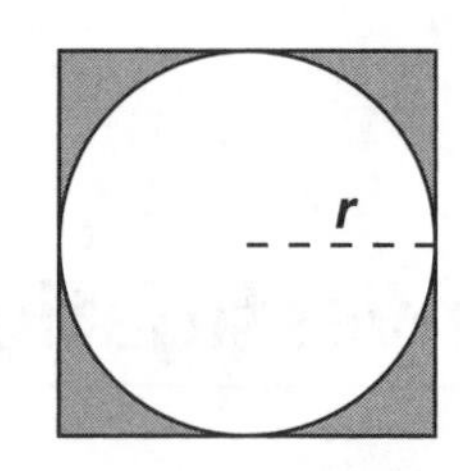

b. The shape is all the area inside the square except a quarter of the area of the circle.

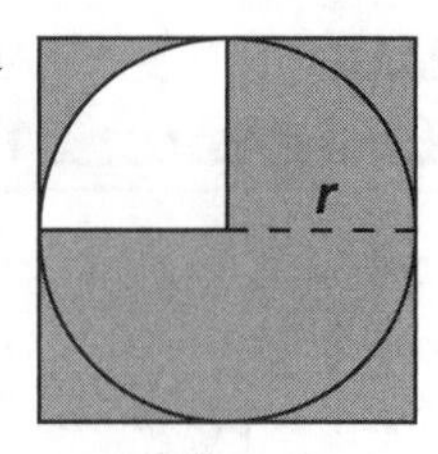

6. a. ii and iv   b. i and iii

c. For part (a), ii and iv are equivalent since:
$(s - 10)^2 = (s - 10)(s - 10) =$
$s(s - 10) - 10(s - 10) =$
$s^2 - 10s - 10s + 100 = s^2 - 20s + 100.$

For part (b), i and iii are equivalent because they both represent the same part of the pool.

d. Answers will vary, but must be equivalent to $A = (s^2 - 20s + 100) + (3s^2 - 10s)$

e. The equation in part (d) is a quadratic relationship.

7. a.

x	$-3x + 6 + 5x$	$6 + 2x$
−3	0	0
−2	2	2
−1	4	4
0	6	6
1	8	8
2	10	10
3	12	12

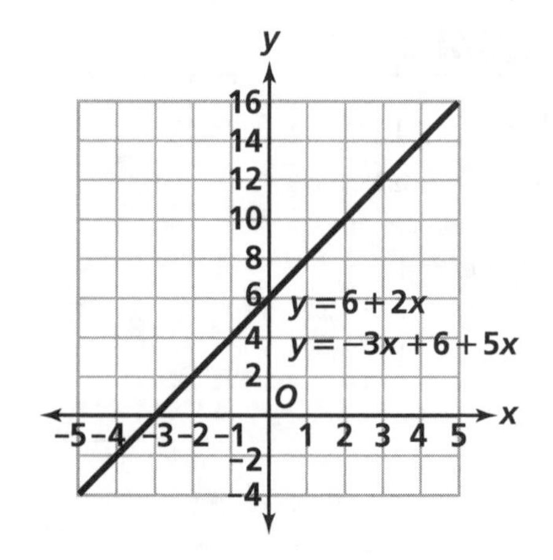

b. The expressions are equivalent because the table values are the same and the graph is a single line. NOTE: These are linear expressions so it is enough to show that they all pass through the same two points.

c. $-3x + 6 + 5x = 6 + -3x + 5x = 6 + (-3 + 5)x = 6 + 2x$

8. a.

x	$10 - 5x$	$5x - 10$
−3	25	−25
−2	20	−20
−1	15	−15
0	10	−10
1	5	−5
2	0	0
3	−5	5

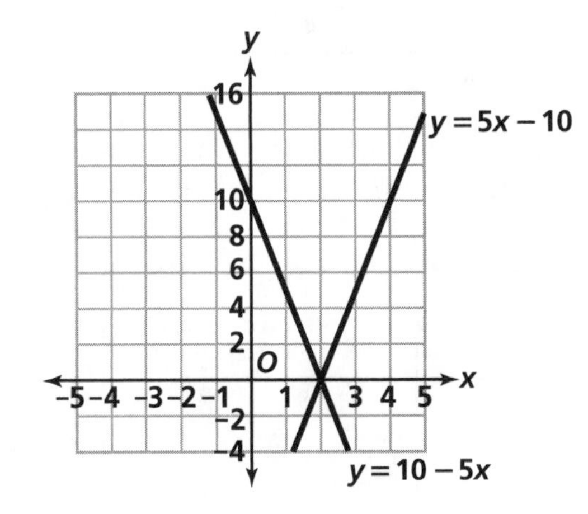

b. The expressions are not equivalent because the table values are different and the graphs are separate lines; one has a negative slope and one has a positive slope.

c. $10 - 5x = -5x + 10 \neq 5x - 10$

9. a.

x	$(3x + 4) + (2x - 3)$	$5x + 1$
−3	−14	−14
−2	−9	−9
−1	−4	−4
0	1	1
1	6	6
2	11	11
3	16	16

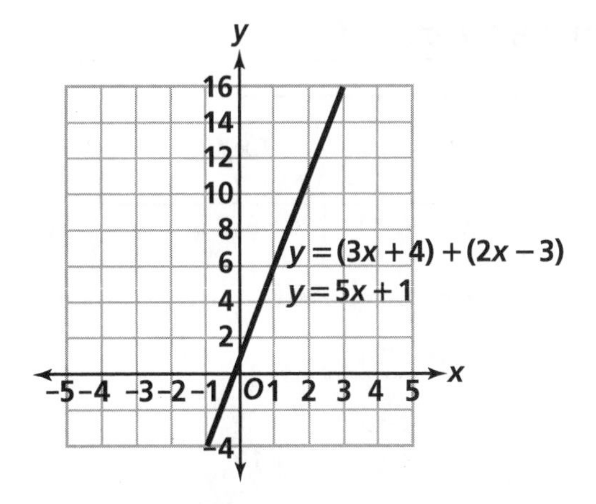

b. The expressions are equivalent because the table values are the same and the graph is a single line. NOTE: These are linear expressions so it is enough to show that they all pass through the same two points.

c. $(3x + 4) + (2x - 3) = 3x + 2x + 4 - 3 = (3 + 2)x + 1 = 5x + 1$

10. a. $3x + 21$

b. $25 - 5x$

c. $8x - 16$

d. $x^2 + 4x + 2x + 8 = x^2 + x(4 + 2) + 8 = x^2 + 6x + 8$

11. a. Possible answers: $2(x - 5x)$ or $x(2 - 10) = -8x$

b. $2(x + 3)$ **c.** $7(2 - x)$

12. a. equal; $3x + 7x = (3 + 7)x = 10x$

b. not equal; $5x - 10x = (5 - 10)x = -5x \neq 5x$

c. equal; $4(1 + 2x) - 3x = 4 + 8x - 3x = 4 + 5x = 5x + 4$
Using the Commutative Property of Addition, $5x + 4 = 4 + 5x$.

d. equal; $5 - 3(2 - 4x) = 5 - 6 + 12x = -1 + 12x$

13. Step (1): Distributive Property
Step (2): Commutative Property
Step (3): Distributive Property
Step (4): Addition

14. Possible answers: $3(2x + 1)$, $x + 5x + 3$, $2x + 2 + 4x + 1$.

15. $(7 + 5)p - p = 11p$

16. $7 + 5(p - p) = 7$

17. Parentheses are not needed.

Connections

18.

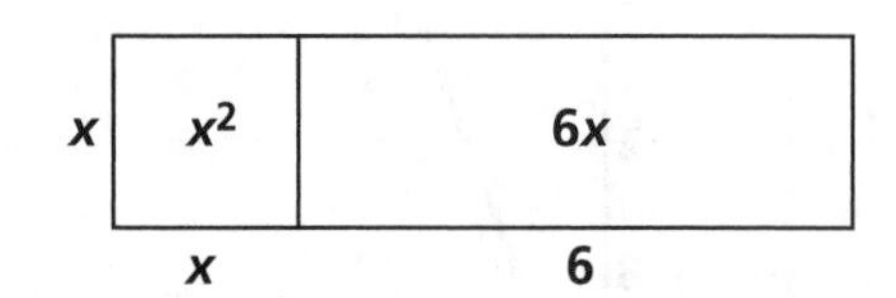

$x(x + 6) = x^2 + 6x$

19.

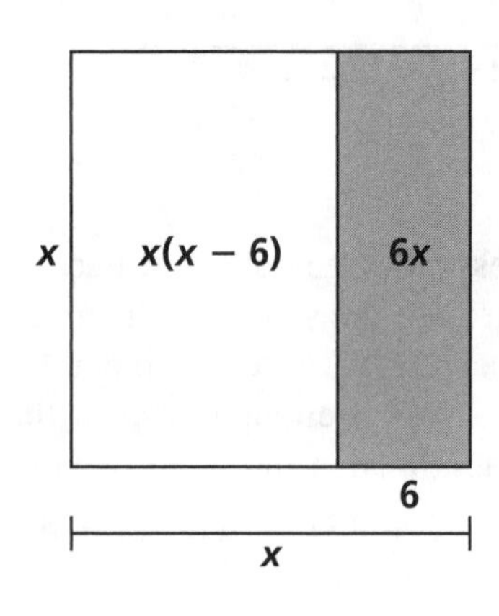

$x(x - 6) = x^2 - 6x$

20.

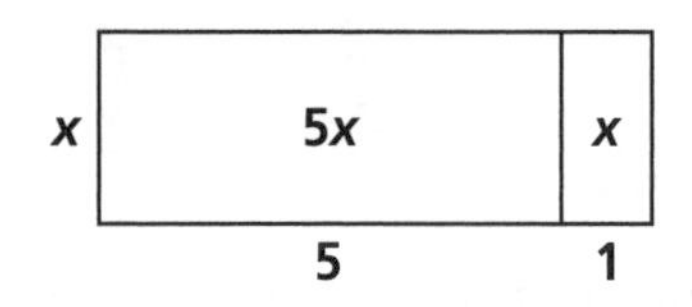

$x(5 + 1) = 5x + x$

21.

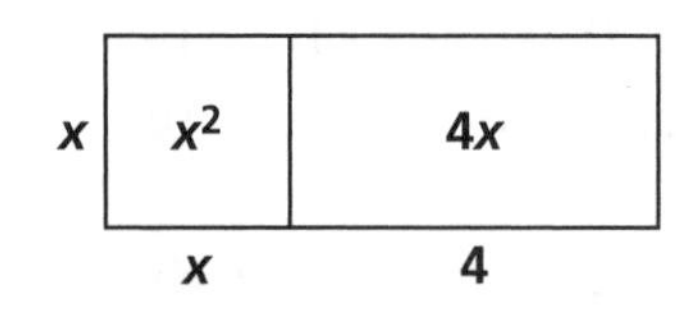

$x^2 + 4x = x(x + 4)$

22.

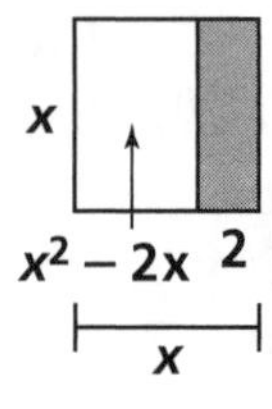

$x^2 - 2x = x(x - 2)$

23.

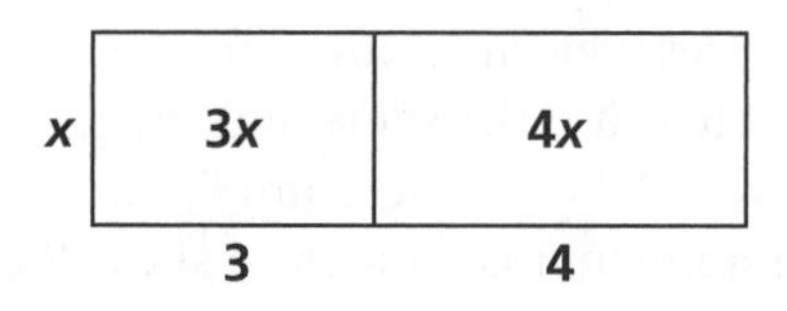

$3x + 4x = x(3 + 4)$ or $7x$

24. **a.** Area of water $= \pi(4)^2 = 16\pi \approx 50$ ft^2

b. Area of border $= \pi(5^2) - \pi(4^2) = 25\pi - 16\pi = 9\pi \approx 28$ ft^2

c. Area of water $= \pi r^2$

d. Area of border $= \pi(r + 1)^2 - \pi r^2$, or $2\pi r + \pi$

25. B

26. J

27.

x	**x^2**	**4x**
1	**x**	**4**
	x	**4**

$(x + 1)(x + 4) = x^2 + 1x + 4x + 4$ or $x^2 + 5x + 4$

28.

x	**x^2**	**6x**
5	**5x**	**30**
	x	**6**

$(x + 5)(x + 6) = x^2 + 5x + 6x + 30$ or $x^2 + 11x + 30$

29.

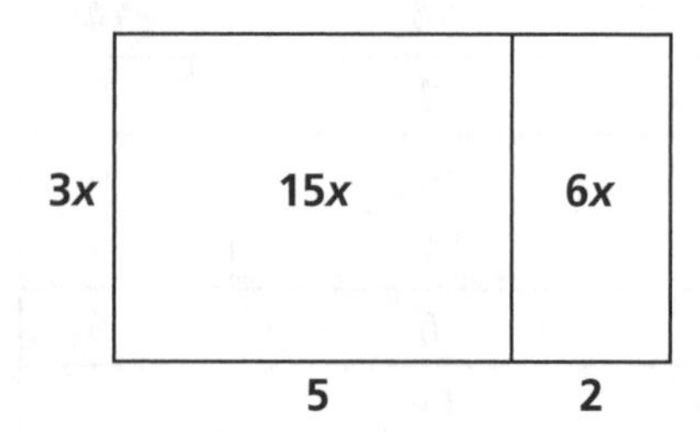

$3x(5 + 2) = 15x + 6x$ or $21x$

30.

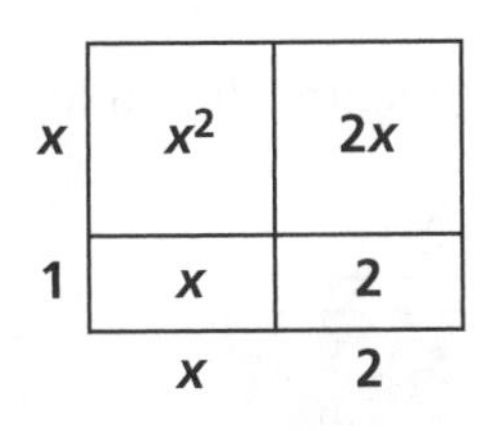

$x^2 + x + 2x + 2 =$

$x^2 + 3x + 2 = (x + 1)(x + 2)$

31.

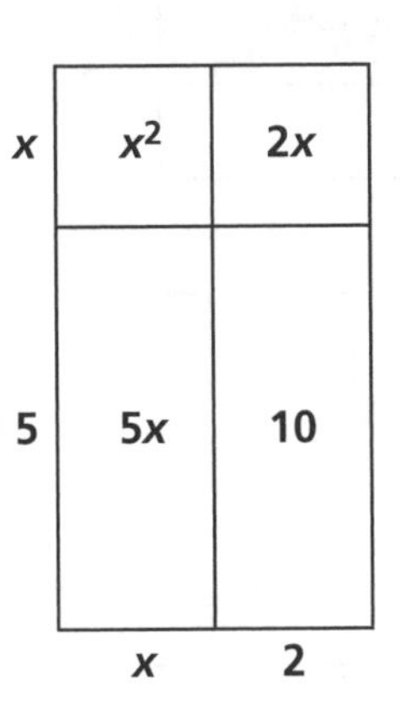

$x^2 + 7x + 10 = (x + 5)(x + 2)$

32.

	x	7
x	x^2	$7x$
7	$7x$	49

$x^2 + 14x + 49 = (x + 7)(x + 7)$

33. $\frac{8}{21}$ **34.** $\frac{17}{6}$ **35.** x

36. $\frac{1}{6}x$ **37.** 28 **38.** 12

39. $\frac{1}{7}$ **40.** 66 **41.** 5

42. -5 **43.** $-54x$ **44.** $3x$

45. $-6x$ **46.** 5 **47.** 12

48. 25 **49.** 3

50. a. Possible answers: $(2x)(4x) + \pi(x)^2$ or $\frac{1}{2}\pi(x)^2 + \frac{1}{2}\pi(x)^2 + 8x^2$

b. The fencing needed for the rectangular region is $4x + 4x = 8x$ since you don't count the two shorter sides. The two half circles each have a perimeter of $\frac{1}{2}\pi(2x)$, which is half of the circumference $\pi(2x)$. So the perimeter is $8x + 2[\frac{1}{2}\pi(2x)]$ or $2\pi x + 8x$.

c. Possible answers: $\pi x + \pi x + 4x + 4x$ or $(2\pi + 8)x$.

51. a. Yes. $8 + 4(s - 1) = 8 + 4s - 4 = 8 - 4 + 4s = 4 + 4s = 4s + 4$

b. Hank

52. a. Since the expression represents her money after one year, she would have the money she put in, which is D, plus the interest the account accrues in that year, which is 0.10 times D, so the expression $D + 0.10D$ is correct.

b. $D(1 + 0.10)$ **c.** $\$1{,}500(1.1) = \$1{,}650$

53. a. Corey's estimate is correct: $C = 200 + 10(50) = 200 + 500 = \$700$.

b. Duncan performed the operations incorrectly by doing the addition first: $C = (200 + 10)50 = \$10{,}500$.

54. a. $S = \frac{200 + 10(20)}{20} = \frac{200 + 200}{20} = \frac{400}{20} = \$20$

b. $S = \frac{200 + 10(N)}{N}$

c. $S = \frac{200 + 10(40)}{40} = \frac{200 + 400}{40} = \frac{600}{40} = \$15$

55. a. The volume of the prism is $6 \times 6 \times 4$ cubic units = 144 cubic units. So the volume of the pyramid is $\frac{144}{3} = 48$ cubic units.

b. A cube with edges 2 units would have volume 8 cubic units. A pyramid that fits inside of this cube would have the given volume.

c. A cube with edge 3 units would have volume 27 cubic units, so a pyramid that fits inside this cube would have the given volume.

d. A cube with edge $3x$ units would have volume $27x^3$ cubic units. So a pyramid with base $3x$ by $3x$ and height $3x$ units would have a volume of $\frac{1}{3}(27x^3) = 9x^3$.

56. a. Sarah performed the calculations correctly.

b. Emily did not use the order of operations correctly. In the second line, she added 4 and 11 before the multiplication of 11 and 3. In the third line, she added 15 and 10 to get 25 instead of multiplying the 15 by 3.

Extensions

57. a. For $s = 1$, 8 tiles are needed.
For $s = 2$, $8 + 4$ tiles are needed.
For $s = 3$, $8 + 4 + 4$ tiles are needed.
Thus, for any s, the number of tiles needed is equal to 8 plus $(s - 1)$ fours, or
$N = 8 + 4(s - 1)$.

b. Percy's equation is equivalent to Stella's equation, $4(s + 1)$. Explanations will vary; they may be based on tables, graphs, the substitution of specific values of s, or the sameness of the expressions.

58. For $2(s + 0.5) + 2(s + 1.5)$, the picture should look like:

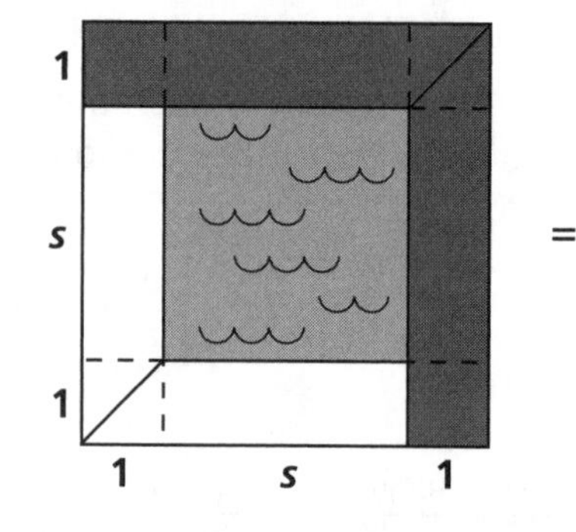

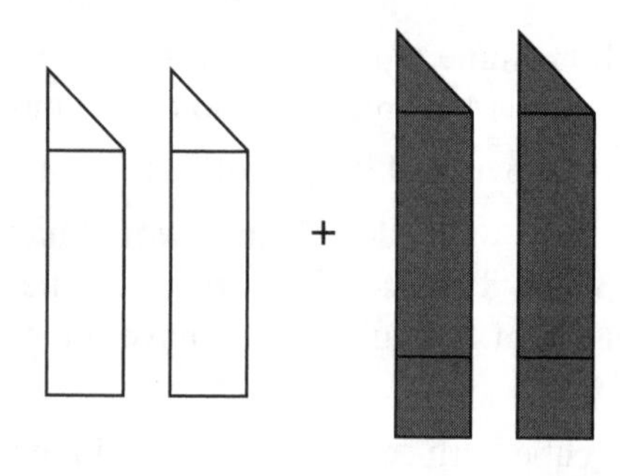

For $4\left[\frac{s + (s + 2)}{2}\right]$, the picture should look like:

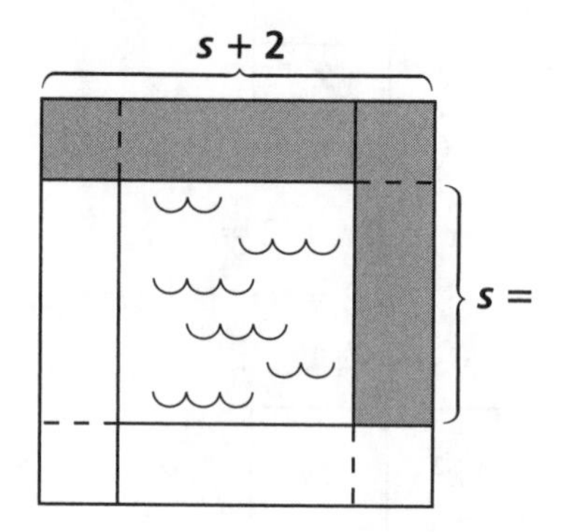

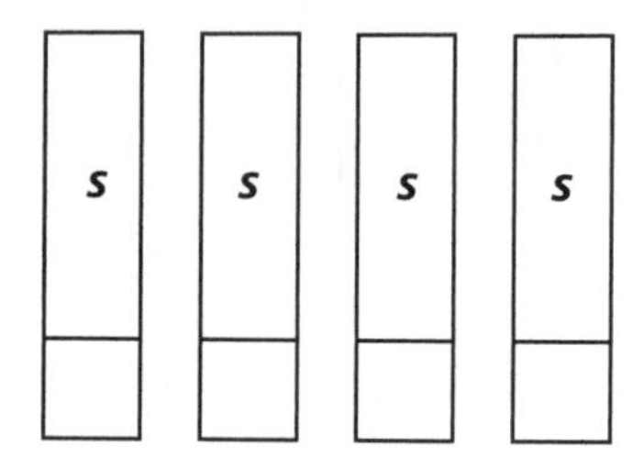

where $4\left[\frac{s + (s + 2)}{2}\right]$ is the area of half the shaded region multiplied by 4. Half the shaded region can be represented by one of the four rectangles to the right of the equal sign.

59. Puzzle 1:

a. $2(n - 3) + 4n + 6n + 1 = 12n - 5$

b. $2(n - 3) + 4n + 6n + 1$

$= 2n - 6 + 4n + 6n + 1$	Distributive Prop.
$= 2n - 6 + (4 + 6)n + 1$	Distributive Prop.
$= 2n - 6 + 10n + 1$	Addition
$= 2n + 10n - 6 + 1$	Comm. Property
$= (2 + 10)n - 5$	Distributive Prop.
$= 12n - 5$	Addition

Puzzle 2:

a. $2n - 3 + 4n + 6(n + 1) = 12n + 3$

b. $2n - 3 + 4n + 6(n + 1)$

$= 2n - 3 + 4n + 6n + 6$	Distributive Prop.
$= 2n - 3 + (4 + 6)n + 6$	Distributive Prop.
$= 2n - 3 + 10n + 6$	Addition
$= 2n + 10n - 3 + 6$	Comm. Property
$= (2 + 10)n + 3$	Distributive Prop.
$= 12n + 3$	Addition

Puzzle 3:

a. $2n - 3 + 4n + 6n + 1 = 12n - 2$; no need for parentheses

b. $2n - 3 + 4n + 6n + 1$

$= 2n - 3 + (4 + 6)n + 1$	Distributive Prop.
$= 2n - 3 + 10n + 1$	Addition
$= 2n + 10n - 3 + 1$	Comm. Property
$= (2 + 10)n - 2$	Distributive Prop.
$= 12n - 2$	Addition

Puzzle 4:

a. $2n - (3 + 4)n + 6n + 1 = n + 1$

b. $2n - (3 + 4)n + 6n + 1$

$= 2n - 7n + 6n + 1$	Addition
$= (2 - 7 + 6)n + 1$	Distributive Prop.
$= n + 1$	Add. and Subtr.

Possible Answers to the Mathematical Reflections

1. Two expressions are equivalent when they are symbolic representations for the same situation. For all values of n, they should give the same result. The same table and the same graph can represent the expressions.

2. The Distributive Property can be used to rewrite expressions as the product of two or more factors (factored form) or as the sum of two or more terms (expanded form). For example, the expression $2x(x + 5)$ can be written as the sum of two terms using the Distributive Property: $2x^2 + 10x$. The expression $6x^2 - 9x$ can be written in factored form using the Distributive Property: $3x(2x - 3)$. The Commutative Property states that we can change the order of addition or multiplication and still have equivalent expressions. For example, $2x + 6 = 6 + 2x$ and $2(x + 3) = (x + 3)2$.

3. To show that two expressions are equivalent, apply the Distributive and Commutative properties to one of the expressions until the original expression is identical to the second expression. If the two expressions are not equivalent, then this procedure will result in a contradiction. For example, the expressions $2(x + 3)$ and $2x + 5$ are not equivalent. If we apply the Distributive Property to the first expression, we get: $2(x + 3) = 2x + 6$ and $2x + 6 \neq 2x + 5$.

Investigation 2 Combining Expressions

Mathematical and Problem-Solving Goals

- Model situations with symbolic statements
- Use several pieces of information to write one symbolic statement.
- Continue to use parentheses and the Distributive Property to write equivalent expressions
- Interpret information represented by equivalent expressions
- Relate parts of a symbolic statement or expression to the underlying relationship and to the context of the problem
- Rewrite an equation that contains two variables by replacing one of the variables by an equivalent expression representing that variable
- Write new algebraic expressions by combining expressions

Mathematics Background

For background on combining expressions, see page 7.

Summary of Problems

Problem 2.1 Walking Together

Problem 2.1 revisits a walkathon from *Moving Straight Ahead*. Students add several expressions and apply the Distributive and Commutative properties to write equivalent expressions. Some of the expressions contain parentheses with which students have not had much experience. This is an opportunity for teachers to assess what understanding of the Distributive Property students bring to the problem.

Problem 2.2 Predicting Profit

Students use two given equations to write one equation by substituting an equivalent expression for one variable in the other equation. They then write a simpler equivalent expression and compare the information that each equation represents in the situation. The equations are used to predict the profit for a given probability of rain and conversely to predict the probability given a certain profit.

Problem 2.3 Area and Profit—What's the Connection?

Students substitute equivalent expressions for quantities in a given equation in order to write equations for area and for profit. To find the profit equation, students substitute one equivalent linear expression for a variable in a quadratic expression. In the previous problem, an equivalent linear expression was substituted for a variable in a linear expression. In these two contexts, the resulting equations for profit and area are the same quadratic relationship, showing that one equation can model two different situations.

	Suggested Pacing	Materials for Students	Materials for Teachers	ACE Assignments
All	$3\frac{1}{2}$ days	Graphing calculators (optional)		
2.1	1 day			1–5, 13–18, 38
2.2	1 day	Poster paper or transparency paper (optional)		6–9, 19–26
2.3	1 day			10–12, 27–37, 39
MR	$\frac{1}{2}$ day			

2.1 Walking Together

Goals

- Use several pieces of information to write one symbolic statement
- Continue to use parentheses and the Distributive Property to write equivalent expressions
- Interpret information represented by equivalent expressions

Launch 2.1

Remind students about the Walkathon from *Moving Straight Ahead*. The same three students are involved with the same amount of money that they collect from their sponsors. You could write the following information on the board:

Leanne: $10 from each of her sponsors.

Gilberto: $2 for each kilometer that he walks from each sponsor.

Alana: $5 plus $0.50 for each kilometer that she walks from each sponsor.

Each student will walk the same number of miles, x; but each student has a different number of sponsors: 16 for Leanne, 7 for Gilberto, and 11 for Alana.

Suggested Question Ask:

- *How could we calculate the total amount of money the three students collect?* (They may say just take the kilometers and calculate the amount each student collects from his/her sponsor and add them together.)

Using student suggestions, find total amounts for different numbers of kilometers. Have students guide the calculations and give reasons for them.

Now challenge the students to write an equation that will calculate the total amount of money collected from the three students for any number of kilometers walked.

Let students work in pairs.

Explore 2.1

As you observe the students, look for ways that they are combining the total amounts for each student. Be sure to share these in the summary.

As students write an equation, ask them how they know it is correct. Suggest that they try to use their equation to compute the money for the number of kilometers you used in the Launch.

Suggested Questions If students have difficulty getting started with Question A ask:

- *How much will Leanne raise per kilometer from each of her sponsors? ($10 total)*
- *How many sponsors does Leanne have?* (16)
- *So, how much will she raise for walking x kilometers?* ($160)
- *How much will Gilberto raise per kilometer from each of his sponsors?* ($2)
- *So, how much will he raise walking x kilometers from each of his sponsors?* ($2x$)
- *How many sponsors does Gilberto have?* (7)
- *So, how much will he raise for walking x kilometers?* [$(2x)(7)$ or $14x$]
- *How much will Alana raise from each of her sponsors?* ($5 + 0.5x$)
- *How many sponsors does Alana have?* (11)
- *So, how much will she raise for walking x kilometers?* [$(5 + 0.5x)(11)$]
- *Now write an equation that shows the total amount for all three.* (Most students can at least write the sum of the previous three expressions to get one expression. Some may recognize that they can apply the Distributive Property to Alana's total.)

For Question B, if students are having trouble you can ask:

- *What would be an equivalent expression for Alana's total?* (If they don't remember the Distributive Property, don't push too hard. It will come up in the summary.)

Summarize 2.1

Have students share their equations for the total amount the walkathon team will raise.

Suggested Questions Ask:

- *What ways do you know for checking whether two expressions are equivalent?* (Students will probably suggest making graphs or tables or substituting a few values into each expression. They may articulate some of their own rules, as well as their present understanding of the Distributive Property.)

Encourage such explanations as the following:

- When there are several quantities in parentheses to be added and a factor outside the parentheses, each quantity must be multiplied by the factor outside the parentheses.
- When there are a certain number of x's and another number of x's, they can be combined by adding the numbers or the coefficients of x.
- When you add or multiply two quantities, it does not matter which one you start with.

Note on vocabulary You might insert vocabulary words such as *term* in place of quantity without disrupting the flow of ideas.

Suggested Questions Ask:

- *Use one of your expressions for the amount the team will raise to find the team's earnings if the students walk 5 kilometers and if they walk 8 kilometers.*
- *Which expression did you use, and why?*

Discuss the advantages and disadvantages of each expression for the total amount raised.

- *What are the advantages and disadvantages of using one equation rather than two or more equations to represent a situation?* (More simplified expressions are usually easier to use for calculating specific values of the variable, but they often don't contain as much information about the context as do more complex expressions.)

Be sure to discuss Question C. It is important to keep the concepts of linear, exponential, and quadratic equations current. Since the expressions for the total amount of money are not readily in the form $y = mx + b$, you need to check to see if they can recognize that this is a linear situation.

Suggested Questions Ask:

- *Does the equation for total money raised represent a linear, exponential, quadratic or none of these relationships? How can you tell?* (Some students may write it in $y = mx + b$ form. Some may use a table or graph. Some may recognize that the highest exponent of x is 1.)
- *What is the slope? y-intercept?* (Note that the slope is the sum of the coefficients of x or the sum of the slopes of the individual sums.)

You can use the following questions to assess students' understanding. Write a few expressions on the board, several of which are equivalent.

- *Identify the expressions that are not equivalent to any other expression in the list:*

$2x + 3 + 7x$	$2x(3 + 7x)$	$9x + 32x + 10x$
$7x + 2x + 3$	$3(3x + 1)$	$2(x + 3) + 7x$

Listening to Students

- Listen to how students talk about the expressions. Do they recognize like terms? You may have talked to them about like terms in Investigation 1. If not, use the expression $2x + 10x$ to illustrate why the expression is equivalent to $12x$ using an area model. Do they recognize that $9x$ and 3 cannot be combined since they are not like terms? So $9x + 3$ is the simplest form possible, meaning that all the operations that can be performed have been performed. The language of "like terms" is not necessary at this time and can be introduced at the teacher's discretion.
- Do they understand the implication of the parentheses?
- Do they relate to the expressions in terms of some invented context?
- Do they suggest various ways to manipulate the expressions? (Perhaps they recognize that some of the expressions are linear and some are quadratic, and realize that this means they cannot be equivalent.)

Presenting a short list of expressions such as that shown above makes an effective class opener, giving students an opportunity to talk about the meaning of the symbols and to connect new knowledge to the interpretation of the expressions. Such experiences will help students move into a world of symbols independent of context. You could also provide two or three linear expressions and ask students to add them or to subtract two of them.

2.1 Walking Together

At a Glance

PACING 1 day

Mathematical Goals

- Use several pieces of information to write one symbolic statement
- Continue to use parentheses and the Distributive Property to write equivalent expressions
- Interpret information represented by equivalent expressions

Launch

Remind students about the Walkathon from *Moving Straight Ahead.* Write the following information on the board:

Leanne: $10 from each of her sponsors.

Gilberto: $2 for each kilometer that he walks from each sponsor.

Alana: $5 plus $0.50 for each kilometer that she walks from each sponsor.

- *How could we calculate the total amount of money the three students collect?*

Using student suggestions, find total amounts for different numbers of kilometers. Have students guide the calculations and give reasons for them. Let students work in pairs.

Explore

As students write an equation, ask them how they know it is correct. Suggest that they try to use their equation to compute the money for the number of kilometers you used in the Launch. If students have trouble with Question A, ask:

- *How much will Leanne (Gilberto, Alana) raise per kilometer from each sponsor?*
- *How many sponsors does Leanne (Gilberto, Alana) have?*
- *So, how much will she (he) raise for walking x kilometers?*
- *Write an equation that shows the total amount for all three.*

For Question B, if students are having trouble, you can ask:

- *What would be an equivalent expression for Alana's total?*

Summarize

Have students share their equations for the total walkathon amount.

- *What ways do you know for checking whether two expressions are equivalent?*
- *Use one of your expressions for the amount the team will raise to find the team's earnings if the students walk 5 kilometers and if they walk 8 kilometers. Which expression did you use, and why?*

Materials

- Student notebooks

continued on next page

Summarize

continued

- *What are the advantages (disadvantages) of using one equation rather than two or more equations to represent a situation?*
- *Does the equation for total money raised represent a linear, exponential, quadratic or none of these relationships? How can you tell? What is the slope? y-intercept?*

Write a few expressions on the board, some of which are equivalent.

- *Identify the expressions that are not equivalent to any other expression in the list:*

$9x + 3$	$2x + 3 + 7x$	$2x + 10x$	$2(x + 3) + 7x$
$3(3x + 1)$	$7x + 2x + 3$	$2x(3 + 7x)$	

ACE Assignment Guide for Problem 2.1

Core 2, 3–5, 13–15

Other *Applications* 1, *Connections* 16–18, *Extensions* 38

Adapted For suggestions about adapting Exercise 1 and other ACE exercises, see the CMP *Special Needs Handbook.*

Connecting to Prior Units 14: *Frogs, Fleas and Painted Cubes*; 15–16: *Say it with Symbols,* Investigation 1; 17–19: *Moving Straight Ahead*

Answers to Problem 2.1

A. 1. a. $M_{Leanne} = 16(10)$

b. $M_{Gilberto} = 7(2x)$

c. $M_{Alana} = 11(5 + 0.5x)$

2. $M_{Total} = 16(10) + 7(2x) + 11(5 + 0.5x)$ or $160 + 14x + 55 + 5.5x$ or some other equivalent form.

NOTE: The x's in the above equations are the same in this context because all three students walk exactly x kilometers together. If the students had walked different distances, we could not use the same variable x in the combined M_{Total} equation since the x's would represent different amounts for each person.

B. 1. $M_{Total} = 160 + 14x + 55 + 5.5x = 215 + 19.5x$

2. The 19.5 represents the combined amount of money that Leanne, Gilberto and Alana make at a per kilometer rate. Leanne makes $10 for each of 16 sponsors, for a total of $160. Gilberto will raise $2 per kilometer from each of his 7 sponsors for a total of $14 per kilometer. Alana will raise $0.50 per kilometer from each of her 11 sponsors for a total of $5.50 per kilometer. This results in a total rate of $14 + 5.5 = 19.5$ per kilometer. The 215 represents the total from the $160 that Leanne raises from her 16 sponsors at $10 each plus the $55 Alana collected from 11 sponsors at $5 each.

3. Possible answer: I used the expression that was written in Question B, part (2), because it was the shortest.

C. The relationship between kilometers walked and money raised is linear. Students may reason about this by using a graph, a table or by noticing the form of the equation $M_{Total} = 215 + 19.5x$ is of the form $y = mx + b$. $m = 19.5$ is the slope and $b = 215$ is the y-intercept.

2.2 Predicting Profit

Goals

- Relate parts of a symbolic statement or expression to the underlying relationship and to the context of the problem
- Rewrite an equation that contains two variables by replacing one of the variables by an equivalent expression representing that variable

In this problem an equation for profit is given based on the number of visitors. The number of visitors is predicted by the probability of rain. So the expression for the number of visitors based on probability of rain is substituted for the variable representing the number of visitors in the profit equation. This gives a new equation for profit that is based on the probability of rain. This is a two-stage process. Given the probability of rain, students can find the profits using this new equation, or they can first find the number of visitors and then substitute this number into the original profit equation.

Launch 2.2

Tell the story about the amusement park. Write the two equations: one that predicts profit, $P = 2.50V - 500$, and one that predicts the number of visitors, $V = 600 - 500R$.

Suggested Question It is worth having a brief conversation about the meaning of the numbers and variables in the equations:

- *What information do the numbers and variables represent in this situation?* (The revenue is $2.50V$ and cost is 500 in the profit equation. In the second equation 600 is the number of visitors if the probability of rain is 0%. For every 1% increase in the probability of rain the number of visitors decreases by 5.)

Challenge the students to find one equation that will predict the profit based on the probability of rain.

Students can work on this problem in pairs.

Explore 2.2

Question A, part (1) is mostly a review. Students need to use the second equation that predicts the number of visitors based on the given probability. Once they have the number of visitors, then use the profit equation to find profit.

Check to see if students are evaluating the expressions by correctly using the Distributive and Commutative properties and the order of operations. This is also a good time to check if students are using percents correctly.

If students are having difficulty writing one equation for profit based on the probability of rain, use the work in Question A to help students find the new equation for profit based on the probability of rain.

Suggested Questions Ask:

- *What is the probability of rain?* (25% or $\frac{1}{4}$ or 0.25)
- *How can you use the probability to find the number of visitors?* (Substitute it for R in the visitor equation.)
- *How can you use the number of visitors to find the profit?* (Substitute the number of visitors for V in the profit equation.)

For Questions B and C, give one or two pairs of students poster paper or blank transparencies to display how they found different expressions for the profit. Ask them to show why the two expressions for profit are equivalent.

Look for ways that students solve the new equation for profit to find the probability of rain given a specific profit in Question C, part (2). Be sure to have students share these strategies in the summary or have them put their solutions on poster paper.

Summarize 2.2

Use the summary to help clarify any misconceptions or weaknesses that you may have observed in the exploration.

Suggested Question Ask the students to explain how the expressions for profit are equivalent. That is:

- *Why does 2.50(600 – 500R) – 500 = 1000 – 1250R?* (Have students demonstrate each step.)

Writing the equation, $P = 2.50(600 - 500R) - 500$, in the form $P = 1{,}000 - 1{,}250R$ provides an opportunity to talk about the slope and intercept of the equation and what each means in this context.

Suggested Questions Ask:

- *Describe the relationship that this equation represents.* (The equation represents a linear situation. The slope of the line represented by the equation is −1,250. That means that for every percent chance of rain, the profits decrease by $12.50.)

Have students share their strategies for Question C, part (2). Use a symbolic method to review what it means to solve an equation and to review the properties of equality. If no one suggests it, use the new equation, $P = 2.50(600 - 500R) - 500$ to demonstrate how to solve the equation for R given a specific value of P, say 600. Ask the class to provide each step in the solution.

If $600 = 2.50(600 - 500R) - 500$
then, $R = 32\%$.

Review Opportunity You can use this opportunity to review other methods for solving an equation.

- *Describe how you can use a table to find the solution when P = 325. What does the solution mean in terms of the original equation P = 2.50(600 – 500R) – 500?* (Enter in the equation $y = 2.50(600 - 500x) - 500$ and follow the table down until y is 325 and see what the corresponding x value is. When students do this, they will have to go by hundredths for their x values in order to get the correct answer, which is 0.15 or 15%.)
- *Describe how you can use a graph to find the solution. What does the solution mean in terms of the original equation?* [Find the point on the line of the equation whose coordinates are (R, 325).]

Question D gives you a chance to see if students can connect these complicated equations to linear relationships and to information given about the patterns of change and y-intercept.

Students will find it interesting to discuss why the profit is –$250 if the probability of rain is 100%.

Suggested Questions Ask:

- *What is the range for the values of the probability?* (0–100% or 0.0 to 1.0)
- *What is the range for the profits?* ($1,000 to −$250)

Finally, ask:

- *Describe why and how we combined the two equations into one equation.*
- *Compare the work we did in this problem of making a new equation to the work in Problem 2.1 for making new equations.*

This summary should help prepare students for solving equations in the next investigation.

2.2 Predicting Profit

At a Glance

PACING 1 day

Mathematical Goals

- Relate parts of a symbolic statement or expression to the underlying relationship and to the context of the problem
- Rewrite an equation that contains two variables by replacing one of the variables by an equivalent expression representing that variable

Launch

Tell the story about the Amusement Park. Write the two equations $P = 2.50V - 500$ and $V = 600 - 500R$ on the board.

- *What information do the numbers and variables represent in this situation?*

Challenge students to find one equation to predict the profit based on the probability of rain. Students can work on this problem in pairs.

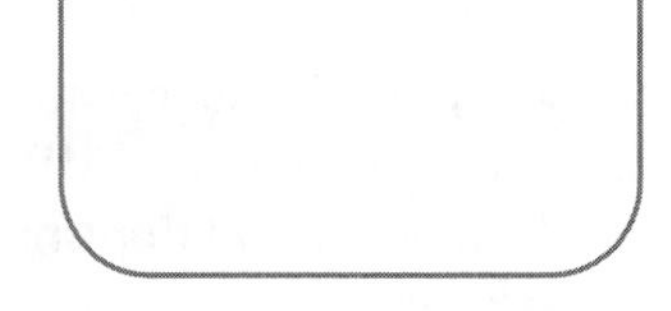

Explore

Question A, part (1), is mostly review. Check that students correctly use the Distributive and Commutative properties and order of operations when evaluating. Make sure students use percents correctly. If students are having difficulty writing one equation for profit based on the probability of rain, ask:

- *What is the probability of rain?*
- *How can you use the probability to find the number of visitors? How can you use the number of visitors to find the profit?*

Give one or two pairs of students poster paper or blank transparencies to display how they found different expressions for the profit and why the two expressions for profit are equivalent.

Materials

- Poster paper (optional)
- Blank transparencies (optional)

Summarize

Ask students to explain why the two expressions for profit are equivalent:

- *Why does $2.50(600 - 500R) - 500$ equal $1000 - 1250R$?*

Talk about the slope and intercepts of the equation and what each means in this context.

- *Describe the relationship that this equation represents.*

Have students share their strategies for Question C, part (2).

If no one suggests it, use the new equation, $P = 2.50(600 - 500R) - 500$ to demonstrate how to solve the equation symbolically for R given a specific value of P, say 600.

Review other methods for solving an equation, like using a table or graph. Discuss why the profit is –\$250 if the probability of rain is 100%.

Ask:

- *What is the range for the values of the probability? What is the range for the profits?*

Materials

- Student notebooks

continued on next page

Summarize

continued

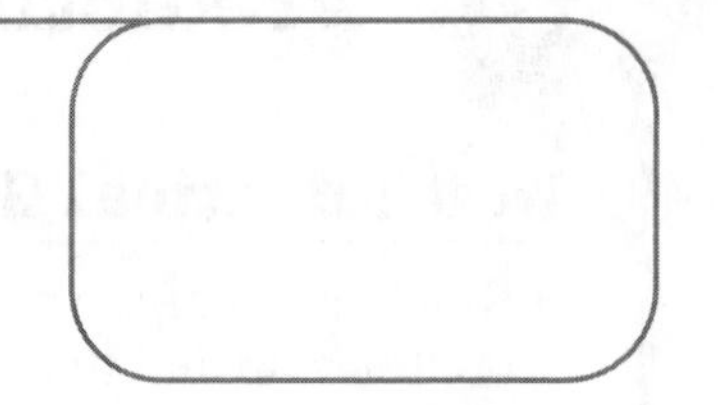

- *Describe why and how we combined the two equations into one equation.*
- *Compare the work we did in this problem of making a new equation to the work in Problem 2.1 for making new equations.*

ACE Assignment Guide for Problem 2.2

Core 6–8, 19–20

Other *Applications* 9, *Connections* 21–26; and unassigned choices from previous problems

Adapted For suggestions about adapting ACE exercises, see the CMP *Special Needs Handbook.*

Connecting to Prior Units 19–26: *Moving Straight Ahead*

Answers to Problem 2.2

A. 1. \$687.50; Substitute 0.25 for R in the equation $V = 600 - 500R$, solve for V, and then substitute that value of V into the equation $P = 2.50V - 500$ to find the profit P.

$V = 600 - 500(0.25)$ $\quad P = 2.50(475) - 500$
$V = 600 - 125$ $\quad P = 1187.50 - 500$
$V = 475$ $\quad P = 687.50$

2. 30%; Substitute 625 for P and solve for V in the equation $P = 2.50V - 500$, and then substitute that value of V into the equation $V = 600 - 500R$ to find the probability it will rain, R.

$$625 = 2.50V - 500$$
$$625 + 500 = 2.50V - 500 + 500$$
$$1125 = 2.50V$$
$$V = 450$$
$$450 = 600 - 500(R)$$
$$450 - 600 = 600 - 500(R) - 600$$
$$-150 = -500R$$
$$R = 0.30 \text{ or } 30\%$$

B.1. $P = 2.50(600 - 500R) - 500$ or any equivalent form.

2. \$687.50; For 25% chance it will rain:

$P = 2.50[600 - 500(0.25)] - 500$
$P = 2.50[600 - 125] - 500$
$P = 2.50[475] - 500$
$P = 687.50$

The answer is the same as the one in Question A, part (1).

C. 1. To find an equivalent expression for the profit, you can use the Distributive Property and multiply 2.50 times 600 and 2.50 times $-500R$. Then combine like terms.

$P = 2.50(600 - 500R) - 500$
$P = 1{,}500 - 1{,}250R - 500$
$P = -1{,}250R + 1000$

The two expressions are equivalent because to get from one to the other you can use the Distributive or Commutative properties. Students may also compare tables and graph or test two points in both (linear) equations to justify equivalence.

2. 30%; Using the equation, $P = -1{,}250R + 1{,}000$ and solving for R when $P = 625$ gives:

$$625 = -1{,}250R + 1{,}000$$
$$625 - 1{,}000 = -1{,}250R + 1{,}000 - 1{,}000$$
$$-375 = -1{,}250R$$

so $R = 0.30$ or 30%, which is the same as the answer for Question A2.

3–4. Answers will vary. Students may use either the two equations or their one equation from Questions B1 or C1.

3. 1,000 (this is the starting value or intercept in the equation $P = -1{,}250R + 1{,}000$) The answer makes sense since if the probability that it will rain is zero, more people should come to the park than if the probability is 100%, thus creating more profit.

4. $-$\$250 or a loss of 250 dollars; Substitute 1 (i.e. 100%) for R in the equation, $P = -1{,}250R + 1{,}000$. If the probability of rain is 100%, there will be fewer visitors to the park, so it will probably lose money. So profit of $-$\$250 makes sense.

D. The relationships in Questions B and C are both linear. They both can be put into the form of $y = mx + b$, the equation of a line. Also they both have constant rates of change.

2.3 Area and Profit—What's the Connection?

Goals

- Model situations with symbolic statements
- Write a new algebraic expression by combining expressions

Launch 2.3

Tell students the story of the two boys, Tony and Paco, and how they are going to rent water tubes at Water World. Tony is trying to find the maximum area of the floor plan given a fixed perimeter and Paco is trying to figure out the maximum profit for renting tubes.

- *Compare these contexts to others you have studied.* (The situation in Question A is very similar to those studied in *Frogs, Fleas and Painted Cubes.* The second situation is similar to the situation in Problem 2.2.)

You may want the students to work on Question A and summarize it before you go to Question B.

Have students work in pairs.

Explore 2.3

Suggested Questions Check that students can write an equation for area in terms of ℓ for Question A, part (1). If they are having difficulty with this you may want to ask"

- *What is the area in terms of length and width?* ($A = \ell w$)
- *Do we have an expression that relates the length and the width?* (Yes, perimeter. $2\ell + 2w = 88$.)
- *Can we use this equation to find an equivalent expression for w in terms of ℓ?* (Yes, solve the equation for w. $w = 44 - \ell$)
- *How can we use this equation to write an equation for area in terms of length, ℓ?* (Use the expression, $44 - \ell$, for w and substitute it for w in the area equation. $A = \ell(44 - \ell)$.)
- *How do you know that the area you got in A2 is the maximum area?* (Some students may remember that it is the rectangle that is most like a square. Some will use the fact that the maximum point lies on a line perpendicular to the horizontal axis that is halfway between the two x-intercepts. In this case $\ell = 22$ and area $= 484$.)

Suggested Questions For Question B, make sure that students read the conditions carefully:

- *Do Equations 1 and 2 in Question B match what we know about the conditions?*
- *Does $n = 54 - (1)p$ make sense?* (Yes, because 54 is the starting point or y-intercept and the number of rentals is decreasing for every \$1 increase in rental price. So the slope is -1.)

If students are confused about profit ask them to explain how to calculate profit.

- *How can you calculate profit?* (Income – Expenses).
- *What is the Income?* [$I = np$ or $I = n(54 - n)$]
- *What are the expenses?* (Expenses $= 10n$)
- *What is profit?* ($D = n(54 - n) - 10n$)

Summarize 2.3

Suggested Questions Ask:

- *Compare the equations for profit and area.* (They have the same relationship. That is $D = n(54 - n) - 10n$ or $D = 44n - n^2$ and $A = (44 - \ell)\ell$ or $A = 44\ell - \ell^2$)
- *Does it matter that in the area equation the variables are A and ℓ and in the profit equation the variables are D and n?*
- *How can you use the information about maximum area in Question A to find the maximum profit in Question B?* (The two equations are the same. Since the maximum area, 484 square meters, occurs when the length is 22 meters, then the maximum profit occurs when 22 water tubes are rented and the maximum profit is \$484.)

- *Compare the methods for combining equations or expressions to write one equation in this investigation.* (In Problem 2.1, we added several expressions representing the amount of money each individual received in the walkathon to find one expression that would calculate the total amount of money collected by the group. In Problems 2.2 and 2.3, we substituted an equivalent expression for a quantity (variable) in an equation containing the quantity (variable) to create one equation. In these situations the two equations contained three variables. For example in Problem 2.2, profit depends on the number of visitors and the number of visitors depends on the probability of rain. We can write one equation for profit in terms of the number of visitors or in terms of the probability of rain. In all three problems we can calculate the final answer about the total amount of money, total profit or area using one equation or in stages using two or more equations.)

Check for Understanding

- *Write an equation for profit in terms of n and p.* [$D = p(54 - p) - 10n$]
- *How is this different from the equation you found in Question B2?*

You may want to call students' attention to the NFL quarterback ratings discussed in the *Did You Know?* in the student edition at the end of this investigation. This rating is based on a series of calculations. You might challenge the students to write one equation for determining the quarterback ratings. ACE Exercise 39 asks students to compute the ratings for a specific quarterback. You may want to substitute a local hero in place of the quarterback given in the book.

2.3 Area and Profit—What's the Connection?

At a Glance

PACING 1 day

Mathematical Goals

- Model situations with symbolic statements
- Write a new algebraic expression by combining expressions

Launch

Tell students the story of the two boys, Tony and Paco, and how they are going to rent water tubes at Water World. Tony is trying to find the maximum area of the floor plan given a fixed perimeter and Paco is trying to figure out the maximum profit for renting tubes.

- *Compare these contexts to others you have studied.*

You may want the students to work on Question A and summarize it before you go to Question B.

Have students work in pairs.

Explore

Check to make sure that students can write an equation for area in terms of ℓ for Question A, part (1). If they are having difficulty with this you may want to ask:

- *What is the area in terms of length and width? Do we have an expression that relates the length and the width?*
- *Can we use this equation to find an equivalent expression for w in terms of ℓ?*
- *How can we use this equation to write an equation for area in terms of length, ℓ?*
- *How do you know that the area you got in Question A part (2) is the maximum area?*

For Question B, make sure that students read the conditions carefully:

- *Do the Equations 1 and 2 in Question B match what we know about the conditions?*
- *Does $n = 54 - (1)p$ make sense?*

If students are confused about profit ask them to explain how to calculate profit.

- *How can you calculate profit? What is the Income?*
- *What are the expenses?*
- *What are the profits?*

Materials

- Poster paper (optional)
- Blank transparencies (optional)

continued on next page

Summarize

Ask students:

- *Compare the equations for profit and area.*
- *Does it matter that in the area equation the variables are A and ℓ and in the profit equation the variables are D and n?*
- *How can you use the information about maximum area in Question A to find the maximum profit in Question B?*
- *Compare the methods for combining equations or expressions to write one equation in this investigation.*

Check for Understanding

- *Write an equation for profit in terms of p.*
- *How is this different from the equation you found in Question B, part (2)?*

Materials

- Student notebooks

ACE Assignment Guide for Problem 2.3

Core 12, 27–29, 39

Other *Applications* 10, 11; *Connections* 30–37; and unassigned choices from previous problems

Adapted For suggestions about adapting ACE exercises, see the CMP *Special Needs Handbook*.

Connecting to Prior Units 13: *Say It With Symbols*, Investigation 1; 27–29: *Frogs, Fleas and Painted Cubes*; 30–35: *Growing, Growing, Growing; 36: Bits and Pieces III*; 37: *Filling and Wrapping*

Answers to Problem 2.3

A. 1. $A = \ell(44 - \ell)$ or $A = 44\ell - \ell^2$; Since $88 = 2(\ell + w)$, then dividing both sides of the equation by 2 gives the equation $44 = \ell + w$ so $w = 44 - \ell$. Thus $A = \ell(44 - \ell)$. Students may multiply through and obtain the equation $A = 44\ell - \ell^2$.

2. The maximum area is 484 ft^2 which occurs when the floor plan is a 22 ft by 22 ft square.

B. 1. Yes; Equation 1 means that for each $1 increase in the price to rent, the number of rentals decreases by 1. The starting value is 54 rentals for a price of $0. Equation 2 means that the daily income equals the number of tube rentals times the price of a rental.

2. $I = n(54 - n)$; First solve $n = 54 - p$ for p obtaining $p = 54 - n$.

Then substitute the expression for p into the income equation in order to get:

$I = n(54 - n)$

3. $D = n(54 - n) - 10$ or $D = 54n - n^2 - 10$; Since D = income − expenses and Expenses = 10 we have that $D = n(54 - n) - 10$ or $D = 54n - n^2 - 10$. D is the daily profit.

4. The equations in Questions B, part (3) and A, part (1) represent the same quadratic relationship. The only difference is that they use different variables.

5. 22 rentals will produce a maximum profit of $484; The maximum value can be found by graphing the equation or looking at the table of the equation $D = 44n - n^2$. Students should also realize that the maximum profit is the same as the maximum area that they found in Question A, part (2).

A price of $32 produces the maximum daily profit; Since the maximum profit occurs at 22 rentals we need to find p when $n = 22$ in the equation $n = 54 - p$. Students may use a graph or table to get the answer or they may solve the equation $22 = 54 - p$ for p using a symbolic method.

Investigation 2

Combining Expressions

In the last investigation, you found several ways to write equivalent expressions to describe a quantity. You also learned several ways to show that two expressions are equivalent. We will continue to answer the questions:

- Are the expressions equivalent? Why?
- What information does each equivalent expression represent?

We will also look at ways to create new expressions and to answer the question:

- What are the advantages and disadvantages of using one equation rather than two or more equations to represent a situation?

2.1 Walking Together

In *Moving Straight Ahead*, Leanne, Gilberto, and Alana enter a walkathon as a team. This means that each person will walk the same number of kilometers. The walkathon organizers offer a prize to the three-person team that raises the most money.

- Leanne has walkathon pledges from 16 sponsors. All of her sponsors pledge \$10 regardless of how far she walks.
- Gilberto has pledges from 7 sponsors. Each sponsor pledges \$2 for each kilometer he walks.
- Alana has pledges from 11 sponsors. Each sponsor pledges \$5 plus \$0.50 for each kilometer she walks.

Notes

Problem 2.1 Adding Expressions

A. 1. Write equations to represent the money M that each student will raise for walking x kilometers.

a. $M_{\text{Leanne}} = ■$

b. $M_{\text{Gilberto}} = ■$

c. $M_{\text{Alana}} = ■$

2. Write an equation for the total money M_{total} raised by the three-person team for walking x kilometers.

B. 1. Write an expression that is equivalent to the expression for the total amount in Question A, part (2). Explain why it is equivalent.

2. What information does this new expression represent about the situation?

3. Suppose each person walks 10 kilometers. Explain which expression(s) you would use to calculate the total amount of money raised.

C. Are the relationships between kilometers walked and money raised linear, exponential, quadratic, or none of these? Explain.

ACE **Homework starts on page 28.**

2.2 Predicting Profit

The manager of the Water City amusement park uses data collected over the past several years to write equations that will help her make predictions about the daily operations of the park.

The daily concession-stand profit in dollars P depends on the number of visitors V. The manager writes the equation below to model this relationship.

$$P = 2.50V - 500$$

She uses the equation below to predict the number of visitors V based on the probability of rain R.

$$V = 600 - 500R$$

- What information might each of the numbers in the equations represent?

Notes ____________________

Problem 2.2 Substituting Equivalent Expressions

A. 1. Suppose the probability of rain is 25%. What profit can the concession stand expect? Explain.

2. What was the probability of rain if the profit expected is \$625? Explain your reasoning.

B. 1. Write an equation that can be used to predict the concession-stand profit P from the probability of rain R.

2. Use this equation to predict the profit when the probability of rain is 25%. Compare your answer with your result in Question A, part (1).

C. 1. Write an equivalent expression for the profit in Question B. Explain why the two expressions are equivalent.

2. Predict the probability of rain on a day when the concession-stand profit is \$625. Compare your answer with the result you found in Question A, part (2).

3. Predict the profit when the probability of rain is 0%. Does your answer make sense? Explain.

4. Predict the profit when the probability of rain is 100%. Does your answer make sense?

D. Do the equations in Questions B and C represent a linear, exponential, or quadratic relationship, or none of these? Explain.

ACE **Homework starts on page 28.**

STUDENT PAGE

STUDENT PAGE

Notes

2.3 Area and Profit—What's the Connection?

In the next problem, you will explore two familiar situations that have an interesting connection.

Tony and Paco will operate the water tube concession stand at Water City. Tony is responsible for designing the building that will store the rafts. Paco is responsible for deciding the rental fee for the tubes.

Problem 2.3 Using Equations

A. Every concession stand must have a rectangular floor space and a perimeter of 88 meters. Tony wants the greatest area possible.

1. Write an equation for the area in terms of the length.
2. What is the maximum area for the rectangular floor space?

B. Paco knows that on a typical day, the number of tube rentals n is related to the price to rent each tube p. Records from other water park locations suggest:

- If the tubes are free (no price), there will be 54 rentals.
- Each increase of $1 in the price will result in one less tube rented.

Paco uses this information to write the following equations:

- Equation 1: $n = 54 - (1)p$
- Equation 2: $I = np$, where I is the daily income

1. Do these equations make sense? Explain.
2. Write an equation for income in terms of the number of rentals n.
3. The expenses for storage and maintenance of the rented tubes are $10 per day. Write an equation for daily profit D in terms of the number of rentals n.

STUDENT PAGE

Notes

4. Compare the equation in part (3) to the equation in Question A, part (1).
5. What number of rentals produces the maximum daily profit? What is the maximum profit? What rental price produces the maximum daily profit?

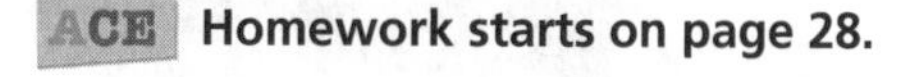

ACE **Homework starts on page 28.**

Did You Know?

The calculation of the quarterback rating in the National Football League (NFL™) uses a series of equations:

Completion Rating: $CR = 5\left(\frac{\text{completions}}{\text{attempts}}\right) - 1.5$

Yards Rating: $YR = \frac{\frac{\text{yards}}{\text{attempts}} - 3}{4}$

Touchdown Rating: $TR = 20\left(\frac{\text{touchdowns}}{\text{attempts}}\right)$

Interception Rating: $IR = 25\left(0.095 - \frac{\text{interceptions}}{\text{attempts}}\right)$

Overall Rating $= 100\left(\frac{CR + YR + TR + IR}{6}\right)$

Go Online PHSchool.com **For:** Information about quarterback ratings **Web Code:** ape-9031

STUDENT PAGE

Notes

Applications Connections Extensions

ACE

Applications

1. The student council is organizing a T-shirt sale to raise money for a local charity. They make the following estimates of expenses and income:

- Expense of \$250 for advertising
- Expense of \$4.25 for each T-shirt
- Income of \$12 for each T-shirt
- Income of \$150 from a business sponsor

a. Write an equation for the income I made for selling n T-shirts.

b. Write an equation for the expenses E for selling n T-shirts.

c. Suppose the student council sells 100 T-shirts. What is the profit?

d. Write an equation for the profit P made for selling n T-shirts.

For Exercises 2–5, use the following information: In *Variables and Patterns*, several students were planning a bike tour. They estimated the following expenses and incomes.

- \$30 for each bike rental
- \$125 for cost of food and camp for each biker
- \$700 for van rental
- \$350 of income for each biker

2. a. Write an equation for the total expenses E for n bikers.

b. Write an equation for the total income I for n bikers.

c. Write an equation for the profit P for n bikers.

d. Find the profit for 25 bikers.

e. Suppose the profit is \$1,055. How many bikers went on the trip?

f. Does the profit equation represent a linear, quadratic, or exponential function, or none of these? Explain.

3. Multiple Choice Suppose someone donates a van at no charge. Which equation represents the total expenses?

A. $E = 125 + 30$ **B.** $E = 125n + 30n$

C. $E = 155$ **D.** $E = 155 + n$

Notes

4. Multiple Choice Suppose people supply their own bikes. Which equation represents the total expenses? (Assume they will rent a van.)

F. $E = 125n + 700$ **G.** $E = 125 + 700 + n$

H. $E = 825n$ **J.** $E = 350n + 125n + 700$

5. Multiple Choice Suppose people supply their own bikes. Which equation represents the profit? (Assume they will rent a van.)

A. $P = 350 - (125 + 700 + n)$ **B.** $P = 350n - 125n + 700$

C. $P = 350n - (125n + 700)$ **D.** $P = 350 - 125n - 700$

For Exercises 6–8, recall the equations from Problem 2.2 ($P = 2.50V - 500$ and $V = 600 - 500R$).

6. Suppose the probability of rain is 50%. What profit can the concession stand expect to make?

7. What is the probability of rain if the profit expected is $100?

8. The manager estimates the daily employee-bonus fund B (in dollars) from the number of visitors V using the equation $B = 100 + 0.50V$.

For: Help with Exercise 8
Web Code: ape-6208

a. Suppose the probability of rain is 30%. What is the daily employee-bonus fund?

b. Write an equation that relates the employee-bonus B to the probability of rain R.

c. Suppose the probability of rain is 50%. Use your equation to calculate the employee-bonus fund.

d. Suppose the daily employee-bonus fund is $375. What is the probability of rain?

Notes

9. A manager of a park claims that the profit P for a concession stand depends on the number of visitors V, and that the number of visitors depends on the day's high temperature T (in Fahrenheit). The following equations represent the manager's claims:

$$P = 4.25V - 300 \qquad V = 50(T - 45)$$

a. Suppose 1,000 people visit the park one day. Predict that day's high temperature.

b. Write an equation for profit based on temperature.

c. Write an equation for profit that is equivalent to the equation in part (b). Explain what information the numbers and variables represent.

d. Find the profit if the temperature is 70°F.

10. A farmer has 240 meters of fence. The farmer wants to build a fence to enclose the greatest possible rectangular land area.

a. Write an equation for the fenced area A in terms of the length ℓ of the rectangular plot.

b. What are the dimensions of the rectangle with the greatest area?

c. Describe how you could find the information in part (b) from a graph of the equation.

d. Does the equation for area represent a linear, quadratic, or exponential function, or none of these? Explain.

11. In Exercise 10, suppose the farmer uses the 240 meters of fence to enclose a rectangular plot on only three sides and uses a creek as the boundary of the fourth side.

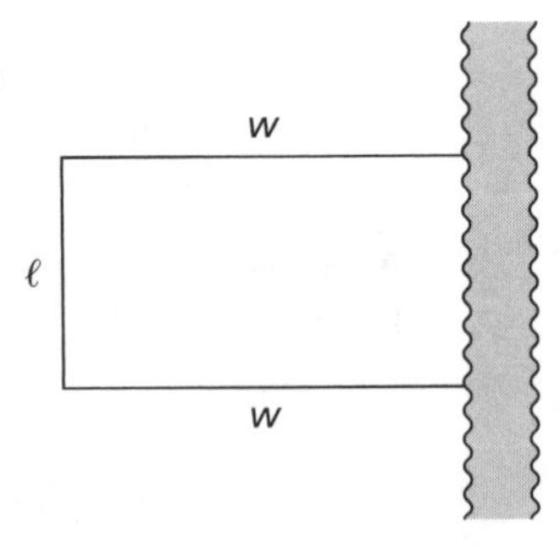

a. Write an equation for the fenced area A in terms of the length ℓ of the rectangular plot.

b. What are the dimensions of the rectangle with the greatest area?

c. Does the equation represent a linear, quadratic, or exponential function, or none of these? Explain.

STUDENT PAGE

Notes

12. The math club is selling posters to advertise National Algebra day. The following equation represents the profits P they expect for selling n posters at x dollars.

$$P = xn - 6n$$

They also know that the number of posters n sold depends on the selling price x, which is represented by this equation:

$$n = 20 - x$$

a. Write an equation for profit in terms of the number of posters sold. **Hint:** First solve the equation $n = 20 - x$ for x.

b. What is the profit for selling 10 posters?

c. What is the selling price of the posters in part (b)?

d. What is the greatest possible profit?

Connections

13. Multiple Choice Which statement is *false* when a, b, and c are different real numbers?

F. $(a + b) + c = a + (b + c)$ **G.** $ab = ba$

H. $(ab)c = a(bc)$ **J.** $a - b = b - a$

For Exercises 14–16, use the Distributive Property and sketch a rectangle to show the equivalence.

14. $x(x + 5)$ and $x^2 + 5x$

15. $(2 + x)(2 + 3x)$ and $4 + 8x + 3x^2$

16. $(x + 2)(2x + 3)$ and $2x^2 + 7x + 6$

For: Multiple-Choice Skills Practice
Web Code: apa-6254

17. Some steps are missing in the solution to $11x - 12 = 30 + 5x$.

$$11x - 12 = 30 + 5x$$
$$11x = 42 + 5x$$
$$6x = 42$$
$$x = 7$$

a. Copy the steps above. Fill in the missing steps.

b. How can you check that $x = 7$ is the correct solution?

c. Explain how you could use a graph or a table to solve the original equation for x.

Notes

18. In the following graph, line ℓ_1 represents the income for selling n soccer balls. Line ℓ_2 represents the expenses of manufacturing n soccer balls.

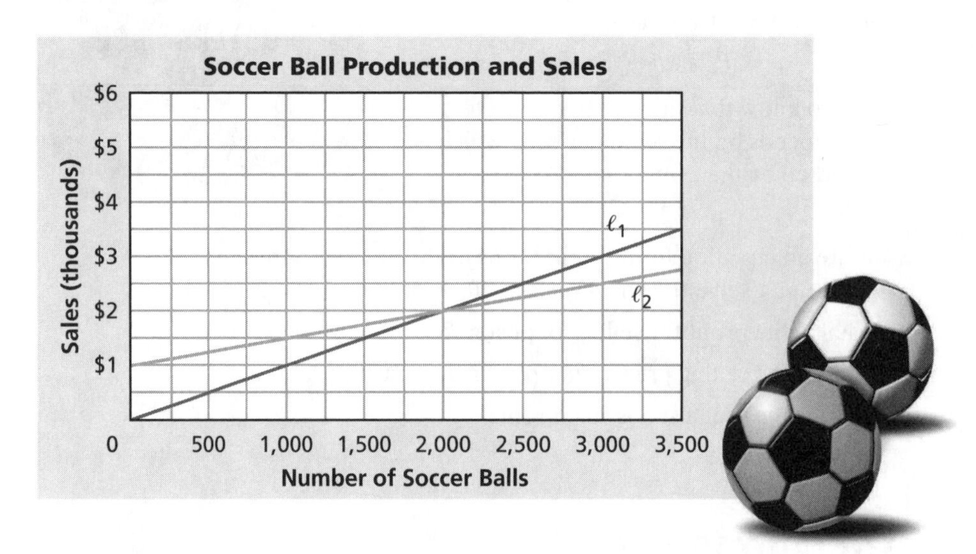

a. What is the start-up expense (the expense before any soccer balls are produced) for manufacturing the soccer balls? NOTE: The vertical axis is in *thousands* of dollars.

b. What are the expenses and income for producing and selling 500 balls? For 1,000 balls? For 3,000 balls? Explain.

c. What is the profit for producing and selling 500 balls? For 1,000 balls? For 3,000 balls? Explain.

d. What is the break-even point? Give the number of soccer balls and the expenses.

e. Write equations for the expenses, income, and profit. Explain what the numbers and variables in each equation represent.

f. Suppose the manufacturer produces and sells 1,750 soccer balls. Use the equations in part (e) to find the profit.

g. Suppose the profit is $10,000. Use the equations in part (e) to find the number of soccer balls produced and sold.

For Exercises 19–24, use properties of equality to solve the equation. Check your solution.

19. $7x + 15 = 12x + 5$

20. $7x + 15 = 5 + 12x$

21. $-3x + 5 = 2x - 10$

22. $14 - 3x = 1.5x + 5$

23. $9 - 4x = \frac{3 + x}{2}$

24. $-3(x + 5) = \frac{2x - 10}{3}$

Notes

25. The writing club wants to publish a book of students' short stories, poems, and essays. A member of the club contacts two local printers to get bids on the cost of printing the books.

Bid 1: cost = $100 + $4 × the number of books printed

Bid 2: cost = $25 + $7 × the number of books printed

a. Make a table of (*number of books printed*, *cost*) values for each bid. Use your table to find the number of books for which the two bids are equal. Explain how you found your answer.

b. Make a graph of the two equations. Use your graph to find the number of books for which the two bids are equal. Explain.

c. For what numbers of books is Bid 1 less than Bid 2? Explain.

26. Use the information about printing costs from Exercise 25.

a. For each bid, find the cost of printing 75 books.

b. Suppose the cost cannot exceed $300. For each bid, find the greatest number of books that can be printed. Explain.

The club decides to request bids from two more printers.

Bid 3: cost = $8 × the number of books printed

Bid 4: cost = $30 + $6 × the number of books printed

c. For what number of books does Bid 3 equal Bid 4? Explain.

27. a. A soccer team has 21 players. Suppose each player shakes hands with each of the other players. How many handshakes will take place?

b. Write an equation for the number of handshakes h among a team with n players.

c. Write an equation for the number of handshakes that is equivalent to the equation in part (b).

Notes

28. **a.** Write an expression that is equivalent to $(x + 2)(x + 5)$.

b. Explain two methods for checking equivalence.

29. For the equation $y = (x + 2)(x + 5)$, find each of the following. Explain how you found each.

a. y-intercept

b. x-intercept(s)

c. maximum/minimum point

d. line of symmetry

For Exercises 30–35, find an equivalent expression.

30. $x^2 \cdot x^3$

31. $x \cdot x^0 \cdot x^5$

32. $\frac{x^2 \cdot x^3}{x}$

33. $\frac{x^8}{x^5}$

34. $\frac{x^5}{x^8}$

35. $\frac{4x^8}{2x^5}$

36. Mary's salary is $30,000 per year. What would be her new salary next year given each condition?

a. She gets a 15% raise.

b. Her salary grows by a factor of 1.12.

c. Her salary increases to 110% of what it is now.

37. Examine the three different cylinders.

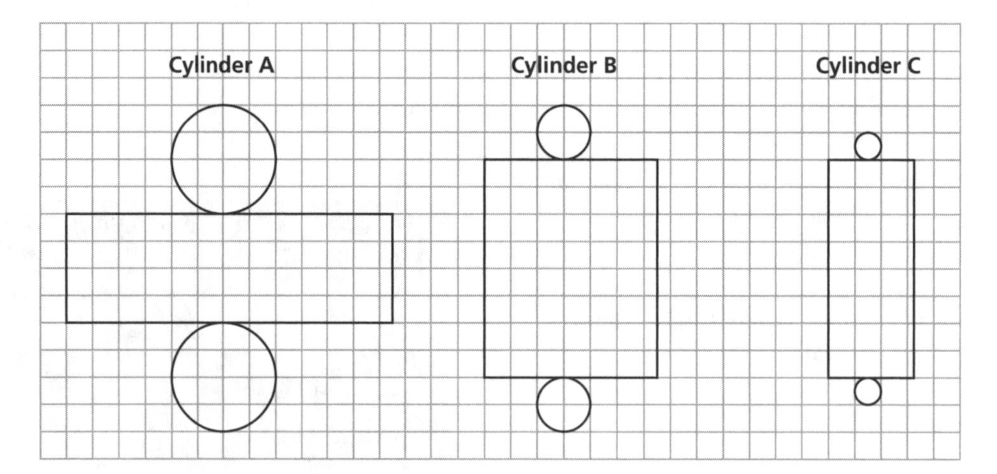

a. Compare the three cylinders.

b. Estimate the surface area of each cylinder. Which cylinder has the greatest surface area? Explain.

c. Which cylinder has the greatest volume? Explain.

Notes

Extensions

38. The Phillips Concert Hall estimates their concession-stand profits P_c and admission profits P_A with the following equations, where x is the number of people (in hundreds):

$$P_c = 15x - 500 \qquad P_A = 106x - x^2$$

The concession-stand profits include revenue from advertising and the sale of food and souvenirs. The admission profits are based on the difference between ticket sales and cost.

a. Write an equation for the total profit for P in terms of the number of people x (in hundreds).

b. What is the maximum profit? How many people must attend in order to achieve the maximum profit?

39. Recall the series of equations used to calculate a quarterback's rating in the *Did You Know?* after Problem 2.3. Tom Brady's statistics for 2004 are shown below. Use the equations and the statistics to find his overall rating that year.

Attempts: 474

Completions: 288

Yards: 3,692

Touchdowns: 28

Interceptions: 14

Connections Extensions

STUDENT PAGE

Notes

Mathematical Reflections 2

In this investigation, you combined expressions or substituted an equivalent expression for a quantity to make new expressions. You also used these expressions to make predictions. These questions will help you summarize what you have learned.

Think about your answers to these questions. Discuss your ideas with other students and your teacher. Then write a summary of your findings in your notebook.

1. Describe a situation in which it is helpful to add expressions to form a new expression. Explain how you can combine the expressions.
2. Describe a situation in which it is helpful to substitute an equivalent expression for a quantity in an equation.
3. What are the advantages and disadvantages of working with one equation rather than two or more equations in a given situation?

STUDENT PAGE

Notes

Investigation 

ACE Assignment Choices

Differentiated Instruction
Solutions for All Learners

Problem 2.1

Core 2, 3–5, 13–15
Other *Applications* 1, *Connections* 16–18, *Extensions* 38

Problem 2.2

Core 6–8, 19–20
Other *Applications* 9, *Connections* 21–26; and unassigned choices from previous problems

Problem 2.3

Core 12, 27–29, 39
Other *Applications* 10, 11; *Connections* 30–37; and unassigned choices from previous problems

Adapted For suggestions about adapting Exercise 1 and other ACE exercises, see the CMP *Special Needs Handbook.*
Connecting to Prior Units 14, 27–29: *Frogs, Fleas and Painted Cubes*; 13, 15, 16: *Say it with Symbols,* Investigation 1; 17–26: *Moving Straight Ahead;* 30–35: *Growing, Growing, Growing; 36: Bits and Pieces III*; 37: *Filling and Wrapping*

Applications

1. **a.** $I = 12n + 150$
   b. $E = 250 + 4.25n$
   c. \$675; If you plug in 100 T-shirts to the income equation you'll get $12(100) + 150 = 1{,}350$ in income and if you plug in 100 to the expense equation, you'll get $E = 250 + 4.25(100) = 675$. So the profit is $1{,}350 - 675 = 675$.
   d. Possible answers:
   $P = 12n + 150 - (250 + 4.25n)$;
   $P = 12n + 150 - 4.25n - 250$ or
   $P = 7.75n - 100$
2. **a.** $E = 125n + 30n + 700$ or $E = 155n + 700$
   b. $I = 350n$
   c. $P = 350n - (125n + 30n + 700)$ or
   $P = 350n - 125n - 30n - 700$ or
   $P = 195n - 700$
   d. \$4,175; Substituting 25 for n into the profit equation we get
   $P = 195(25) - 700 = 4{,}175$
   e. 9 bikers; Substituting 1,055 in for P in the equation $P = 195n - 700$ and solving for n gives that $1{,}055 = 195n - 700$ or $1{,}755 = 195n$. Dividing both sides by 195 we get that the number of bikers is 9.
   f. The profit equation is a linear equation because it can be written in the form $y = mx + b$, it has a constant rate of change and a linear graph (any of these three are acceptable answers).
3. B
4. F
5. C
6. \$375; Since the probability of rain is 50% or 0.50, the number of predicted visitors is $V = 600 - 500(0.50) = 350$. Based on this number the profit will be
   $P = 2.50(350) - 500 = 375$
7. 72%; If students use the combined equation which is $P = -1{,}250R + 1{,}000$ and solve for R when $P = 100$ they should get 72%. If students use both equations separately, then for $P = 100$ the number of visitors would be 240 which can be found by solving the equation $100 = 2.50n - 500$ for n. So to find the probability of rain we must solve the other equation $240 = 600 - 500R$ for R and we get 0.72 or 72%.
8. **a.** \$325; Combining both equations into one results in the equation,
   $B = 100 + 0.50(600 - 500R)$ or
   $B = 400 - 250R$. So if the probability of rain is 30%, the daily employee-bonus fund is \$325. Students may use both equations

separately to find the number of visitors, $V = 600 - 500R$ when $R = 30\%$ which is 450. Then substitute 450 into the equation $B = 100 + 0.50V$ and solve for V getting \$325.

b. $B = 100 + 0.50(600 - 500R)$ or $B = 400 - 250R$

c. \$275; $B = 400 - 250(0.5)$ gives $B = \$275$

d. 10%; Solving the equation $\$375 = 400 - 250R$ for R gives $R = 0.1$ or 10%.

9. a. 65°;

$$
\begin{aligned}
V &= 50(T - 45)\\
1{,}000 &= 50(T - 45)\\
1{,}000 &= 50T - 2250\\
1{,}000 + 2250 &= 50T - 2250 + 2250\\
3{,}250 &= 50T\\
\frac{3{,}250}{50} &= \frac{50T}{50}\\
65 &= T
\end{aligned}
$$

b. To find the profit based on the temperature, substitute $50(T - 45)$ for V in the equation $P = 4.25V - 300$ and get $P = 4.25[50(T - 45)] - 300$.

c. $P = -9862.5 + 212.5T$; To simplify $P = 4.25[50(T - 45)] - 300$ first distribute the 50 by multiplying it by T and -45, multiply each of those terms by 4.25, and then combine like terms:

$$
\begin{aligned}
P &= 4.25[50(T - 45)] - 300\\
P &= 4.25[50T - 2250] - 300\\
P &= -9562.5 + 212.5T - 300\\
P &= -9862.5 + 212.5T
\end{aligned}
$$

The 212.50 represents the rate of change for the profit as the temperature increases 1 degree. The y-intercept is -9862.5. However, -9862.5 does not have a physical meaning since T must be always greater than or equal to 45° to have a positive number of visitors. T represents the independent variable or the temperature and P represents the dependent variable or the profit, which depends on the temperature because it changes at the rate of \$212.50 per 1° change in temperature.

d. \$5,012.50; Students may choose to use either of their equations from parts (b) or (c).

10. a. $A = \ell(120 - \ell)$; since $A = \ell w$, we need to write w in terms of ℓ. The only thing we know about the situation is that the perimeter is 240. So using the equation $240 = 2\ell + 2w$ solving for w we get $w = 120 - \ell$ and thus $A = \ell(120 - \ell)$.

b. The maximum area is when ℓ and w each equal 60.

c. If you graph the equation $A = \ell(120 - \ell)$ you would get a parabola that opens down. To find the maximum area you look at the maximum point on the parabola or the vertex. The x-coordinate is the length of the rectangle with the largest area. To find the width plug this x-coordinate into the equation $w = 120 - \ell$ and solve for w.

d. The equation is quadratic because it is the product of two linear factors that are in terms of ℓ. The equation $A = \ell(120 - \ell)$ can be written as $A = 120\ell - \ell^2$ where the exponent on ℓ is 2 and this is the highest exponent to which ℓ is raised.

11. a. $A = \ell(120 - 0.5\ell)$. Since $A = \ell w$ we need to write w in terms of ℓ. The only thing we know about the situation is that the fencing is 240 meters. So using the equation $240 = w + \ell + w$, we get that $w = 120 - 0.5\ell$.

b. The length would be 120 meters and so the width could be found using the equation $w = 120 - 0.5\ell$ so the width would be 60 meters.

c. The equation is quadratic because it is the product of two linear factors that are in terms of ℓ. The equation $A = \ell(120 - 0.5\ell)$ can be written as $A = 120\ell - 0.5\ell^2$ where the exponent on ℓ is 2 and this is the highest exponent to which ℓ is raised.

12. a. First we need to write the equation $n = 20 - x$ in terms of $x = 20 - n$. So substituting into $P = xn - 6n$ we get that $P = (20 - n)n - 6n$ or $P = 20n - n^2 - 6n$ which is equivalent to $P = 14n - n^2$.

b. \$40; using the equation $P = 14n - n^2$, substitute 10 in for n. The profit is $P = 14(10) - 10^2 = 40$.

c. The selling price can be found using the equation $n = 20 - x$. So when $n = 10$ the selling price is \$10.

d. \$49; the greatest profit can be found by making a table or graph for the profit equation $P = 20n - n^2 - 6n = 14n - n^2$. The greatest profit occurs when they sell 7 posters, which yields a value of $P = 14(7) - 7^2 = 49$.

Connections

13. J; Students can try an example like $a = 1$ and $b = 2$ to check that J is false. The other letters are true: F and H are the Associative Property of Addition and Multiplication, respectively, and G is the Commutative Property of Multiplication.

14. $x(x + 5) = x^2 + 5x$

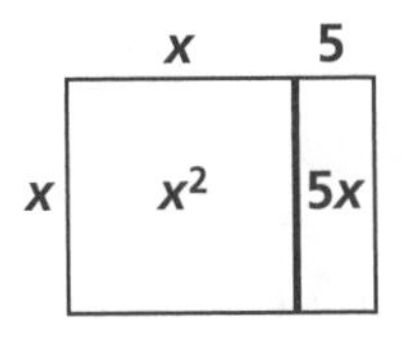

15. $(2 + x)(2 + 3x) = (2 + x)2 + (2 + x)3x = 4 + 2x + 6x + 3x^2 = 4 + 8x + 3x^2$

	2	3x
2	4	6x
x	2x	3x²

16. $(x + 2)(2x + 3) = (x + 2)2x + (x + 2)3 = 2x^2 + 4x + 3x + 6 = 2x^2 + 7x + 6$

	2x	3
x	2x²	3x
2	4x	6

17.a.

$$
\begin{aligned}
11x - 12 &= 30 + 5x \\
11x - 12 + 12 &= 30 + 12 + 5x \\
11x &= 42 + 5x \\
11x - 5x &= 42 + 5x - 5x \\
6x &= 42 \\
\frac{6x}{6} &= \frac{42}{6} \\
x &= 7
\end{aligned}
$$

b. To check, substitute 7 into the original equation for x and see if the values on each side of the equal sign are equal to each other.

$$
\begin{aligned}
11x - 12 &= 30 + 5x \\
11(7) - 12 &= 30 + 5(7) \\
77 - 12 &= 30 + 35 \\
65 &= 65
\end{aligned}
$$

c. To solve the equation using a graph, first graph each of the equations $y = 11x - 12$ and $y = 30 + 5x$ and use the x-value of their point of intersection for the solution. To solve the equation using a table, look on the tables for each equation and see for which value of x their y-values coincide.

18. a. \$1,000

b.

Number of Soccer Balls	Income from Soccer Balls	Expenses of Soccer Balls
500	\$500	\$1,250
1,000	\$1,000	\$1,500
3,000	\$3,000	\$2,500

c. To find the profit of soccer balls, subtract the expenses from the income. See table below.

Number of Soccer Balls	Profit of Soccer Balls (\$)
500	500 − 1,250 = −750
1,000	1,000 − 1,500 = −500
3,000	3,000 − 2,500 = 500

d. The break-even point is at 2,000 soccer balls; the income and expenses are both \$2,000.

e. Income = 1 times the number of soccer balls or

$I = 1n$

Expenses = 1,000 + 0.5 times number of soccer balls or

$E = 1{,}000 + 0.5n$

Profit = Income − Expenses or

$P = 1n - (1{,}000 + 0.5n)$ or

$P = n - 1{,}000 - 0.5n$, or

$P = 0.5n - 1000$

f. \$−125 or a loss of \$125; (Figure 1).

g. 22,000 ; Profit = −1,000 + 0.5(number of soccer balls)

$$\$10{,}000 = -1{,}000 + 0.5n$$
$$10{,}000 + 1{,}000 = -1{,}000 + 1{,}000 + 0.5n$$
$$11{,}000 = 0.5n$$
$$\frac{11{,}000}{0.5} = \frac{0.5n}{0.5}$$
$$22{,}000 = n$$

The number of soccer balls produced and sold if the profit is \$10,000 is 22,000.

19. One possible solution:

$$7x + 15 = 12x + 5$$
$$7x - 7x + 15 = 12x - 7x + 5$$
$$15 = 5x + 5$$
$$15 - 5 = 5x + 5 - 5$$
$$10 = 5x$$
$$\frac{10}{5} = \frac{5x}{5}$$
$$2 = x$$

Check:

$$7x + 15 = 12x + 5$$
$$7(2) + 15 = 12(2) + 5$$
$$14 + 15 = 24 + 5$$
$$29 = 29$$

20. $x = 2$; The solution is the same as Exercise 19 because the Commutative Property does not change the value of the variables when solving an equation.

21. One possible solution:

$$-3x + 5 = 2x - 10$$
$$-3x - 2x + 5 = 2x - 2x - 10$$
$$-5x + 5 = -10$$
$$-5x + 5 - 5 = -10 - 5$$
$$-5x = -15$$
$$\frac{-5x}{-5} = \frac{-15}{-5}$$
$$x = 3$$

Check:

$$-3x + 5 = 2x - 10$$
$$-3(3) + 5 = 2(3) - 10$$
$$-9 + 5 = 6 - 10$$
$$-4 = -4$$

22. One possible method:

$$14 - 3x = 1.5x + 5$$
$$14 - 3x - 14 = 1.5x + 5 - 14$$
$$-3x = 1.5x - 9$$
$$-3x - 1.5x = 1.5x - 9 - 1.5x$$
$$(-3 - 1.5)x = -9$$
$$-4.5x = -9$$
$$\frac{-4.5x}{-4.5} = \frac{-9}{-4.5}$$
$$x = 2$$

Check:

$$14 - 3(2) = 1.5(2) + 5$$
$$14 - 6 = 3 + 5$$
$$8 = 8$$

Figure 1

Number of Soccer Balls	Income (\$) = # of Soccer Balls I = 1*n*	Expenses (\$) = 1,000 + 0.5 (# of soccer balls)	Profit (\$) = Income − Expenses or *P* = 0.5*n* − 1,000
1,750	1,750	1,000 + 0.5(1,750) = 1,000 + 875 = 1,875	1,750 − 1,875 = −125, or 0.5(1,750) − 1,000 = 875 − 1,000 = −125

23. One possible solution:

$$9 - 4x = \frac{(3 + x)}{2}$$
$$2(9 - 4x) = 2 \times \frac{(3 + x)}{2}$$
$$18 - 8x = 3 + x$$
$$18 - 8x - x = 3 + x - x$$
$$18 - 9x = 3$$
$$18 - 9x - 18 = 3 - 18$$
$$-9x = -15$$
$$\frac{-9x}{-9} = \frac{-15}{-9}$$
$$x = 1\tfrac{2}{3}$$

Check:

$$9 - 4(1\tfrac{2}{3}) = \frac{3 + (1\frac{2}{3})}{2}$$
$$9 - 6\tfrac{2}{3} = \frac{4\frac{2}{3}}{2}$$
$$2\tfrac{1}{3} = 2\tfrac{1}{3}$$

24. One possible solution:

$$-3(x + 5) = \frac{(2x - 10)}{3}$$
$$-3x - 15 = \frac{(2x - 10)}{3}$$
$$3(-3x - 15) = 3 \times \frac{(2x - 10)}{3}$$
$$-9x - 45 = 2x - 10$$
$$-9x - 2x - 45 = 2x - 2x - 10$$
$$-11x - 45 = -10$$
$$-11x - 45 + 45 = -10 + 45$$
$$-11x = 35$$
$$\frac{-11x}{-11} = \frac{35}{-11}$$
$$x = -3\tfrac{2}{11}$$

Check:

$$-3(-3\tfrac{2}{11} + 5) = \frac{2x - 10}{3}$$
$$-3(1\tfrac{9}{11}) = \frac{2(-3\frac{2}{11}) - 10}{3}$$
$$\frac{-60}{11} = \frac{\frac{-70}{11} - 10}{3}$$
$$\frac{-60}{11} = \frac{\frac{-180}{11}}{3}$$
$$\frac{-180}{11} = \frac{-180}{11}$$

25. a. The two bids are equal when the y-values for a common x-value are equal. This occurs when $x = 25$ and $y = 200$, meaning the bids are both $200 for 25 books.

x (Number of books printed)	Y = 100 + 4x	Y = 25 + 7x
10	$140	$ 95
15	160	130
20	180	165
25	200	200
30	220	235

b.

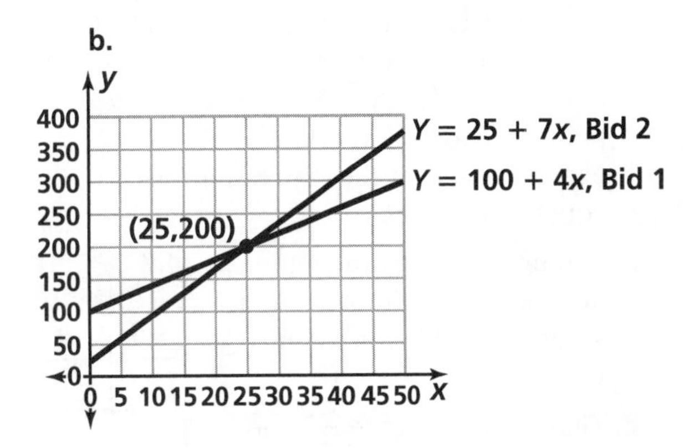

c. For 25 books, the bids are equal. The graph shows that for more than 25 books, Bid 1 is less than Bid 2 because the graph for Bid 1 is lower than the graph for Bid 2 for $x > 25$. For example, if the number of books is 26, Bid 1 is $204 and Bid 2 is $207. Since Bid 2 increases more with each book, if the number of books is greater than 25, Bid 1 is lower.

26. a. Bid 1: $100 + 4(75) = \$400$,
Bid 2: $25 + 7(75) = \$550$
(Students might also find these values from the table or the graph.)

b. The greatest number of books that can be printed is 50 for Bid 1 and 39 for Bid 2. Explanations will vary. Students might extend their tables or graphs, use trial and error, or apply methods for solving linear equations.

c. The related equations are $y = 8x$ and $y = 30 + 6x$. The two bids are equal when $x = 15$ and $y = 120$, meaning they are both $120 for 15 books. Explanations will vary; students may use tables, graphs, or begin to see a pattern and solve the equations $8x = 30 + 6x$ symbolically.

27. a. 210; $(21 \times 20) \div 2 = 420 \div 2 = 210$

b. $h = \frac{n(n-1)}{2}$

c. $h = \frac{n^2 - n}{2}$ or $h = \frac{1}{2}(n^2 - n)$

28. a. $x^2 + 7x + 10$ or $x^2 + 2x + 5x + 10$

b. Answers will vary. Students may use an area model to justify that their expressions are equivalent. They may use a graph or a table to show that their expressions are equivalent. (Teacher: Note that if three points satisfy different quadratic expressions, then the expressions are equivalent.)

29. a. y-intercept is 10; Students may find this by looking at a graph or a table for when $x = 0$.

b. The x-intercepts are -2 and -5. Students can find the x-intercepts by looking at a graph or a table for when $y = 0$.

c. The minimum is at $x = -3.5$ where the value of y is -2.25. The students may use a table or graph. There is no maximum.

d. The line of symmetry is the vertical line through the value $x = -3.5$.

X	Y
−5	0
−4	−2
−3	−2
−2	0
−1	4
0	10
1	18
2	28
3	40
4	54
5	70
6	88

30. x^5 **31.** x^6 **32.** x^4

33. x^3 **34.** $\frac{1}{x^3}$ **35.** $2x^3$

36. a. $34,500; she gets $30{,}000 \times 1.15 = 34{,}500$.

b. $33,600; since $30{,}000 \times 1.12 = 33{,}600$.

c. $33,000; since $30{,}000 \times 1.10 = 33{,}000$.

37. a. Cylinder A is fatter and shorter than either of the other 2 cylinders. Cylinder C is the same height as Cylinder B but skinnier. Cylinders B and C are both twice as tall as Cylinder A.

b. Cylinder A has the largest surface area. Students may count squares on the grid pattern to estimate the surface area. If they use formulas they will probably use the actual measurements. In general, Cylinder A has radius 2 and height 4 and surface area $= 2(\pi(2)^2) + (\pi(4)(4) = 24\pi$. Cylinder B has radius 1 and height 8 and surface area $= 2(\pi(1)^2) + (\pi)(2)(8) = 18\pi$. Cylinder C's surface area is 8.5π.

c. Cylinder A; Since volume equals $\pi r^2 h$ we need to find when r^2h is the greatest. For Cylinder A, $r^2h = 16$; for Cylinder B, $r^2h = 8$; and for Cylinder C, $r^2h = 2$.

Extensions

38. a. $P = 15x - 500 + 106x - x^2$

b. The maximum profit is 3,160.25 which occurs between 6000 and 6100 people.

39. Completion Rating:

$$CR = 5(\tfrac{288}{474}) - 1.5 \approx 1.5$$

Yards Rating:

$$YR = \frac{\frac{3692}{474} - 3}{4} \approx 1.2$$

Touchdown Rating:

$$TR = 20(\tfrac{28}{474}) \approx 1.18$$

Interception Rating:

$$IR = 25(0.095 - \tfrac{14}{474}) \approx 1.64$$

Overall Rating:

$$OR = 100\frac{(CR + YR + TR + IR)}{6}$$

$$\approx 100\frac{(1.5 + 1.2 + 1.18 + 1.64)}{6}$$

$$= 92$$

Possible Answers to Mathematical Reflections

1. If you have two or more equations for the amount of money each person collects for walking n kilometers, you can add them to find the total amount t of money collected by the group. For example if
$M_{Leanne} = 16(10)$
$M_{Gilberto} = 7(2n)$
$M_{Alana} = 11(5 + 0.5n)$; then
$t = 16(10) + 7(2n) + 11(5 + 0.5n) = 19.5n + 215$.

2. Answers will vary. If you have two equations and they have a variable in common like V, the number of visitors in Problem 2.2 where $P = 2.50V - 500$ and $V = 600 - 500R$, you can combine the equations into one by taking the expression 600 – 500R for V and substituting it into the equation, $P = 2.50V - 500$. The equation becomes $P = 2.50(600 - 500R) - 500$. By combining them into one equation, if you know the probability of rain and want to predict the profit, you only have to do one calculation instead of two separate calculations.

3. The advantage of working with one equation is that you only have to solve one equation. If you have to find more than one data point such as in the previous example—finding the profit when the probability of rain is 10%, 20%, 30%, etc, then you can graph the equation or make a table in your calculator and find all the profit values at once. A disadvantage of combining into one equation is that you may not be able to see the individual patterns that are involved in the separate equations and you may lose sense of the context of the problem. For example, the equation $V = 600 - 500R$ tells you that when the probability of rain is 0 there will be 600 visitors and that as the probability of rain increases, the number of visitors decreases. If profit is written in terms of the probability of rain, you lose the information about the number of visitors.

Investigation 3 Solving Equations

Mathematical and Problem-Solving Goals

- Develop a strategy for distributing a negative sign over a sum or difference in a linear expression
- Develop a strategy for solving linear equations with parentheses
- Continue to develop understanding and some fluency with factoring quadratic expressions
- Connect the x-intercepts of a quadratic function to solving a quadratic equation $0 = ax^2 + bx + c$
- Solve quadratic equations by factoring
- Use solutions of equations to make predictions and decisions
- Interpret information provided by equivalent expressions in context

In this investigation students continue to use the Distributive and Commutative properties of numbers to write equivalent expressions. The student uses the equivalent expressions with the properties of equalities to solve more complex linear equations and to solve quadratic equations by factoring.

Mathematics Background

For background on solving equations, see pages 7–9.

Summary of Problems

Problem 3.1 Solving Linear Equations

Students are intoduced to solving equations that involve parentheses and negative signs.

Problem 3.2 Comparing Costs

Problem 3.2 presents two linear equations with parentheses that represent the costs for tiles needed to surround a pool. The students are asked to find the number of tiles when the costs are equal without using tables or graphs.

Problem 3.3 Factoring Quadratic Expressions

Students revisit factoring quadratic expressions, which was first done in *Frogs, Fleas, and Painted Cubes.*

Problem 3.4 Solving Quadratic Equations

The connections between a factored form of $ax^2 + bx + c$, the x-intercepts of the graph of the equation $y = ax^2 + bx + c$, and the solutions to $0 = ax^2 + bx + c$ are explored. The two equivalent forms for a quadratic expression are used to predict the x- and y-intercepts, the maximum or minimum point, and the line of symmetry of the graph of a quadratic equation.

	Suggested Pacing	Materials for Students	Materials for Teachers	ACE Assignments
All	5 days	Graphing calculators (optional)	Graphing calculator (optional), overhead graphing calculator display (optional)	
3.1	1 day		Transparency 3.1	1–7, 29–32, 47–49
3.2	1 day	Large poster paper or blank transparencies (optional)		8–17, 33–37, 50, 53
3.3	$1\frac{1}{2}$ days		Transparency 3.3A, 3.3B	18–20, 38–41, 51–52
3.4	$1\frac{1}{2}$ days		Transparency 3.4	21–28, 42–46, 54–57
MR	$\frac{1}{2}$ day			

3.1 Solving Linear Equations

Goals

- Develop a strategy for distributing a negative sign over a sum or difference in a linear expression
- Develop a strategy for solving linear equations with parentheses on one side of the equation

Mathematics Background

For background on motivating the distribution of a negative sign over a sum or difference, see p 6.

Launch 3.1

Use the Getting Ready to review the strategies for solving linear equations. Ask the class to provide a reason for each step.

For steps (1) and (2), the property of equality was used; it states that subtracting the same quantity from both sides of the equation maintains equality. In (1), the quantity was $4x$; for (2) it was 25.

Suggested Questions Ask:

- *Could you begin with a different first step?* (Yes, students could have subtracted 100 or 25 from both sides.)
- *How could you check that 25 is the correct solution?* (By substituting 25 for x in the equation $100 + 4x = 25 + 7x$.)
- *Describe another method for finding the solution to the equation.* (Graph the equations $y = 100 + 4x$ and $y = 25 + 7x$ in a graphing calculator and trace the graphs to find the x-coordinate of the intersection point. Find the table for the two equations and find when the y-coordinates are the same. At this value, find the x-coordinate to find the answer.)

By the end of this discussion, students should be comfortable with using the principles of equality to solve equations. The principles state that equality is maintained by

- adding or subtracting the same quantity to both sides of an equation
- multiplying or dividing both sides of an equation by the same nonzero quantity

The following questions provide a quick review from *Moving Straight Ahead.*

Suggested Questions Ask:

- *What does 7x mean?* ($7x$ means 7 times x or $x + x + x + x + x + x + x$)
- *Why does 7x – 4x equal 3x?* [Using the Distributive Property, $7x - 4x = x(7 - 4) = x \times 3$ or $3x$.]
- *Why does 3x divided by 3 equal x?* (Since $3x = x + x + x$ or three groups of x, when you divide 3 groups of x into 3 groups you get x in each group)

Put the equation $P = 5s - (100 + 2s)$ on the board. Tell the story about the club selling cards to raise money.

- *What affects the profit?* (The number of boxes sold, which is the income, and the expenses, or costs. Profit = income – expenses.)

Try to keep the problem open. Ask each student to read Question A parts (1) and (2) on their own before moving into groups. Do Questions A and B and then discuss these parts. Then let the class apply the strategies that they developed in Questions A and B to solve the equations in Question C.

Let the class work in pairs or groups of 3.

Explore 3.1

If students are struggling interpreting the information represented, point to various parts of the equation and ask what information each part represents.

For Question A, part (3), some students may need to be reminded what break-even means. (The break-even point is when Income = Expenses, or in this case, when profit equals zero.)

Look at the ways students are solving the equation. Suggest to students solving by graph or table to try solving without a table or graph.

Look for how students are distributing the negative sign. If you notice that they are not doing it correctly, suggest that they try substituting a value into the original expression for profit and the new equivalent expression to see if their expressions are equivalent. This will tell them that they do not have an equivalent expression. You might also remind students that subtraction can be thought of as adding the opposite quantity. For example, $5 - 3 = 5 + -3$. In this problem, $-(100 + 2s)$ is the same as $-1(100 + 2s)$. This is a good time to check on students' use of the order of operations. In Question A, part (5), in the expression $5s - 2(50 + s)$, the multiplication of -2 by $(50 + s)$ is the first step in finding an equivalent expression. Students may need to be reminded again while they work on Question C. There are many opportunities in the ACE Exercises in this unit to review or practice order of operations.

Summarize 3.1

Call on students to answer each part. Be sure they give a reason for each step, or have someone else give a reason for each step as a student presents his/her solution.

Suggested Question Ask:

- *In Question A, part (2), is there another way to solve this equation, $200 = 5s - (100 + 2s)$?* (Some will suggest using tables or graphs. Be sure to have a symbolic method illustrated. Most students will distribute the negative sign and then add the constant 100 to both sides or combine $5s$ and $-2s$. Some may subtract $5s$ from both sides of the equation as the first step. For some students you may need to write the equation as $200 = 5s + -1(100 + 2s)$. This should help them understand the role of the minus sign in front of parentheses and the need to apply the Distributive Property.)

Be sure to summarize the strategies for solving equations with parentheses.

Be aware of how students use the order of operations.

Then let the class solve the equations in Question C.

Call on different groups to show their solutions, including how they check to see if they were correct. Pick one or two of the equations and ask students to show the solution on a graph.

3.1 Solving Linear Equations

At a Glance

PACING 1 day

Mathematical Goals

- Develop a strategy for distributing a negative sign over a sum or difference in a linear expression
- Develop a strategy for solving linear equations with parentheses on one side of the equation

Launch

Use the Getting Ready to review strategies for solving linear equations. Ask the class to give a reason for each step and discuss how to check the answer.

Review the principles of equality: add or subtract the same quantity on both sides of an equation, and multiply or divide by the same nonzero quantity.

Ask students to explain the following to see that their reasoning includes an understanding of $7x$ as 7 times x or $x + x + x + x + x + x + x$.

- *Why does $7x - 4x$ equal $3x$? Why does $3x$ divided by 3 equal x?*

Put $P = 5x - (100 + 2x)$ on the board. Tell the story about the club selling cards to raise money.

- *What affects the profit?*

Keep the problem open. Ask students to read Question A, parts (1) and (2), before moving into groups. Let the class work in pairs or groups of three.

Materials
- Transparency 3.1

Vocabulary
- properties of equality

Explore

Point to various parts of the equation and ask what information each part represents. For Question A, part (3), students may need to be reminded what break-even means.

Look at the ways students are solving the equation. Suggest to students who are solving by graph or table to try solving without a table or graph.

If students are incorrectly distributing the negative sign, have them substitute values into the original expression for profit and the new equivalent expression to see if their expressions are equivalent.

Remind students that subtraction can be thought of as adding the opposite quantity, and that $-(100 + 2x)$ is the same as $-1(100 + 2x)$, in which we distribute -1 over $(100 + 2x)$.

Check students' use of the order of operations, especially in A(2) and A(5).

Summarize

Be sure they give a reason for each step or have someone else give a reason for each step as a student presents his/her solution.

- *In Question A, part (2), is there another way to solve this equation, $200 = 5s - (100 + 2s)$?*

Summarize strategies for solving equations with parentheses.

Be aware of students' use of the order of operations.

Have students solve the equations in Question C. Pick one or two of the equations and ask students to show the solution on a graph.

Materials
- Student notebooks

ACE Assignment Guide for Problem 3.1

Core 1, 4–7, 30, 31, 49
Other *Applications* 2, 3; *Connections* 29, 32; *Extensions* 47, 48

Adapted For suggestions about adapting ACE exercises, see the CMP *Special Needs Handbook.*
Connecting to Prior Units 29, 30: *Moving Straight Ahead;* 31, 32: *Accentuate the Negative*

Answers to Problem 3.1

A. **1.** The $5s$ represents the income, so the school choir makes \$5 for each box of greeting cards they sell. The $100 + 2s$ represents the expenses, so the start-up cost is \$100 and it costs \$2 to produce each box of greeting cards.

2. 100 boxes; The equation which students must solve is $200 = 5s - (100 + 2s)$

3. 34 boxes; The solution to the equation $P = 5s - (100 + 2s)$ when $P = 0$ is $s = 33.333$. So to break even, the school choir must sell 34 boxes.

4. $P = 3s - 100$; The 3 represents the income made per box sold and the 100 is the startup cost. Students may find other equivalent expressions such as $P = 5s - 100 - 2s$, but these expressions do not provide as much new information.

5. Yes, $5s - 2(50 + s)$ is equivalent to $5s - (100 + 2s)$ by applying the Distributive Property to factor out a common factor of 2. Students can also check two different values for s and show that they produce the same value for P in each expression since the expressions are linear. Or students can use a graph or table to show that both expressions are equivalent.

B. One possible strategy: To solve an equation like $200 = 5s - (100 + 2s)$, first replace the right hand expression with the equivalent expression $5s - 100 - 2s$. This expression is equivalent since we can rewrite the equation as $200 = 5s + -1(100 + 2s)$ and then distribute the -1. Make sure students recognize that replacing an expression in an equation with an equivalent expression doesn't change the equality. Then we have $200 = 5s - 100 - 2s$. We can replace $5s - 100 - 2s$ with the equivalent expression $3s - 100$ getting $200 = 3s - 100$. Using the properties of equality on $200 = 3s - 100$ we get:

$$200 + 100 = 3s - 100 + 100 \quad \text{(add 100 to both sides)}$$
$$300 = 3s \quad \text{(combine like terms)}$$
$$100 = s \quad \text{(divide both sides by 3)}$$

To solve an equation involving parentheses, distribute the number in front of the parentheses and then combine like terms. Next, continue to use the properties of equality to write simpler equations until it is easy to read the solution.

C. Be sure students check their work!

1.
$$\begin{aligned} 0 &= 5 + 2(3 + 4x) \\ 0 &= 5 + 6 + 8x \\ 0 &= 11 + 8x \\ 0 - 11 &= 11 + 8x - 11 \\ -11 &= 8x \\ -\tfrac{11}{8} &= x \end{aligned}$$

2.
$$\begin{aligned} 0 &= 5 - 2(3 + 4x) \\ 0 &= 5 - 6 - 8x \\ 0 &= -1 - 8x \\ 0 + 1 &= -1 - 8x + 1 \\ 1 &= -8x \\ -\tfrac{1}{8} &= x \end{aligned}$$

3.
$$\begin{aligned} 0 &= 5 + 2(3 - 4x) \\ 0 &= 5 + 6 - 8x \\ 0 &= 11 - 8x \\ 0 - 11 &= 11 - 8x - 11 \\ -11 &= -8x \\ \tfrac{11}{8} &= x \end{aligned}$$

4.
$$\begin{aligned} 0 &= 5 - 2(3 - 4x) \\ 0 &= 5 - 6 + 8x \\ 0 &= -1 + 8x \\ 0 + 1 &= -1 + 8x + 1 \\ 1 &= 8x \\ \tfrac{1}{8} &= x \end{aligned}$$

3.2 Comparing Costs

Goal

- Solve linear equations that have parentheses on both sides of the equation

Launch 3.2

Describe the problem. Put the two equations on the overhead for the cost of tiles.

Suggested Questions Ask:

- *Do these equations make sense given the information about the two companies?* (Students should be able to relate parts of the equation and the role of parentheses to the given information.)
- *What information does the constant number on each side of the equals sign represent?* (For *Cover and Surround It*, 1000 is the start-up cost, which includes the first 12 tiles. Similarly for *Tile and Beyond*, 740 is the start-up cost, which include the first 10 tiles.)
- *What information does the number in front of the parentheses represent?* (For *Cover and Surround It*, the 25 means that the cost of each tile is $25 for any tile over 12. For the other company the cost per tile over 10 is $32.)

You can let the class work on Question A and then summarize before doing Question B.

Let the class work in groups of 2–3.

Explore 3.2

This problem is very similar to the last problem, except it requires a few more steps.

If students make a graph for the two equations, check if they represent the situations accurately. For *Cover and Surround It* they should have a horizontal line for tiles up to 12, which represents a fixed charge of $1,000 up to 12 tiles, then the graph of $1{,}000 + 25(N - 12)$ beyond the first 12 tiles. Similarly, for *Tile and Beyond*, they should have a horizontal line for tiles up to 10, which represents a fixed charge of $740 up to 10 tiles, then the graph of $740 + 32(N - 10)$ beyond the first 10 tiles.

Look for different ways that students might solve the problem. See the first question in the summary.

You might have some groups put their work, including graphical representations on large poster paper or blank transparency paper for the discussion.

Summarize 3.2

Call on a group to present their work for Question A, parts (1) and (2). Have the rest of the class validate their work and/or ask questions of the group.

Suggested Questions Ask:

- *Did any group use a different first step?* (Some may have subtracted 1,000 or 740 from both sides of the equation, before distributing the number in front of the parentheses. Or after subtracting one of the constant terms, they could divide both sides by the number in front of the parentheses. If this happens, be sure they divide correctly.)
- *For the expression on the right side of the equality $740 + 32(N - 10)$, can we add 740 and 32 as a first step?* (No. Following the order of operations, multiplication comes before addition when finding an equivalent expression.)
- *Describe how you could use a table or graph to solve this equation.* (If you have an overhead display for the graphing calculator, you could use it to illustrate how a table or graph might be used.)
- *How can you determine the number of tiles for which the* Tile and Beyond Company *is the cheaper of the two?* (Some may suggest to substitute a number that is less than the number of tiles for when the two costs are equal. The lesser of the costs indicates which plan is cheaper.)

If no one suggests using a graph, ask:

- *How can you decide which is cheaper by using a table or graph?* (On the graph look at the parts of the line graphs that are to the left of the point of intersection. The line that is the lowest will have costs that are the cheaper of the two. You might have students describe on the graph why this is true and by how much cheaper the lower company is. It is the difference in the vertical heights for any given value of N.)

Go over Question A. Discuss the graphs of each equation. Each graph contains a horizontal line and a non-horizontal line. See answer.

Let the class work on Question B individually, or you can assign Question B as part of the homework.

You could end by posing an equation to solve. It might have some fractions or decimals. For example, $10.5 - \frac{3}{2}(5 - 6x) = 12 + 3(5x - \frac{1}{2}x)$.

3.2 Comparing Costs

At a Glance

PACING 1 day

Mathematical Goal

- Solve linear equations that have parentheses on both sides of the equation

Launch

Describe the problem. Put the two equations for the cost of tiles on the overhead. You can let the class work on Question A and then summarize before doing Question B.

Let the class work in groups of 2–3.

Explore

This problem is very similar to the last problem, except that it requires a few more steps.

You might have some groups put their work including graphical representation on large poster paper or blank transparency paper for the discussion.

Materials

- Large poster paper or transparency paper (optional)

Summarize

Call on a group to present their work for Question A, parts (1) and (2). Have the rest of the class validate their work and/or ask questions of the group. Ask:

- *Did any group use a different first step?*
- *Can we add 740 and 32 as a first step?*
- *Describe how you could use a table or graph to solve this equation.*
- *How can you determine the number of tiles for which the* Tile and Beyond Company *is the cheaper of the two?*

If no one suggests using a graph, ask:

- *How can you decide which is cheaper by using a table or graph?*

Go over Question A and then let the class work on Question B individually, or assign Question B as part of the homework.

Discuss the graphical representation.

Materials

- Student notebooks

ACE Assignment Guide for Problem 3.2

Core 8–15, 34

Other *Applications* 16, 17; *Connections* 33, 35–37, *Extensions* 50, 53; and unassigned choices from previous problems

Adapted For suggestions about adapting ACE exercises, see the CMP *Special Needs Handbook.*
Connecting to Prior Units 33: *Filling and Wrapping; Frogs, Fleas and Painted Cubes*; 36, 37: *Covering and Surrounding*

Answers to Problem 3.2

A. 1. 40;
$$\begin{aligned} 1{,}000 + 25(N-12) &= 740 + 32(N-10) \\ 1{,}000 + 25N - 300 &= 740 + 32N - 320 \\ 700 + 25N &= 420 + 32N \\ 700 - 420 + 25N &= 420 - 420 + 32N \\ 280 + 25N &= 32N \\ 280 + 25N - 25N &= 32N - 25N \\ \frac{280}{7} &= \frac{7N}{7} \\ 40 &= N \end{aligned}$$

2. One possible way to check that the solution is correct is to put the value for N, 40, into each equation, solve for cost, and see if it is the same value.

3. Students may graph each equation and find the point at which the two lines intersect in order to determine the number of tiles for which the cost estimates are equal. If students used a table to determine the number of tiles for which the cost is equal, they would look for the number of tiles for which both companies have the same cost values.

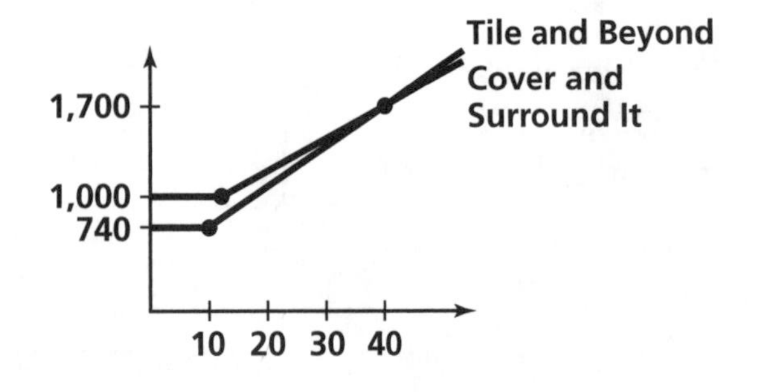

4. *Tile and Beyond* is cheaper than *Cover and Surround It* when the number of tiles is less than 40. On the graph *Tile and Beyond* has cost values that are lower than *Cover and Surround* It when the value for N is less than 40 tiles, and this holds true for the table as well.

B. NOTE: The solutions below make use of the idea of combining *like* terms. For example, $3x - 8x = -5x$ may be used by some students. Others may still need to think of this idea as $3x - 8x = (3-8)x = -5x$ using the Distributive Property. Be sure that students check answers!

1.
$$\begin{aligned} 3x &= 5 + 2(3 + 4x) \\ &= 5 + 6 + 8x \\ 3x &= 11 + 8x \\ 3x - 8x &= 11 + 8x - 8x \\ -5x &= 11 \\ x &= -\frac{11}{5} \end{aligned}$$

2.
$$\begin{aligned} 10 + 3x &= 2(3 + 4x) + 5 \\ &= 6 + 8x + 5 \\ 10 + 3x &= 11 + 8x \\ 10 + 3x - 11 &= 11 + 8x - 11 \\ -1 + 3x &= 8x \\ -1 + 3x - 3x &= 8x - 3x \\ -1 &= 5x \\ -\frac{1}{5} &= x \end{aligned}$$

3.
$$\begin{aligned} 3x &= 5 - 2(3 + 4x) \\ &= 5 - 6 - 8x \\ 3x &= -1 - 8x \\ 3x + 8x &= -1 - 8x + 8x \\ 11x &= -1 \\ x &= -\frac{1}{11} \end{aligned}$$

4.
$$\begin{aligned} 7 + 3(1 - x) &= 5 - 2(3 - 4x) \\ 7 + 3(1 - x) &= 5 - 6 + 8x \\ 7 + 3 - 3x &= -1 + 8x \\ 10 - 3x &= -1 + 8x \\ 10 - 3x + 1 &= -1 + 8x + 1 \\ 11 - 3x &= 8x \\ 11 - 3x + 3x &= 8x + 3x \\ 11 &= 11x \\ 1 &= x \end{aligned}$$

3.3 Factoring Quadratic Equations

Goals

- Continue to develop understanding and some fluency with factoring quadratic expressions
- Factor more quadratic expressions of the form $ax^2 + bx + c$, where a does not equal 1
- Connect the x-intercepts of a quadratic function to solving a quadratic equation $0 = ax^2 + bx + c$

Launch 3.3

Write the equation $y = x^2 + 5x$ on the board.

Suggested Questions Ask students to:

- *Describe the shape of the graph.* (Students should be able to do this without making a sketch or using a calculator.)
- *How can you use a table or graph to find the x-intercepts?*
- *What are the coordinates of the x-intercepts?* [$(0, 0)$ and $(-5, 0)$]
- *What is the value of y for each x-intercept?* ($y = 0$)
- *Finding the x-intercepts is the same as solving the equation, $0 = x^2 + 5x$, for x. This is called solving a quadratic equation for x when $y = 0$.*

Put up Transparency 3.3A, which shows the connection between finding the x-intercepts of the graph of a quadratic equation and solving the equation if $y = 0$ using a table or graph.

Suggested Questions Ask:

- *What is the factored form of $x^2 + 5x$?* [$x(x + 5)$]
- *What is the relationship between the factored form of $x^2 + 5x$ and the x-intercepts of the graph of $y = x^2 + 5x$?* [The factored form of $x^2 + 5x$ which is $x(x + 5)$ is related to the x-intercepts. When y is zero, each x-intercept is the value for x that makes each factor equal to zero, in this case, $x = 0$ and $x + 5 = 0$ or $x = -5$. Therefore 0 and -5 are the x-intercepts.]

If students don't suggest one, ask them:

- *How would you use an area model to get the factored form?* (In the first expression the dimensions of the rectangle are x and $x + 5$. The areas of the subparts of the rectangle are x^2 and $5x$.)
- *Finding the x-intercepts using the factored form of a quadratic expression is the same as solving the equation $0 = ax^2 + bx + c$. To do this we need to review how to factor a quadratic expression.*

Put up Transparency 3.3B and go over the questions.

Suggested Questions Ask:

- *Does Trevor's area model match the expression $x^2 + 5x + 6$?* (Yes, since the sum of the areas of the four rectangles is $x^2 + 3x + 2x + 6$ or $x^2 + 5x + 6$.)
- *Find the factors of $x^2 + 5x + 6$.* [$(x + 2)$ and $(x + 3)$]
- *What are the x-intercepts of the equation for $y = x^2 + 5x + 6$?* (-2 and -3)
- *Describe the relationship between the x-intercepts of $y = x^2 + 5x + 6$ and the factored form of the expression, $x^2 + 5x + 6$.* [Students may recognize that the x-intercepts in this case are the additive inverse of the 2 and 3 in the factored form. The x-intercepts are the value of x when each of the factors $(x + 2)$ and $(x + 3)$ are set equal to zero.]

Put up another expression such as $x^2 + 7x + 12$ and ask the class to write it in factored form.

Suggested Questions Ask:

- *Can you factor this expression without using the area model?*
- *What clues in the area model will help you factor this expression?* (Students should begin to notice that if m and n are the x-intercepts, or solutions, then $mn = 12$, the constant term, and $m + n = 7$, the coefficient of the x term. That is, a pair of corresponding factors of 12 must have a sum of 7. This is true because the coefficient of x is 1.)

- *How could you use an area model to factor $2x^2 + 6x$?* (The dimensions of the rectangle are either x and $2x + 6$, $2x$ and $x + 3$, or 2 and $x^2 + 3x$. The area of the sub parts of the rectangle is $2x^2$ and $6x$ or x^2, x^2 and $6x$. See area models below.)

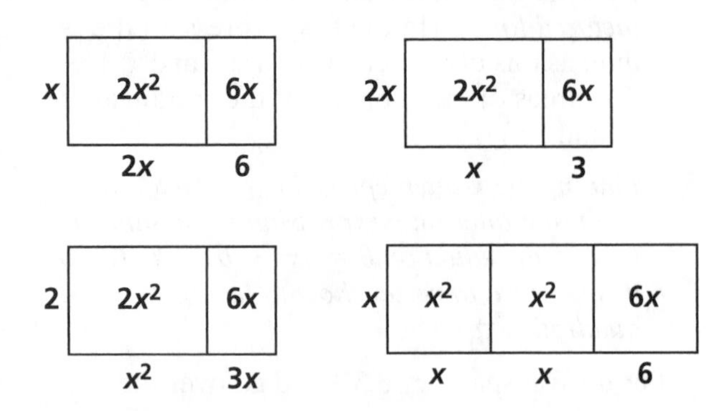

- *What are the x-intercepts for the equation $y = 2x^2 + 6x$?*

Go over Question A as whole class discussion. Ask students to think about Jaime's method and explain what he is doing.

You could first let the class work on Questions B and C, summarize these questions, and then work on Question D.

Let the class work in pairs.

Explore 3.3

If students are having trouble factoring, suggest that they use an area model.

Have students check if they can adapt Jaime's method for Questions B and C.

Suggested Question Ask:

- *Will Jaime's method work?* (NOTE to teacher: It works on any quadratic of the form $ax^2 + bx + c$ where $a = 1$.)

In *Prime Time* students considered just whole numbers as factor pairs, but in Question B students will have to consider integer values. If they struggle with Question B parts (2) and (3), refer them to the first bullet of Jaime's method, which includes integer values in the factor pairs.

Summarize 3.3

Go over Questions B and C. In Question C, part (1d), $x^2 - 4$ is the difference of two squares. Its factored form is $(x + 2)(x - 2)$. An area model for this special quadratic was explored in Investigation 2 of *Frogs, Fleas, and Painted Cubes.* You might want to have a student present an area model for this expression.

Suggested Questions You may also want to ask students:

- *Will Jaime's method for factoring work for Question C, part (1d)?* (Yes, but students may need help to realize that they need two numbers that multiply to -4 and add to zero since $x^2 - 4$ is equivalent to $x^2 + 0x - 4$. The factor pair that multiplies to -4 and adds to zero is 2 and -2.)

Write the expressions for Question D on the overhead.

- *What is different about these expressions?* (The coefficient of x^2 is not 1.)
- *Can we use Jaime's method?* (Let the students try but they will quickly see that Jaime's method does not take care of the coefficient of x^2.)
- *Let's go back to an area model to see if we can adjust Jaime's method.* (Students should see that factored pairs of c and factored pairs of a must combine to get b.)

For example, write $2x^2 + 7x + 6$ on the board.

- *What are possibilities for factors of 2?* (2 and 1)
- *So we have $(2x + ■)(x + ■) = 2x^2 + 7x + 6$. What are possibilities for factors of 6?* (6 and 1 or 2 and 3.)
- *Now what are possibilities for ■ in $(2x + ■)(x + ■)$?* [$(2x + 6)(x + 1)$ or $(2x + 1)(x + 6)$ or $(2x + 2)(x + 3)$ or $(2x + 3)(x + 2)$].
- *How do we know which one is correct?* (Use an area model or multiply each out using the Distributive Property.)

For Question D, part (1a) ask:

- *What does each term have in common?* (Each term has a common factor of 2.)
- *Can you use this information to write an equivalent expression?* [Yes, the Distributive Property allows you to write $2x^2 + 8x + 8$ as $2(x^2 + 4x + 4)$.]

- *Is this in factored form?* (yes)
- *Can we predict the solutions or x-intercepts from this form?* (No, but we can write $x^2 + 4x + 4$ in factored form as $(x + 2)(x + 2)$ using Jaime's method. So the factored form is $2(x + 2)(x + 2)$.)

For Question D, part (1a), you can tell the students that $(x + 2)(x + 2)$ can be written as $(x + 2)^2$. You could connect this expression, $2x^2 + 8x + 8$, to the graph of $y = 2x^2 + 8x + 8$ in order to introduce students to the idea that when a root is repeated for a quadratic, there is only one x-intercept.

Now let the class work the rest of Question D or assign it as homework.

NOTE: In the examples above we were only looking for whole number factors. There may be temptation to spend lots of time on factoring. Factoring quadratic expressions is a "guess and check" procedure. The examples are quite contrived since picking whole numbers randomly for a, b, and c in the expression $ax^2 + bx + c$ will have a probability near zero of being factorable over the real numbers.

It is important to be clear that the relation between the factored and expanded forms depends on the Distributive Property. Understanding the Distributive Property is key to using factored and expanded form successfully in a variety of situations.

Suggested Questions At this point ask students to factor the following and summarize the strategies.

- *How could we factor the following?*
  1. $x^2 + 7x + 12$ [Since $a = 1$, we can use Jaime's method $(x + 3)(x + 4)$]
  2. $3x^2 + 8x + 5$ [Since $a \neq 1$, we can't use Jaime's method. Use area model or consider the combinations of the factor pairs for 3 and 5. $(3x + 5)(x + 1)$]
  3. $2x^2 + 14x + 24$ [After the 2 is factored out, we can use Jaime's method, $2(x + 3)(x + 4)$. Have students compare to the factors of $x^2 + 7x + 12$.]

INVESTIGATION 3

3.3 Factoring Quadratic Equations

At a Glance

PACING $1\frac{1}{2}$ days

Mathematical Goals

- Continue to develop understanding and some fluency with factoring quadratic expressions
- Factor more quadratic expressions of the form $ax^2 + bx + c$ where a does not equal 1
- Connect the x-intercepts of a quadratic function to solving a quadratic equation $0 = ax^2 + bx + c$

Launch

Write the equation $y = x^2 + 5x$ on the board. Ask students to:

- *Describe the shape of the graph.*
- *How can you use a table or graph to find the x-intercepts?*
- *What are the coordinates of the x-intercepts?*
- *What is the value of y for each x-intercept?*

Finding the x-intercepts is the same as solving the equation $0 = x^2 + 5x$ for x. This is called solving a quadratic equation for x when $y = 0$.

Put up Transparency 3.3A.

- *What is the factored form of $x^2 + 5x$? What is the relationship between the factored form of $x^2 + 5x$ and the x-intercepts of the graph of $y = x^2 + 5x$?*

Put up Transparency 3.3B.

- *Does Trevor's area model match the expression $x^2 + 5x + 6$?*
- *What are the x-intercepts of the equation for $y = x^2 + 5x + 6$? Describe the relationship between the x-intercepts of $y = x^2 + 5x + 6$ and the factored form of the expression $x^2 + 5x + 6$.*
- *Can you factor $x^2 + 7x + 12$ without using the area model?*
- *What clues in the area model help you factor this expression?*
- *How could you use an area model to factor $2x^2 + 6x$?*
- *What are the x-intercepts for the equation $y = 2x^2 + 6x$?*

Go over Question A as whole class discussion. You could first let the class work on Questions B and C, summarize these questions, and then work on Question D.

Materials

- Transparencies 3.3A and 3.3B

Vocabulary

- roots

Explore

For students having trouble factoring, suggest they use an area model. For Questions B and C, see if students can adapt Jaime's method:

- *Will Jaime's method work?*
- *Will Jaime's method for factoring work for Question C, part (1d)?*

continued on next page

Summarize

Materials
- Student notebooks

For Question D:

- *What is different about these expressions? Can we use Jaime's method? Let's go back to an area model to see if we can adjust Jaime's method.*

Write $2x^2 + 7x + 6$ on the board.

- *What are the possibilities for factors of 2?*
- *So we have $(2x + ■)(x + ■) = 2x^2 + 7x + 6$. What are the possibilities for factors of 6? Now what are the possibilities for ■ in $(2x + ■)(x + ■)$? How do we know which one is correct?*

For Question D, part (1a) ask:

- *What does each term have in common? Can you use this information to write an equivalent expression? Is this in factored form?*
- *Can we predict the solutions or x-intercepts from this form?*

Connect $2x^2 + 8x + 8$ to the graph of $y = 2x^2 + 8x + 8$ to introduce students to when a repeated root results in only one x-intercept. Ask students to factor the following and summarize strategies.

- *How could we factor the following?*

1. $x^2 + 7x + 12$ **2.** $3x^2 + 8x + 5$ **3.** $2x^2 + 14x + 24$

ACE Assignment Guide for Problem 3.3

Core 18–20
Other *Connections* 38–41, *Extensions* 51–52; and unassigned choices from previous problems

Adapted For suggestions about adapting ACE exercises, see the CMP *Special Needs Handbook*.
Connecting to Prior Units 38: *Looking for Pythagoras*; 39, 40: *Covering and Surrounding*; 41: *Filling and Wrapping and Looking for Pythagoras*

Answers to Problem 3.3

A. 1. The area model that represents why Jaime's method worked is shown to the right. The simplest way to represent x^2 is x times x. Next Jaime needed to decide how to represent 12. He had three choices that gave him 12 in the lower right hand rectangle. He picked the pair (2, 6) because they added to 8, which was the coefficient of the middle term in $x^2 + 8x + 12$. This happened because when he used 2 and 6, they created rectangles with an area of $2x$ and $6x$, which made for a total area of $8x$ when he added them.

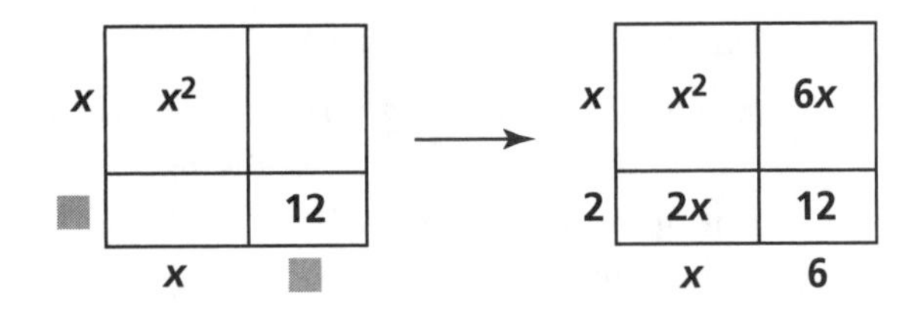

2. If Jaime had used another factor pair like 3 and 4, then the area model would have the x^2-rectangle and the 12-rectangle; however it would have also had a $3x$- and a $4x$-rectangle which would add to $7x$, not $8x$. So the factor pair 3 and 4 would not work. There is only one factor pair that will work for an expression using Jaime's method (though the factor pair may be commuted: 2 and 6 and 6 and 2).

B. 1. The factor pairs for 4 are (1, 4), (2, 2). Since $1 + 4 = 5$, the factored form of $x^2 + 5x + 4$ is $(x + 4)(x + 1)$. To show that this factored form is correct, students may make an area model with one side of length $x + 4$ and the other of $x + 1$ and show that the area of the rectangle is $x^2 + 5x + 4$. They can also make a table or graph for the two expressions $(x + 4)(x + 1)$ and $x^2 + 5x + 4$ and note that they are the same.

2. The factor pairs for 4 are (1, 4) and (2, 2). However, even though $1 + 4 = 5$, the middle term is actually -5. So for this one, Jaime's method must be modified to consider negative values in the factor pairs. Since -1×-4 still is 4, and $-1 + (-4) = -5$, the factored form of $x^2 - 5x + 4$ is $(x - 4)(x - 1)$.
3. The factor pairs for -4 are $(-1, 4)$, $(1, -4)$ and $(-2, 2)$. Since $1 + -4 = -3$, the factored form of $x^2 - 3x - 4$ is $(x - 4)(x + 1)$.
4. The factor pairs for 4 are (2, 2), $(-2, -2)$. Since $2 + 2 = 4$, the expression in factored form is $(x + 2)(x + 2)$.

C. 1. The expressions are similar to those in Question B in that they are all quadratic. However some of these expressions have $a \neq 1$ in the expression $ax^2 + bx + c$, whereas in Question B, $a = 1$ for all the expressions. Also, the expressions in Question C have two terms because either b or c equals zero, whereas the expressions in Question B have three terms.

2. Jaime's method will only work if the coefficient of x^2 is 1. So it only works directly for parts (a) or (d). However students can use Jaime's method for Question B if they first factor out a 4 from both the $4x^2$ and $32x$. See below for explanations.

a. Students may think of the c in the form $ax^2 + bx + c$ as 0. So the factor pair (0, 4) works since $0 \times 4 = 0$ and $0 + 4 = 4$. So the factors are $(x)(x + 4)$. Students may also apply the Distributive Property directly to factor out the common factor x or use an area model.

b. Students must factor out the 4 in order to use Jaime's method. If they do so, they will have $4(x^2 + 8x)$, which if they think of the factor pair (0, 8), yields $0 + 8 = 8$. So the factored form is $4(x)(x + 8)$. Students may also apply the Distributive Property directly to factor out the common factor $4x$ or use an area model.

c. Students may apply the Distributive Property by factoring out $2x$ and writing $2x(3x - 2)$ or they may use an area model. Also Jaime's method could be adjusted to fit quadratic expressions in which the coefficient of x^2 is not 1. See answer to Question D, part (2). NOTE: there are other valid area models for this expression. See two of them below:

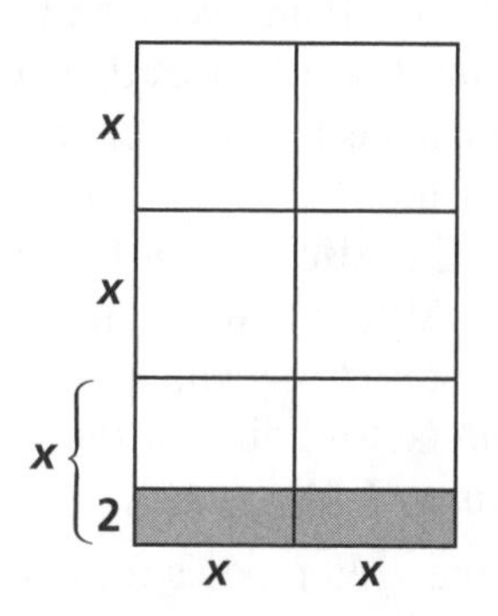

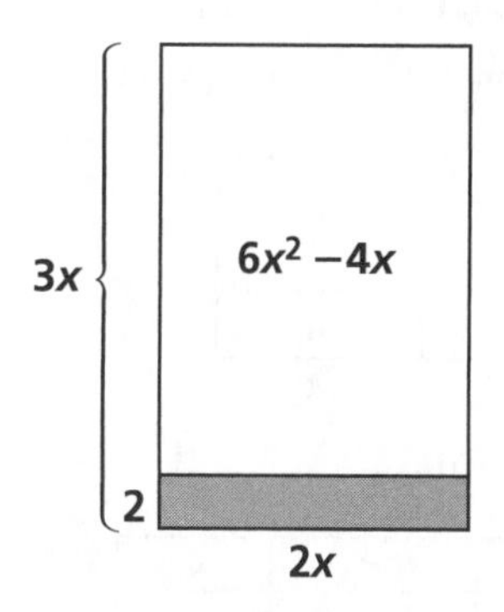

d. The factor pair $(2, -2)$ works since $2 + -2 = 0$, which is the coefficient of the middle term. So the factored form is $(x + 2)(x - 2)$. Students may also use an area model. Two are provided. For example, the area of the shaded part of the second figure below is $(x - 2)(x + 2) = x^2 - 2x + 2x - 4 = x^2 - 4$.

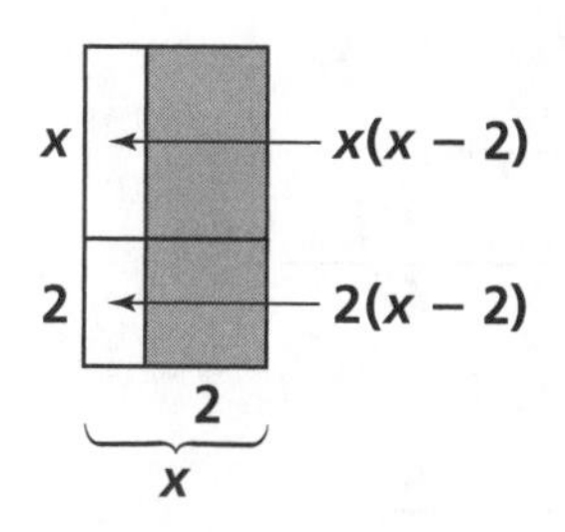

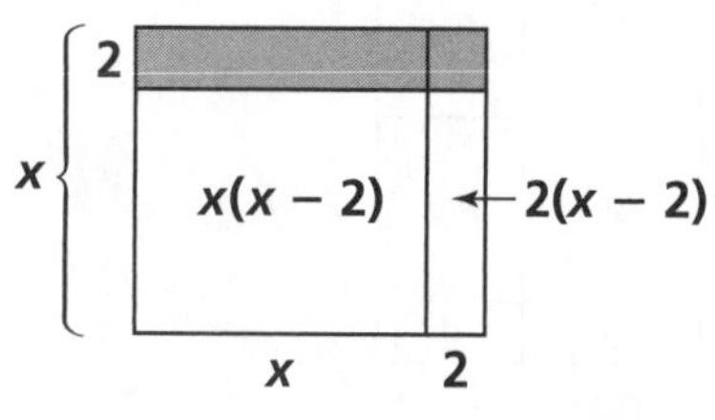

$x(x - 2) + 2(x - 2) = x^2 - 4$

D. 1. They are different in that the coefficients of x^2 are not 1. They are similar because they all are of the form $ax^2 + bx + c$, where a, b, c all are $\neq 0$.

2. Jaime's method will not work on these because his method requires that the coefficient of x^2 be 1. However students can adapt Jaime's method for a, b, and c. For example, for Question D, part (1c), $2x^2 + 9x + 4$, students would need to look at the factor pairs for 4 which are (1, 4) and (2, 2) and the factor pairs for the 2 in front of x^2 which are (2, 1).

Looking at the area models for each one of these combinations:

Combination 1: (2, 1) and (4, 1)

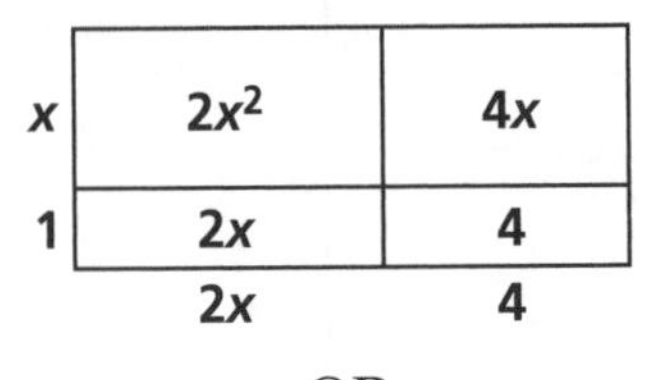

OR

	x	x	4
1	x	x	4
x	x²	x²	4x

2x² + 6x + 4

Combination 2: (2, 1) and (1, 4)

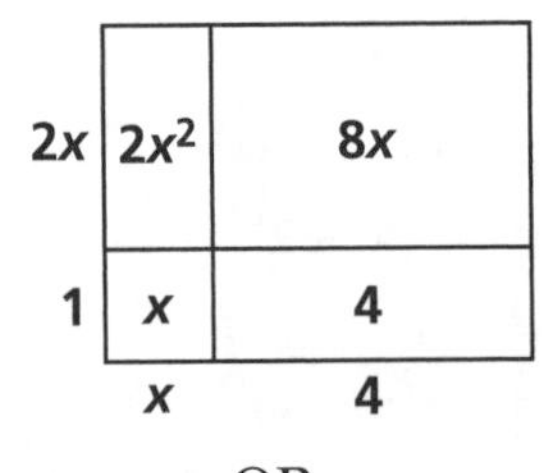

OR

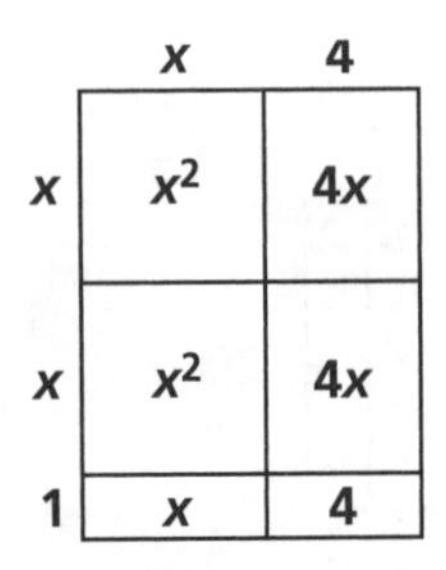

2x² + 9x + 4

Combination 3: (2, 1) and (2, 2)

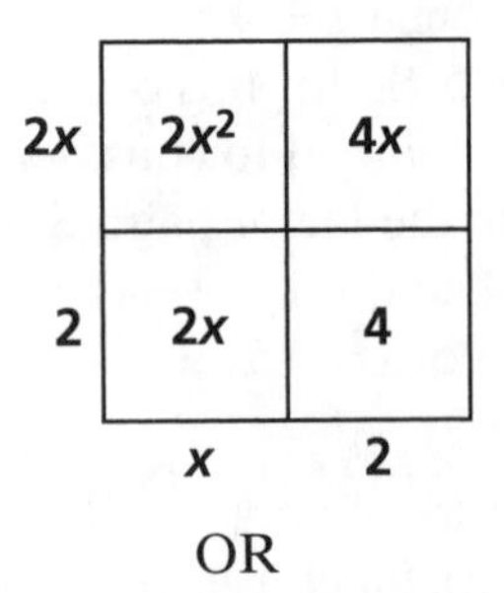

OR

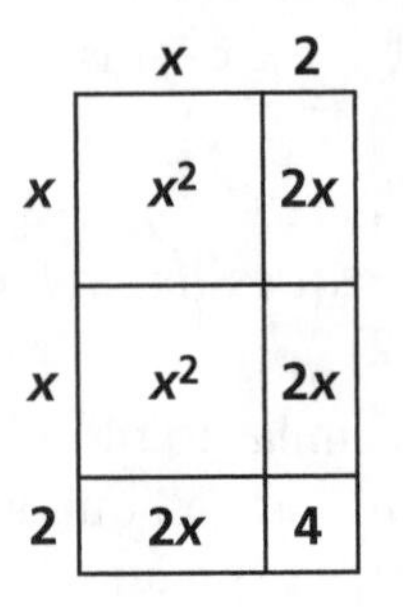

2x² + 6x + 4

We see that combination 2 gives $2x^2 + 9x + 4$.

So in adjusting Jaime's methods, students consider factor pairs of a and c in $ax^2 + bx + c$ and find combinations of the pairs for which the middle coefficient b is satisfied.

The factored forms are:

a. $(2x + 4)(x + 2) = 2(x + 2)(x + 2)$

b. $(2x + 1)(2x + 1)$

c. $(2x + 1)(x + 4)$

To explain why expressions are equivalent, students may check that three different x-values give the same y-value in each expression. They may use a graph or table to show the expressions produce the same graph or table. Or they may use the Distributive or Commutative properties to show equivalence.

3.4 Solving Quadratic Equations

Goals

- Solve quadratic equations by factoring
- Use solutions of equations to make predictions and decisions
- Interpret information provided by equivalent expressions in context

Launch 3.4

Write the equation from the Getting Ready, $0 = x^2 + 8x + 12$, on the overhead. Go over the questions. The factoring parts are review. We are trying to get students to understand how the product of two quantities could equal 0. They connect the process of factoring a quadratic expression to solving a quadratic equation, $0 = ax^2 + bx + c$.

Let the class work on this as individuals or pairs. They can come together in small groups of 2–3 to discuss their solutions.

Explore 3.4

If students have factored incorrectly, challenge the student to show that his/her factored expression is correct by multiplying it out using the Distributive Property or trying three numerical values for the factored and expanded form to see if they are equivalent expressions.

You may want some pairs to put their work for an equation on a large poster paper along with the graph and table showing alternate ways to solve the equations.

Summarize 3.4

Go over each part. Take time to connect solving quadratic equations to the bigger picture of quadratic relationships. Solving a quadratic equation, $0 = ax^2 + bx + c$, is the same as finding the x-intercepts of the graph of $y = ax^2 + bx + c$. Go over Question D, which introduces a context where being able to factor in order to solve a quadratic equation is useful.

Check for Understanding

Solve each of the following equations for x:

$6 - 4(x + 4) = 2x \qquad 2x^2 - 18x + 28 = 0$

Suggested Question Ask:

- *How could you use a graph or table to solve these equations?*

3.4 Solving Quadratic Equations

At a Glance

PACING $1\frac{1}{2}$ days

Mathematical Goals

- Solve quadratic equations by factoring
- Use solutions of equations to make predictions and decisions
- Interpret information provided by equivalent expressions in context

Launch

Write the equation from the Getting Ready, $0 = x^2 + 8x + 12$, on the board. First we write $x^2 + 8x + 12$ in factored form as $(x + 2)(x + 6)$. This expression is the product of two linear factors.

- *If $(x + 2)(x + 6) = 0$, what must be true about one of the linear factors?*
- *How can this information help us find the solutions to $0 = (x + 2)(x + 6)$?*
- *How can this information help us find the x-intercepts of $y = x^2 + 8x + 12$?*

We are trying to get students to understand how the product of two quantities could equal 0 and connect the process of factoring a quadratic expression to solving a quadratic equation, $0 = ax^2 + bx + c$. Let the class work on this as individuals or pairs and come together in small groups of 2–3 to discuss their solutions.

Explore

If students have factored incorrectly, challenge the student to show that his/her factored expression is correct by multiplying it out using the Distributive Property or trying three numerical values for the factored and expanded form to see if they are equivalent.

You may want some pairs to put their work for an equation on a large poster paper along with the graph and table showing alternate ways to solve the equations.

Materials

- Poster paper (optional)

Summarize

Go over each part. Take time to connect solving quadratic equations to the bigger picture of quadratic relationships. Solving a quadratic equation, $0 = ax^2 + bx + c$, is the same as finding the x-intercepts of the graph of $y = ax^2 + bx + c$. Go over Question D, which introduces a context where being able to factor in order to solve a quadratic equation is useful.

Check for Understanding

- *Solve each of the following equations for x:*

  $6 - 4(x + 4) = 2x$ $\qquad$ $2x^2 - 18x + 28 = 0$
- *How could you use a graph or table to solve these equations?*

Materials

- Student notebooks

ACE Assignment Guide for Problem 3.4

Core 21–26, 43
Other *Connections* 27–28, 42, 44–46; *Extensions* 54–57; and unassigned choices from previous problems

Adapted For suggestions about adapting ACE exercises, see the CMP *Special Needs Handbook*.
Connecting to Prior Units 42–46: *Frogs, Fleas and Painted Cubes*

Answers to Problem 3.4

A. **1.** $(x + 4)(x + 6)$

2. For the product of two numbers to equal 0, one or both factors must equal 0. So for the equation $(x + 4)(x + 6) = 0$, either $x + 4 = 0$ or $x + 6 = 0$. So either $x = -4$ or $x = -6$. So the equation $x^2 + 10x + 24 = 0$ has two solutions.

3. The solutions to $0 = x^2 + 10x + 24$ are the x-intercepts since you are finding x when the y-value is 0.

B. **1.** $x = -1$ or $x = -\frac{7}{2}$

2. $x = 5$ or $x = 2$

3. To find the solutions, students must first factor using Jaime's method or an area model. So the equation becomes $0 = (x + 3)(x + 3)$ and the solution is $x = -3$.

4. To find the solutions, students must first factor using Jaime's method or an area model. So the equation becomes $0 = (x + 4)(x - 4)$ and the solutions are $x = -4$ or $x = 4$.

5. To find the solutions, students must first factor using Jaime's method or an area model. So the equation becomes $0 = (x + 8)(x + 2)$, and the solutions are $x = -8$ or $x = -2$.

6. To find the solutions, students must first factor using an area model or some other method. So the equation becomes $0 = (2x + 3)(x + 2)$ and the solutions are $x = -1.5$ or $x = -2$.

7. To check the solutions students can substitute their x-values into the equation.

C. **1.** $x = 0$ or $x = 9$

2. $x = 0$ or $x = -2.5$

3. If students factor first, they should get $2x(x + 16) = 0$, so $x = 0$ or $x = -16$. Students may also make an area model to find the factors.

4. If students factor first, they should get $9x(2 - x) = 0$, so $x = 0$ or $x = 2$.

To check the solutions, students can either substitute their x-values into the equation or look at a table and see if the x-values they found correspond to a y-value of 0. They can also look at the graph and see if the x-intercepts are the x-values they found.

D. **1.** The pole vaulter is looking for the time when he/she will land the jump.

2. No, the maximum height given in this equation is 16 feet, which occurs at 1 second. The maximum height can be found by graphing and looking at the y-coordinate of the vertex, using a table, or by looking at the factored form of the equation $h = 32t - 16t^2 = 16t(2 - t)$. Since the zeros are 0 and 2, the maximum occurs directly between 0 and 2, which is 1 second. Substituting 1 second into the original equation yields a maximum height of 16 feet, which is less than 17.5 feet.

Investigation 3

Solving Equations

A problem often requires finding solutions to equations. In previous units, you developed strategies for solving linear and quadratic equations. In this investigation, you will use the properties of real numbers to extend these strategies.

3.1 Solving Linear Equations

How do you solve the following linear equation for x?

$$100 + 4x = 25 + 7x$$

Getting Ready for Problem 3.1

The steps below show one way to solve $100 + 4x = 25 + 7x$.

$$\begin{aligned}
& & 100 + 4x &= 25 + 7x \\
&(1) & 100 + 4x - 4x &= 25 + 7x - 4x \\
& & 100 &= 25 + 3x \\
&(2) & 100 - 25 &= 25 + 3x - 25 \\
& & 75 &= 3x \\
&(3) & 75 \div 3 &= 3x \div 3 \\
& & 25 &= x
\end{aligned}$$

- Provide an explanation for each numbered step in the solution.
- The solution above begins by subtracting $4x$ from both sides of the equation. Could you begin with a different first step? Explain.
- How can you check that $x = 25$ is the correct solution?
- Describe another method for finding the solution to the equation.

STUDENT PAGE

Notes

The example in the Getting Ready uses the **properties of equality** that you learned in *Moving Straight Ahead.*

- You can add or subtract the same quantity to both sides of an equation to write an equivalent equation.
- You can multiply or divide both sides of an equation by the same non-zero number to write an equivalent equation.

You will continue to use these properties as well as the Distributive and Commutative properties to solve more equations.

Problem 3.1 Solving Linear Equations

A. A school choir is selling boxes of greeting cards to raise money for a trip.

The equation for the profit in dollars P in terms of the number of boxes sold s is:

$P = 5s - (100 + 2s)$

1. What information do the expressions $5s$ and $100 + 2s$ represent in the situation? What information do 100 and $2s$ represent?

2. Use the equation to find the number of boxes the choir must sell to make a $200 profit. Explain.

3. How many boxes must the choir sell to break even? Explain.

4. Write a simpler expression for profit. Explain what information the variables and numbers represent.

5. One of the choir members wrote the following expression for profit: $5s - 2(50 + s)$. Explain whether this expression is equivalent to the original expression for profit.

B. Describe how to solve an equation that has parentheses like $200 = 5s - (100 + 2s)$ without using a table or graph.

C. Solve each equation for x when $y = 0$. Check your solutions.

1. $y = 5 + 2(3 + 4x)$ **2.** $y = 5 - 2(3 + 4x)$

3. $y = 5 + 2(3 - 4x)$ **4.** $y = 5 - 2(3 - 4x)$

ACE Homework starts on page 45.

STUDENT PAGE

STUDENT PAGE

Notes

3.2 Comparing Costs

Ms. Lucero wants to install tiles around her square swimming pool. She receives two estimates:

- *Cover and Surround It* has a fixed charge of $1,000 for design and material delivery costs. They charge $25 per tile after the first 12 tiles.
- *Tile and Beyond* has a fixed charge of $740 for design and material delivery costs. They charge $32 per tile after the first 10 tiles.

The equations below show the estimated costs C (in dollars) of buying and installing N border tiles.

Cover and Surround It:	$C_C = 1{,}000 + 25(N - 12)$
Tile and Beyond:	$C_T = 740 + 32(N - 10)$

Recall that you can use *subscripts* to show different uses for a variable: C_C means cost for *Cover and Surround It*; C_T means cost for *Tile and Beyond*.

- Do the equations make sense given the description above for each company's charges?

Ms. Lucero wants to know when the costs of each company are the same.

How can Ms. Lucero use the equation $C_C = C_T$ to answer her question?

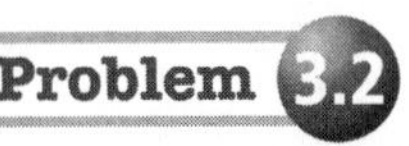

Problem 3.2 Solving More Linear Equations

A. **1.** Without using a table or graph, find the number of tiles for which the two costs are equal.

2. How can you check that your solution is correct?

3. How can you use a graph or table to find the number of tiles for which the two costs are equal?

4. For what numbers of tiles is *Tile and Beyond* cheaper than *Cover and Surround It* ($C_T < C_C$)? Explain your reasoning.

B. Use the techniques that you developed in Problem 3.1 and in Question A to solve each equation for x. Check your solutions.

1. $3x = 5 + 2(3 + 4x)$

2. $10 + 3x = 2(3 + 4x) + 5$

3. $3x = 5 - 2(3 + 4x)$

4. $7 + 3(1 - x) = 5 - 2(3 - 4x)$

ACE Homework starts on page 45.

STUDENT PAGE

STUDENT PAGE

Notes ______________________________

3.3 Factoring Quadratic Expressions

Sometimes mathematical problems that appear to be different are actually the same. Finding the x-intercepts of $y = x^2 + 5x$ is the same as solving $x^2 + 5x = 0$ for x. The *solutions* to $x^2 + 5x = 0$ are also called the *roots* of the equation. In *Frogs, Fleas, and Painted Cubes* you found the solutions or roots by using a table or graph of $y = x^2 + 5x$ as shown.

x	y	
−7	14	
−6	6	
−5	0	← x-intercept or solution
−4	−4	
−3	−6	
−2	−6	
−1	−4	
0	0	← x-intercept or solution
1	6	
2	14	
3	24	

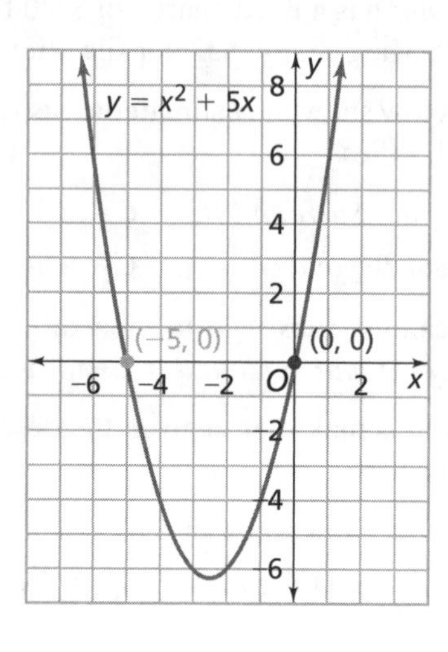

- What is the factored form of $x^2 + 5x$?
- What is the relationship between the factored form of $x^2 + 5x$ and the x-intercepts of the graph of $y = x^2 + 5x$?

Getting Ready for Problem 3.3

To factor the expression $x^2 + 5x + 6$, Trevor draws the area model at the right.

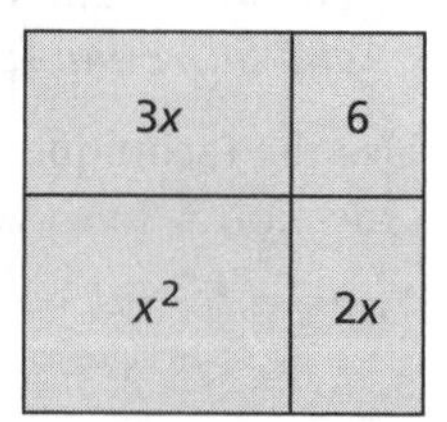

- Does the model match $x^2 + 5x + 6$?
- Find the factors of $x^2 + 5x + 6$.
- What are the x-intercepts of the graph of $y = x^2 + 5x + 6$?
- Describe the relationship between the x-intercepts of the graph of $y = x^2 + 5x + 6$ and the factored form of $x^2 + 5x + 6$.

Notes

Algebra provides tools, such as factoring, that can help solve quadratic equations like $x^2 + 5x = 0$ without using tables or graphs. Before using this tool, you need to review how to write quadratic expressions in factored form.

Problem 3.3 Factoring Quadratic Expressions

A. Jaime suggests the method below to factor $x^2 + 8x + 12$.

- Find factor pairs of 12 such as 1 and 12, 2 and 6, 3 and 4, -1 and -12, -2 and -6, and -3 and -4.
- Pick the factor pair whose sum is 8: $2 + 6 = 8$.
- Write the factored form: $(x + 2)(x + 6)$.

1. Use an area model to show why Jaime's method works for the expression $x^2 + 8x + 12$.

2. Could Jaime have used another factor pair, such as 1 and 12 or 3 and 4, to make an area model for $x^2 + 8x + 12$? Explain.

B. Use a method similar to Jaime's to write each expression in factored form. Show why each factored form is correct.

1. $x^2 + 5x + 4$ **2.** $x^2 - 5x + 4$

3. $x^2 - 3x - 4$ **4.** $x^2 + 4x + 4$

C. 1. Examine the following expressions. How are they similar to and different from those in Question B?

a. $x^2 + 4x$ **b.** $4x^2 + 32x$

c. $6x^2 - 4x$ **d.** $x^2 - 4$

2. Will Jaime's method for factoring work on these expressions? If so, use his method to write them in factored form. If not, find another way to write each in factored form.

D. 1. Examine the following expressions. How are they similar to and different from those in Question B?

a. $2x^2 + 8x + 8$

b. $4x^2 + 4x + 1$

c. $2x^2 + 9x + 4$

2. Will Jaime's method work on these expressions? If so, write them in factored form. If not, find another way to write each in factored form. Explain why your expression is equivalent to the original expression.

ACE Homework starts on page 45.

Notes

3.4 Solving Quadratic Equations

In the last problem, you explored ways to write a quadratic expression in factored form. In this problem, you will use the factored form to find solutions to a quadratic equation.

If you know that the product of two numbers is zero, what can you say about the numbers?

Getting Ready for Problem 3.4

- How can you solve the equation $0 = x^2 + 8x + 12$ by factoring?

First write $x^2 + 8x + 12$ in factored form to get $(x + 2)(x + 6)$. This expression is the product of two linear factors.

- When $0 = (x + 2)(x + 6)$, what must be true about one of the linear factors?
- How can this information help you find the solutions to $0 = (x + 2)(x + 6)$?
- How can this information help you find the x-intercepts of $y = x^2 + 8x + 12$?

Problem 3.4 Solving Quadratic Equations

A. **1.** Write $x^2 + 10x + 24$ in factored form.

2. How can you use the factored form to solve $x^2 + 10x + 24 = 0$ for x?

3. Explain how the solutions to $0 = x^2 + 10x + 24$ relate to the graph of $y = x^2 + 10x + 24$.

B. Solve each equation for x without making a table or graph.

1. $0 = (x + 1)(2x + 7)$

2. $0 = (5 - x)(x - 2)$

3. $0 = x^2 + 6x + 9$

4. $0 = x^2 - 16$

5. $0 = x^2 + 10x + 16$

6. $0 = 2x^2 + 7x + 6$

7. How can you check your solutions without using a table or graph?

Notes

C. Solve each equation for x without making a table or graph. Check your answers.

1. $0 = x(9 - x)$
2. $0 = -3x(2x + 5)$
3. $0 = 2x^2 + 32x$
4. $0 = 18x - 9x^2$

D. You can approximate the height h of a pole-vaulter from the ground after t seconds with the equation $h = 32t - 16t^2$.

1. Suppose the pole-vaulter writes the equation $0 = 32t - 16t^2$. What information is the pole-vaulter looking for?
2. The pole-vaulter wants to clear a height of 17.5 feet. Will the pole-vaulter clear the desired height? Explain.

ACE **Homework starts on page 45.**

Notes

Did You Know?

You can find the solutions to many quadratic equations using tables or graphs. Sometimes, however, these methods will give only approximate answers. For example, the solutions to the equation $x^2 - 2 = 0$ are $x = \sqrt{2}$ and $x = -\sqrt{2}$. Using a table or graph, you only get an approximation for $\sqrt{2}$.

You can try a factoring method, but the probability of readily factoring any quadratic expression $ax^2 + bx + c$, where a, b, and c are real numbers is small.

We know that the Greeks used a geometric method to solve quadratic equations around 300 B.C. Mathematicians from India probably had methods for solving these equations around 500 B.C., but their methods remain unknown.

For years, mathematicians tried to find a general solution to $ax^2 + bx + c = 0$. In a book published in 1591, François Viète was the first person to develop a formula for finding the roots of a quadratic equation. It is called the *quadratic formula* and is given below.

$$x = \frac{-b \pm \sqrt{b^2 - 4ac}}{2a}$$

This formula can be used for any quadratic equation. You will learn more about this formula in later mathematics courses.

For: Information about François Viète
Web Code: ape-9031

STUDENT PAGE

STUDENT PAGE

Notes

Applications

1. The organizers of a walkathon discuss expenses and income. They make the following estimates:

- Expense for advertisement: \$500
- Expense for participant T-shirts: \$6 per child, \$8.50 per adult
- Income from business sponsors: \$1,000
- Expense for emergency medical services: \$250
- Income from registration fees: \$5 per child, \$15 per adult

a. Suppose 30 adults and 40 children participate in the walkathon. Find the total income, the total expenses, and the profit. Show your work.

b. Write an equation showing the profit P in the form:

P = (expression for income) − (expression for expenses).

c. Write another expression for profit that is equivalent to the one in part (b).

d. Suppose 30 adults and 40 children participate. Use your equation from part (b) or part (c) to find the profit. Compare your answer to the profit you calculated in part (a).

e. Suppose 100 children participate and the profit is \$1,099. How many adults participated? Show your work.

Notes

2. Marcel and Kirsten each try to simplify the following equation:
$P = (1{,}000 + 5c + 15a) - (500 + 6c + 8.50a + 250)$

They are both incorrect. Study the steps in their reasoning and identify their mistakes.

a. Marcel

$$\begin{aligned} P &= (1{,}000 + 5c + 15a) - (500 + 6c + 8.50a + 250) \\ &= 1{,}000 + 5c + 15a - 500 + 6c + 8.50a + 250 \\ &= 1{,}000 - 500 + 250 + 5c + 6c + 15a + 8.50a \\ &= 750 + 11c + 23.50a \quad \textit{incorrect answer} \end{aligned}$$

b. Kirsten

$$\begin{aligned} P &= (1{,}000 + 5c + 15a) - (500 + 6c + 8.50a + 250) \\ &= 1{,}000 + 5c + 15a - 500 - 6c - 8.50a - 250 \\ &= 1{,}000 - 500 - 250 + 5c - 6c + 15a - 8.50a \\ &= 250 + c + 6.50a \quad \textit{incorrect answer} \end{aligned}$$

3. According to the equation $V = 200 + 50(T - 70)$, the number of visitors to a park depends on the day's high temperature T (in Fahrenheit). Suppose 1,000 people visited the park one day. Predict that day's high temperature.

Homework Help Online
PHSchool.com
For: Help with Exercise 3
Web Code: ape-6303

For Exercises 4–7, solve each equation for *x* using the techniques that you developed in Problem 3.1. Check your solutions.

4. $10 + 2(3 + 2x) = 0$
5. $10 - 2(3 + 2x) = 0$
6. $10 + 2(3 - 2x) = 0$
7. $10 - 2(3 - 2x) = 0$

8. The two companies from Problem 3.2 decide to lower their costs for a Fourth of July sale. The equations below show the lower estimated costs C (in dollars) of buying and installing N border tiles.

Cover and Surround It: $C_C = 750 + 22(N - 12)$
Tile and Beyond: $C_T = 650 + 30(N - 10)$

a. Without using a table or graph, find the number of tiles for which the cost estimates from the two companies are equal.

STUDENT PAGE

Notes

b. How can you check that your solution is correct?

c. Explain how a graph or table could be used to find the number of tiles for which the costs are equal.

d. For what numbers of tiles is *Tile and Beyond* cheaper than *Cover and Surround It*? Explain your reasoning.

e. Write another expression that is equivalent to the expression for *Tile and Beyond's* cost estimate (C_T). Explain what information the variables and numbers represent.

9. The school choir from Problem 3.1 has the profit plan $P = 5s - (100 + 2s)$. The school band also sells greeting cards. The equation for the band's profit is $P = 4s - 2(10 + s)$. Find the number of boxes that each group must sell to have equal profits.

For Exercises 10–17, solve each equation for x without using tables or graphs. Check your solutions.

10. $8x + 16 = 6x$

11. $8(x + 2) = 6x$

12. $6 + 8(x + 2) = 6x$

13. $4 + 5(x + 2) = 7x$

14. $2x - 3(x + 6) = -4(x - 1)$

15. $2 - 3(x + 4) = 9 - (3 + 2x)$

16. $2.75 - 7.75(5 - 2x) = 26$

17. $\frac{1}{2}x + 4 = \frac{2}{3}x$

18. Write each product in expanded form.

a. $(x - 2)(x + 2)$

b. $(x - 5)(x + 5)$

c. $(x - 4)(x + 4)$

d. $(x - 12)(x + 12)$

Applications

STUDENT PAGE

STUDENT PAGE

Notes

19. Write each of these quadratic expressions in equivalent factored form.

a. $x^2 + 5x + 4$ **b.** $8 + x^2 + 6x$

c. $x^2 - 7x + 10$ **d.** $x^2 + 7x$

e. $x^2 - 6 + 5x$ **f.** $2x^2 - 5x - 12$

g. $x^2 - 7x - 8$ **h.** $x^2 - 5x$

Go Online
PHSchool.com
For: Multiple-Choice Skills Practice
Web Code: apa-6354

20. Write each of these expressions in factored form.

a. $x^2 - 16$ **b.** $x^2 - 36$

c. $x^2 - 49$ **d.** $x^2 - 400$

e. $x^2 - 64$ **f.** $x^2 - 144$

For Exercises 21–23, solve each equation for x. Check your solutions by using calculator tables or graphs.

21. $x^2 + 1.5x = 0$ 22. $x^2 + 6x + 8 = 0$ 23. $8x - x^2 = 0$

24. The equation $H = -16t^2 + 8t$ describes the height of a flea (in feet) after t seconds during a jump.

a. Is the flea's jump equation linear, quadratic, or exponential?

b. Write an expression that is equivalent to $-16t^2 + 8t$.

c. Without using a graph or a table, find the time when the flea lands on the ground. Explain how you found your answer.

25. Use an area model to factor each expression.

a. $x^2 + 8x + 15$ **b.** $x^2 - 9$ **c.** $2x^2 + 5x + 3$

26. Use your answers to Exercise 25 to solve each equation.

a. $x^2 + 8x + 15 = 0$ **b.** $x^2 - 9 = 0$ **c.** $2x^2 + 5x + 3 = 0$

Notes

In Exercises 27 and 28, each solution contains an error.

- Find the error, and correct the solution.
- How would you help a student who made this error?

27.

$6x^2 - x = 1$

Solution

$6x^2 - x - 1 = 0$

$(3x - 1)(2x + 1) = 0$

$3x - 1 = 0$ or $2x + 1 = 0$

$x = \frac{1}{3}$ or $x = -\frac{1}{2}$

incorrect answer

28.

$24n^2 - 16n = 0$

Solution

$24n^2 - 16n = 0$

$24n^2 = 16n$

$n = \frac{16}{24}$ or $n = \frac{2}{3}$

partially correct answer

Connections

29. In Problem 3.1, the equation for profit P in terms of the number of boxes sold s is $P = 5s - (100 + 2s)$. The number of boxes sold also depends on the number of choir members.

a. Suppose each member sells 11 boxes. Write an equation that will predict profit from the number of choir members n.
Hint: First find an expression for the number of boxes sold.

b. Write an equivalent expression for profit in part (a). Explain what the variables and numbers represent.

c. Suppose the choir has 47 members. What is the profit?

d. Suppose the profit is $1,088. How many choir members are there?

e. In part (d), how many boxes were sold?

30. The equations $N = 2s + 2(s + 2)$ and $N = 4(s + 2) - 4$ both represent the number of 1-foot square border tiles needed to surround a square pool with sides of length s in feet.

a. Suppose $N = 48$. Solve $N = 2s + 2(s + 2)$ for s.

b. Suppose $N = 48$. Solve $N = 4(s + 2) - 4$ for s.

c. How do your answers for parts (a) and (b) compare? Explain.

Notes

31. Multiple Choice If $\frac{3}{4}(x - 4) = 12$, what is the value of x?

A. 6 **B.** 8 **C.** $18\frac{1}{3}$ **D.** 20

32. Multiple Choice What is the value of $x^2(7 - x) + 1$ when $x = 5$?

F. 201 **G.** 28 **H.** 51 **J.** 75

33. In Problem 3.2, you found the number of tiles for which the cost estimates for the two companies were equal. What is the side length of the largest square pool that can be surrounded by that number of tiles? Explain your reasoning.

For Exercises 34 and 35, use the Distributive and Commutative properties to simplify each expression. Check that the original expression and your simplified expression are equivalent by testing several *x* values in both expressions.

34. $2(9x + 15) - (8 + 2x)$

35. $(7x - 12) - 2(3x + 10)$

Each figure in Exercises 36–40 has an area of 24 square meters. Find each labeled dimension.

36.

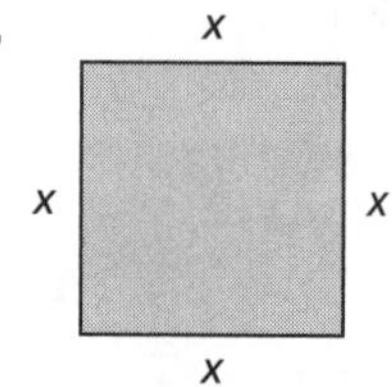

37.

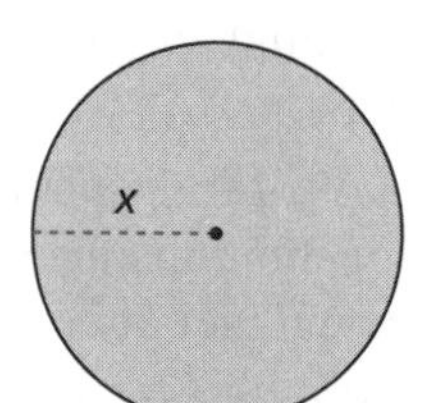

38.

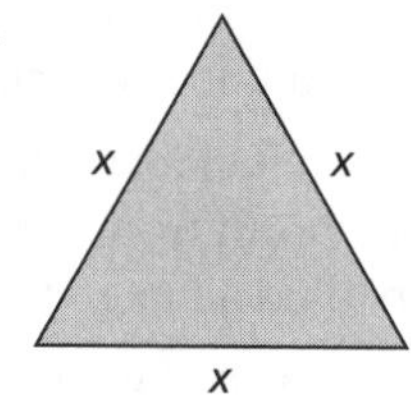

39.

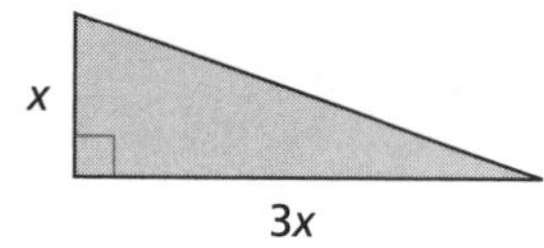

40.

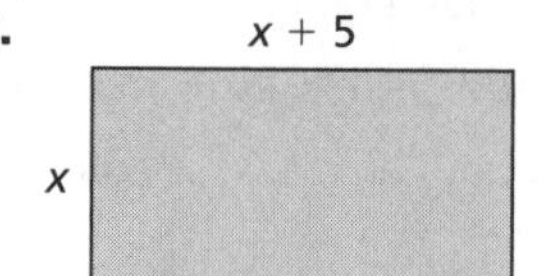

STUDENT PAGE

Notes

41. An oil company ships oil in spherical tanks that are 3 meters in diameter. The company now wants to ship oil in cylindrical tanks that are 4 meters high, but have the same volume as the spheres. What radius must the cylindrical tanks have?

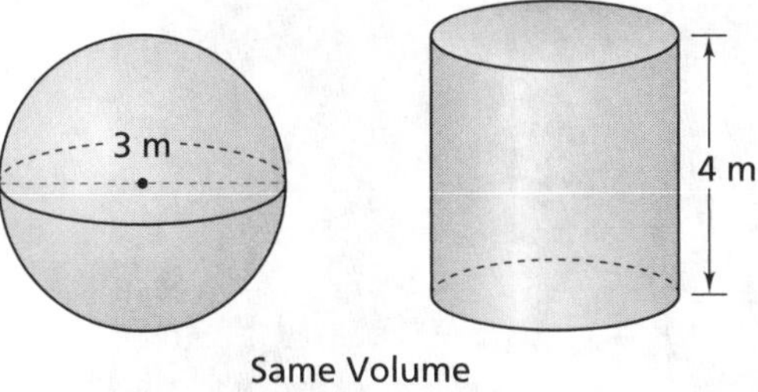

Same Volume
Not drawn to scale

42. Write a quadratic equation that has

a. one solution (one x-intercept)

b. two solutions (two x-intercepts)

43. John wants to know if he can bounce a superball over his house. You can approximate the height h of the superball on one bounce with the equation $h = 48t - 16t^2$, where t is the number of seconds after the ball hits the ground.

a. How long is the ball in the air?

b. Suppose his house is 30 feet tall. Will the ball make it over his house? Explain.

44. You can write quadratic expressions in factored and expanded forms. Which form would you use for each of the following? Explain.

a. to determine whether a quadratic relationship has a maximum point or a minimum point

b. to find the x- and y-intercepts of a quadratic relationship

c. to find the line of symmetry for a quadratic relationship

d. to find the coordinates of the maximum or minimum point for a quadratic relationship

Notes

45. Each team in a lacrosse league must play each of the other teams. The number of games g played in a league with n teams is $g = n^2 - n$. What are the x-intercepts for the graph of this equation? Explain what information they represent.

46. The height (in feet) of an arch above a point x feet from one of its bases is approximated by the equation $y = 0.2x(1{,}000 - x)$. What is the maximum height of the arch? Explain.

Extensions

For Exercises 47 and 48, find the value of c for which $x = 3$ is the solution to the equation.

47. $3x + c = 2x - 2c$

48. $3x + c = cx - 2$

49. Write two linear equations that have the solution $x = 3$. Are there more than two equations with a solution of $x = 3$? Explain.

50. Insert parentheses into the expression $13 = 3 + 5x - 2 - 2x + 5$ so that the solution to the equation is $x = 1$.

STUDENT PAGE

Notes

51. Write the following in expanded form.

a. $(x - .2)(x + .2)$ **b.** $(x - 12.5)(x + 12.5)$

c. $(x - \sqrt{5})(x + \sqrt{5})$ **d.** $(x - \sqrt{2})(x + \sqrt{2})$

52. Factor.

a. $x^2 - 100$ **b.** $x^2 - 1.44$

c. $x^2 - 7$ **d.** $x^2 - 24$

53. Below are the graphs of $y = 1.5x + 6$ and $y = -2x + 15$. The scale on the x-axis is 1, and the scale on the y-axis is 3.

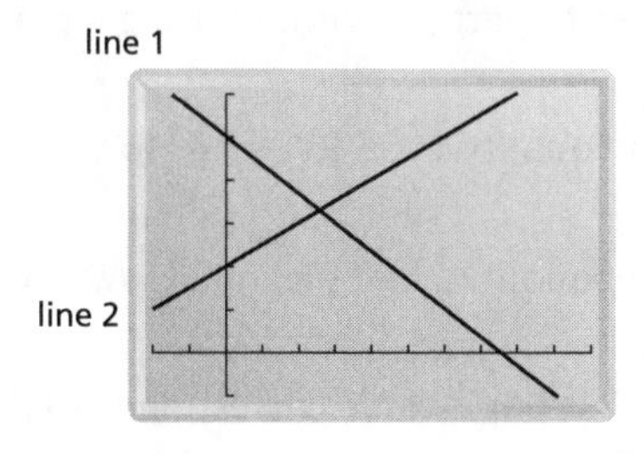

a. Is $y = 1.5x + 6$ or $y = -2x + 15$ the equation of line 1?

b. Find the coordinates of the point of intersection of the two lines.

c. How could you find the answer to part (b) without using a graph or a table?

d. What values of x satisfy the inequality $1.5x + 6 < -2x + 15$? How is your answer shown on the graph?

e. What values of x satisfy the inequality $1.5x + 6 > -2x + 15$? How is your answer shown on the graph?

Notes

54. Use the graph of $y = x^2 - 9x$ below. The scale on the x-axis is 1. The scale on the y-axis is 2.

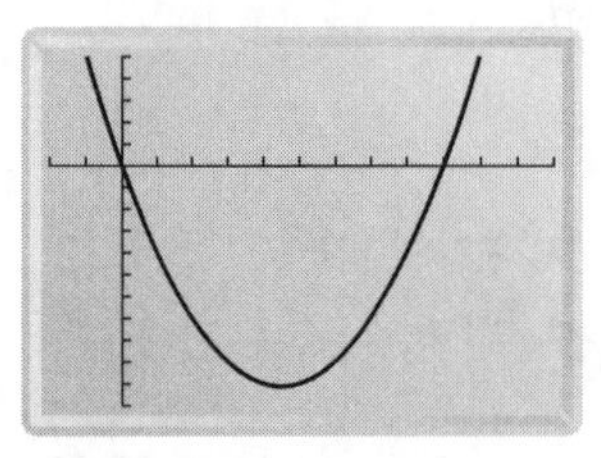

a. What are the coordinates of the x-intercepts?

b. How could you find the answer to part (a) without using a graph or a table?

c. What values of x satisfy the inequality $x^2 - 9x < 0$? How is your answer shown on the graph?

d. What values of x satisfy the inequality $x^2 - 9x > 0$? How is your answer shown on the graph?

e. What is the minimum y-value? What x-value corresponds to this minimum y-value?

55. Use the quadratic formula from the *Did You Know?* after Problem 3.4 to solve each equation.

a. $x^2 - 6x + 8 = 0$

b. $-x^2 - x + 6 = 0$

c. $10 - 7x + x^2 = 0$

d. $4x^2 - x = 0$

e. $2x^2 - 12x + 18 = 0$

f. $3x + x^2 - 4 = 0$

For Exercises 56 and 57, use what you have learned in this investigation to solve the equation. Show your work and check your solutions.

56. $x^2 + 5x + 7 = 1$

57. $x^2 + 6x + 15 = 6$

Notes

Mathematical Reflections 3

In this investigation, you learned methods for solving linear and quadratic equations. These questions will help you summarize what you have learned.

Think about your answers to these questions. Discuss your ideas with other students and your teacher. Then write a summary of your findings in your notebook.

1. Describe some general strategies for solving linear equations, including those with parentheses. Give examples that illustrate your strategies.
2. Describe some strategies for solving quadratic equations of the form $ax^2 + bx + c = 0$. Give examples.
3. How are the solutions of linear and quadratic equations related to graphs of equations?

Notes

Investigation 3

ACE Assignment Choices

Differentiated Instruction
Solutions for All Learners

Problem 3.1

Core 1, 4–7, 30, 31, 49
Other *Applications* 2, 3; *Connections* 29, 32; *Extensions* 47, 48

Problem 3.2

Core 8–15, 34
Other *Applications* 16, 17; *Connections* 33, 35–37, *Extensions* 50, 53; and unassigned choices from previous problems

Problem 3.3

Core 18–20
Other *Connections* 38–41, *Extensions* 51–52; and unassigned choices from previous problems

Problem 3.4

Core 21–26, 43
Other *Connections* 27–28, 42, 44–46; *Extensions* 54–57; and unassigned choices from previous problems

Adapted For suggestions about adapting Exercise 8 and other ACE exercises, see the CMP *Special Needs Handbook*.
Connecting to Prior Units 29, 30: *Moving Straight Ahead;* 31, 32: *Accentuate the Negative;* 33, 42–46: *Frogs, Fleas and Painted Cubes;* 36, 37, 39, 40: *Covering and Surrounding;* 38: *Looking for Pythagoras*; 41: *Filling and Wrapping and Looking for Pythagoras*

Applications

1. a. Income will be
$1{,}000 + 5(40) + 15(30) = \$1{,}650$.
Expenses will be
$500 + 250 + 6(40) + 8.50(30) = \$1{,}245$.
The profit is thus $\$1{,}650 - \$1{,}245 = \$405$.

b. $P = (1{,}000 + 5c + 15a) - (750 + 6c + 8.50a)$

c. $P = 1{,}000 + 5c + 15a - 750 - 6c - 8.50a$
$P = 250 - c + 6.50a$

d. $P = 250 - 40 + 6.50(30)$
$P = 250 - 40 + 195$
$P = 210 + 195$
$P = \$405$

The answer is the same as in part(a): \$405 profit.

e. $P = 250 - c + 6.50a$
$\$1{,}099 = 250 - 100 + 6.50a$
$1{,}099 = 150 + 6.50a$
$1{,}099 - 150 = 150 - 150 + 6.50a$
$949 = 6.50a$
$\frac{949}{6.50} = \frac{6.50a}{6.50}$
$146 = a$

There are 146 adults registered for the event.

2. a. When evaluating the second set of parentheses, Marcel distributed the minus sign to the 500, but not to the other three terms.

b. Kirsten combined $5c - 6c$ and got c instead of $-c$.

3. $1{,}000 = 200 + 50(T - 70)$
$1{,}000 = 200 + 50T - 3500$
$1{,}000 = 50T - 3300$
$4{,}300 = 50T$
$86 = T$

4. -4; $10 + 2(3 + 2x) = 0$
$10 + 6 + 4x = 0$
$16 + 4x = 0$
$16 + 4x - 16 = 0 - 16$
$4x = -16$
$x = -4$

ACE ANSWERS 3

5. 1; $10 - 2(3 + 2x) = 0$

$$10 - 6 - 4x = 0$$
$$4 - 4x = 0$$
$$4 - 4x - 4 = 0 - 4$$
$$-4x = -4$$
$$x = 1$$

6. 4; $10 + 2(3 - 2x) = 0$

$$10 + 6 - 4x = 0$$
$$16 - 4x = 0$$
$$16 - 4x - 16 = 0 - 16$$
$$-4x = -16$$
$$x = 4$$

7. –1; $10 - 2(3 - 2x) = 0$

$$10 - 6 + 4x = 0$$
$$4 + 4x = 0$$
$$4 + 4x - 4 = 0 - 4$$
$$4x = -4 \text{, so } x = -1$$

8. a. 17;

$$750 + 22(N - 12) = 650 + 30(N - 10)$$
$$750 + 22N - 264 = 650 + 30N - 300$$
$$486 + 22N = 350 + 30N$$
$$486 - 350 + 22N = 350 - 350 + 30N$$
$$136 + 22N = 30N$$
$$136 + 22N - 22N = 30N - 22N$$
$$\frac{136}{8} = \frac{8N}{8}$$
$$17 = N$$

NOTE: for this context to make sense, $N \geq 12$.

b. One possible way to check that the solution is correct is to put the value for N, 17, into each equation, solve for cost and see if both equations have the same value.

c. The point on the graphs at which the two lines intersect is the number of tiles for which the cost estimates are equal. Using a table one would look for the number of tiles for which both companies have the same cost values.

d. *Tile and Beyond* is cheaper when the number of tiles is less than 17.

e. $C = 650 + 30(N - 10)$

$C = 650 + 30N - 300$

$C = 30N + 350$

The 30 means that each tile costs 30 dollars and the 350 is the start-up cost, including the first 10 tiles.

9. 80 boxes; Students may graph the two equations and find the x-coordinate of the intersection point. Or they may make a table for each equation and find for which x-coordinate the profits are equal. If students solve symbolically:

$$4s - 2(10 + s) = 5s - (100 + 2s)$$
$$4s - 20 - 2s = 5s - 100 - 2s$$
$$2s - 20 = 3s - 100$$
$$2s - 20 + 100 = 3s - 100 + 100$$
$$2s + 80 = 3s$$
$$2s + 80 - 2s = 3s - 2s$$
$$80 = s$$

10. One possible answer method:

$$8x + 16 = 6x$$
$$8x + 16 - 8x = 6x - 8x$$
$$16 = -2x$$
$$-8 = x$$

Check:

$$8(-8) + 16 = 6(-8)$$
$$-64 + 16 = -48$$
$$-48 = -48$$

11. One possible answer method:

$$8(x + 2) = 6x$$
$$8x + 16 = 6x$$
$$8x + 16 - 8x = 6x - 8x$$
$$16 = -2x$$
$$-8 = x$$

Check:

$$8(-8 + 2) = 6(-8)$$
$$8(-6) = -48$$
$$-48 = -48$$

12. One possible answer method:

$$6 + 8(x + 2) = 6x$$
$$6 + 8x + 16 = 6x$$
$$22 + 8x = 6x$$
$$22 + 8x - 8x = 6x - 8x$$
$$22 = -2x$$
$$-11 = x$$

Check:

$$6 + 8(x + 2) = 6x$$
$$6 + 8(-11 + 2) = 6(-11)$$
$$6 + 8(-9) = -66$$
$$6 + (-72) = -66$$
$$-66 = -66$$

13. One possible answer method:

$$4 + 5(x + 2) = 7x$$
$$4 + 5x + 10 = 7x$$
$$14 + 5x - 5x = 7x - 5x$$
$$14 = 2x$$
$$7 = x$$

Check:

$$4 + 5(7 + 2) = 7(7)$$
$$4 + 5(9) = 49$$
$$49 = 49$$

14. One possible answer:

$$2x - 3(x + 6) = -4(x - 1)$$
$$2x - 3x - 18 = -4x + 4$$
$$-x - 18 = -4x + 4$$
$$-x - 18 - 4 = -4x + 4 - 4$$
$$-x - 22 = -4x$$
$$-x - 22 + x = -4x + x$$
$$-22 = -3x$$
$$\frac{22}{3} = x \text{ or } x = 7\frac{1}{3}$$

Check:

$$2(\tfrac{22}{3}) - 3(\tfrac{22}{3} + 6) = -4(\tfrac{22}{3} - 1)$$
$$\frac{44}{3} - 22 - 18 = -\frac{88}{3} + 4$$
$$\frac{44}{3} - 40 = -\frac{88}{3} + \frac{12}{3}$$
$$\frac{44}{3} - \frac{120}{3} = -\frac{88}{3} + \frac{12}{3}$$
$$-\frac{76}{3} = -\frac{76}{3}$$

15. One possible answer:

$$2 - 3(x + 4) = 9 - (3 + 2x)$$
$$2 - 3x - 12 = 9 - 3 - 2x$$
$$-3x - 10 = 6 - 2x$$
$$-3x - 10 - 6 = 6 - 2x - 6$$
$$-3x - 16 = -2x$$
$$-3x - 16 + 3x = -2x + 3x$$
$$-16 = x$$

Check:

$$2 - 3(-16 + 4) = 9 - (3 + 2(-16))$$
$$2 - 3(-12) = 9 - (3 - 32)$$
$$2 + 36 = 9 - (-29)$$
$$38 = 38$$

16. One possible answer:

$$2.75 - 7.75(5 - 2x) = 26$$
$$2.75 - 38.75 + 15.5x = 26$$
$$-36 + 15.5x = 26$$
$$-36 + 36 + 15.50x = 26 + 36$$
$$15.50x = 62$$
$$x = 4$$

Check:

$$2.75 - 7.75(5 - 2(4)) = 26$$
$$2.75 - 7.75(5 - 8) = 26$$
$$2.75 - 7.75(-3) = 26$$
$$2.75 + 23.25 = 26$$

17.

$$\frac{1}{2}x + 4 = \frac{2}{3}x$$
$$\frac{1}{2}x + 4 - \frac{1}{2}x = \frac{2}{3}x - \frac{1}{2}x$$
$$4 = \frac{1}{6}x$$
$$4 \div \frac{1}{6} = x$$
$$24 = x$$

Check:

$$\frac{1}{2}(24) + 4 = \frac{2}{3}(24)$$
$$12 + 4 = 16$$
$$16 = 16$$

18. **a.** $x^2 - 4$ **b.** $x^2 - 25$

c. $x^2 - 16$ **d.** $x^2 - 144$

19. **a.** $(x + 1)(x + 4)$ **b.** $(x + 2)(x + 4)$

c. $(x - 5)(x - 2)$ **d.** $x(x + 7)$

e. $(x - 1)(x + 6)$ **f.** $(2x + 3)(x - 4)$

g. $(x + 1)(x - 8)$ **h.** $x(x - 5)$

20. **a.** $(x + 4)(x - 4)$ **b.** $(x + 6)(x - 6)$

c. $(x - 7)(x + 7)$ **d.** $(x + 20)(x - 20)$

e. $(x - 8)(x + 8)$ **f.** $(x - 12)(x + 12)$

21.

$$x^2 + 1.5x = 0$$
$$x(x + 1.5) = 0$$
$$x = 0 \text{ or } x = -1.5$$

22.

$$x^2 + 6x + 8 = 0$$
$$(x + 2)(x + 4) = 0$$
$$x = -2 \text{ or } x = -4$$

23.

$$8x - x^2 = 0$$
$$x(8 - x) = 0$$
$$x = 0 \text{ or } x = 8$$

24. **a.** The jump equation is quadratic.

b. $-8t(2t - 1)$ or $8t(-2t + 1)$. Some students may write an equivalent form like $2(-8t^2 + 4t)$ for example, which is equivalent; however this will not help them when they try to solve symbolically in part (c), since there is still a quadratic factor in this expression.

c. $\frac{1}{2}$; The flea lands on the ground when the height is 0 ft. So by solving the equation $0 = -16t^2 + 8t$, which is the same as solving $0 = 8t(-2t + 1)$, students should get $8t = 0$ or $-2t + 1 = 0$. So $t = 0$ which is when the flea starts the jump or $t = \frac{1}{2}$ which is when the flea lands back on the ground.

25. **a.**

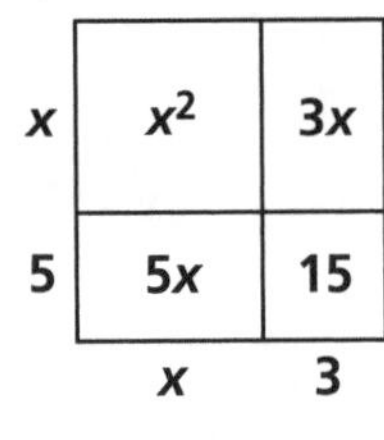

$x^2 + 8x + 15$

b.

	x	3
3		
x − 3	x(x − 3)	3(x − 3)

(The full side length is x.)

$x(x - 3) + 3(x - 3) = x^2 - 9$

c.

	x	x	3
1	x	x	3
x	x²	x²	3x

$2x^2 + 5x + 3$

NOTE: there are other area models that use $2x + 3$ and $x + 1$.

26. **a.**

$$x^2 + 8x + 15 = 0$$
$$(x + 5)(x + 3) = 0$$
$$x + 5 = 0 \text{ or } x + 3 = 0$$
$$x = -5 \text{ or } x = -3$$

b.

$$x^2 - 9 = 0$$
$$(x - 3)(x + 3) = 0$$

OR

$$x^2 - 9 = 0$$
$$x^2 = 9$$
$$x = 3 \text{ or } -3$$

c.

$$2x^2 + 5x + 3 = 0$$
$$2x^2 + 2x + 3x + 3 = 0$$
$$2x(x + 1) + 3(x + 1) = 0$$
$$(2x + 3)(x + 1) = 0$$
$$x = -1 \quad \text{OR} \quad x = \frac{-3}{2}$$

27. $6x^2 - x = 1$

Solution:

$$6x^2 - x - 1 = 0$$
$$(3x + 1)(2x - 1) = 0$$
$$3x + 1 = 0 \quad \text{OR} \quad 2x - 1 = 0$$
$$x = -\frac{1}{3} \quad \text{OR} \quad x = \frac{1}{2}$$

- The factors the student gave were $(3x - 1)(2x + 1)$, which are the wrong factors, since when you use the Distributive Property you get $6x^2 - 2x + 3x - 1$ or $6x^2 + x - 1$, and you need the middle term to be $-1x$ not $1x$. With trial and error, students may find that if the signs are switched, the correct factorization can be found. So the correct factorization is $(3x + 1)(2x - 1)$ with solutions of $\frac{1}{2}$ and $-\frac{1}{3}$.
- To help the student, first I would tell them to check their answers in the original equation so they can see if they got the answer right. When factoring $6x^2 - x - 1$, students may suggest an alteration of Jaime's method that they found in Problem 3.3, or they can make an area model.

28.
- The mistake is that the student divided each side of the equation by n. By doing this, the solution of $n = 0$ disappears so the student is only partially correct.
- To help the student, first I would tell them to factor the expression $24n^2 - 16n$ by factoring out $8n$ and getting the new equation $8n(3n - 2) = 0$ to solve. By setting the expression equal to zero, you get $n = 0$ or $n = \frac{2}{3}$.

Connections

29. a. Substitute $11n$ (total number of boxes sold based on the number of choir members) for s, the number of boxes sold, in the equation $P = 5s - (100 + 2s)$ and you will get: $P = 5(11n) - [100 + 2(11n)]$

b. You can simplify the new equation for profit in part (a) by multiplying inside the parentheses, multiplying outside the parentheses, then applying the Distributive Property by multiplying -1 by the numbers inside the brackets, and then combining like terms.

$$P = 5(11n) - [100 + 22n]$$
$$P = 55n - 100 - 22n$$
$$P = 33n - 100$$

c. If the number of choir members is 47, you would substitute it for n in the equation and solve for P:

$$P = 33(47) - 100$$
$$P = 1551 - 100$$
$$P = \$1451$$

d. Substitute \$1,088 for P and solve for n:

$$\$1{,}088 = 33n - 100$$
$$\$1{,}088 + 100 = 33n - 100 + 100$$
$$\$1{,}188 = 33n$$
$$\frac{\$1{,}188}{33} = \frac{33n}{33}$$
$$36 = n$$

There are 36 choir members when the profit is \$1,088.

e. The number of boxes s is 11 times the number of choir members, $s = 11n$. Therefore, when there are 36 choir members, there are $36(11) = 396$ boxes.

30. a. 11; $48 = 2s + 2(s + 2)$
$$48 = 2s + 2s + 4$$
$$44 = 4s$$
$$11 = s$$

b. 11; $48 = 4(s + 2) - 4$
$$48 = 4s + 8 - 4$$
$$48 = 4s + 4$$
$$48 - 4 = 4s + 4 - 4$$
$$44 = 4s$$
$$s = 11$$

c. The answers are the same since the expressions are equivalent expressions. So for any N-value, the corresponding s-value for both equations is the same.

31. D; Since $\frac{3}{4}(20 - 4) = \frac{3}{4}(16) = 12$.

32. H; Since $5^2(7 - 5) + 1 = 25(2) + 1 = 50 + 1 = 51$

33. The largest square pool that can be built for the 40 tiles is a 9 tile by 9 tile pool because that would use (9 tiles × 4 sides) + the 4 corner tiles would be 40 tiles.

34. $16x + 22$;
$$2(9x + 15) - (8 + 2x) = 18x + 30 - 8 - 2x = 16x + 22$$

35. $x - 32$;
$$(7x - 12) - 2(3x + 10) = 7x - 12 - 6x - 20 = x - 32$$

36. Approximately 4.899 meters; since $x^2 = 24$ so $x = \sqrt{24} \approx 4.899$

37. Approximately 2.76 meters; Using the formula $A = \pi x^2$ we get $24 = \pi x^2$ and so $x^2 = \frac{24}{\pi}$ so $x \approx 2.76$

38. $x \approx 7.44$ meters; The height can be found using the Pythagorean theorem. When the height (altitude) is drawn, the resulting triangle has a side of length $\frac{1}{2}x$ and a hypotenuse of x. Substitute these into the Pythagorean theorem to solve $(\frac{1}{2}x)^2 + h^2 = x^2$ for the height, h. So the height is $\frac{\sqrt{3}}{2}x$. Since the area is 24, you can use the equation $24 = \frac{1}{2}(x)(\frac{\sqrt{3}}{2}x)$ to find the value of x. Simplifying the right side gives $24 = \frac{\sqrt{3}}{4}x^2$. Dividing both sides by $\frac{\sqrt{3}}{4}$, you get that $x^2 \approx 55.4256$ so $x \approx 7.44$.

39. The triangle has base 12 and height 4; since $24 = \frac{1}{2}(3x)(x) = \frac{1}{2}(3x^2) = \frac{3}{2}x^2$ and $24 = \frac{3}{2}x^2$ simplifies to $16 = x^2$, the dimensions of the triangle are 4 and $3 \times 4 = 12$.

40. 3 and 8 meters; Since $(x + 5)x = 24$ we need two factors of 24 which are 5 apart. These are 8 and 3 so $x = 3$. The dimensions of the rectangle are 3 and 8.

41. About 1.06 meters; The volume of the sphere is $V = \frac{4}{3}\pi(\frac{3}{2})^3 = \frac{108}{24}\pi$ and the volume of the cylinder is $V = \pi x^2 4$, so we need $x^2 4 = \frac{108}{24}$. Dividing each side by 4 we get that $x^2 = \frac{108}{96}$. So the radius, x, of the cylindrical tank must be $\sqrt{\frac{108}{96}}$, or about 1.06 meters. (NOTE to teacher: This is an opportunity to see how students deal with irrational numbers involving fractions.)

42.a. Some possible answers: $y = x^2 + 4x + 4$, $y = x^2 + 6x + 9$, $y = x^2 - 4x + 4$

b. Some possible answers: $y = x^2 - 16$, $y = x^2 + 7x + 10$ and $y = x^2 + 6x - 7$

43. a. 3 seconds; to find out how long the ball is in the air, students could find out at what time the ball hits the ground or when height is zero. Students can do this by looking at a table or a graph for the value of t for which h is zero. Alternatively, they can solve the equation $0 = 48t - 16t^2$ for t. Since solving $0 = 48t - 16t^2$ is the same as solving $16t(3 - t) = 0$, we have $t = 0$ or $t = 3$. So since the ball is back on the ground after 3 seconds, it is in the air for 3 seconds.

b. Yes; The maximum height of the ball will occur at $t = 1.5$. At this time the height of the ball will be 36, which can be found on a graph, on a table, or by substituting 1.5 into the equation to get $48(1.5) - 16(1.5)^2 = 36$, which is greater than 30 feet.

44. a. If the coefficient of the x^2 term is positive, then the graph has a minimum point. If the coefficient of the x^2 term is negative, then the graph has a maximum point. Either form can be used, but the coefficient of x^2 is immediately available in the expanded form. In the factored form, some mental calculation may have to be done to find the coefficient.

b. The y-intercept can be read directly from the expanded form (the constant term), while the x-intercepts can be determined easily from the factored form (the values that make the factors zero).

c. The line of symmetry is a vertical line perpendicular to the x-axis through a point with an x-coordinate half way between the x-intercepts. The factored form can be used to find this point.

d. The x-coordinate of the maximum/minimum point lies on the line of symmetry. The factored form can be used to find the x-coordinate. To find the y-coordinate, substitute the value of x into either form to calculate the y-value.

45. a. If $g = n^2 - n$, then $g = n(n - 1)$. The x-intercepts are $n = 0$ or $n = 1$. This means that for a league with 0 teams or 1 team, there are no league games.

46. a. 50,000 feet; the x-intercepts are 0 and 1,000. (The equation $0.2x(1{,}000 - x) = 0$ has solutions $x = 0$ and $x = 1{,}000$.) The axis of symmetry would be $x = 500$, so the maximum occurs when the x-coordinate is 500. This makes the height $h = 0.2(500)(1{,}000 - 500) = 0.2(250{,}000) = 50{,}000$ feet.

Extensions

47. c = −1; when $x = 3$ for $3x + c = 2x - 2c$

$$\begin{aligned} 3(3) + c &= 2(3) - 2c \\ 9 + c &= 6 - 2c \\ 9 - 6 + c &= 6 - 6 - 2c \\ 3 + c &= -2c \\ 3 + c - c &= -2c - c \\ \frac{3}{-3} &= \frac{-3c}{-3} \\ -1 &= c \end{aligned}$$

48. c = 5.5; when $x = 3$ for $3x + c = cx - 2$

$$\begin{aligned} 3(3) + c &= c(3) - 2 \\ 9 + c &= 3c - 2 \\ 9 + 2 + c &= 3c - 2 + 2 \\ 11 + c &= 3c \\ 11 + c - c &= 3c - c \\ \frac{11}{2} &= \frac{2c}{2} \\ 5.5 &= c \end{aligned}$$

49. Some possible answers: $2x = 6$, $9 - x = 6$, $15 = 2x + 9$ or $10 = 5(x - 1)$. Not everyone will have the same equation.

50. Answers may vary. Possible answer: The parentheses should be around $(2 - 2x)$:

$$13 = 3 + 5x - (2 - 2x) + 5$$
$$13 = 3 + 5(1) - (2 - 2(1)) + 5$$
$$13 = 3 + 5(1) - (2 - 2) + 5$$
$$13 = 3 + 5(1) - 0 + 5$$
$$13 = 3 + 5 - 0 + 5$$
$$13 = 8 - 0 + 5$$
$$13 = 8 + 5$$
$$13 = 13$$

51. **a.** $x^2 - 0.04$

b. $x^2 - 156.25$

c. $x^2 - 5$

d. $x^2 - 2$

52. **a.** $(x - 10)(x + 10)$

b. $(x - 1.2)(x + 1.2)$

c. $(x - \sqrt{7})(x + \sqrt{7})$

d. $(x - \sqrt{24})(x + \sqrt{24})$

53. **a.** The equation of line 1 is $y = -2x + 15$. The equation of line 2 is $y = 1.5x + 6$.

b. $x \approx 2.6$; $y \approx 10$. (Previous discussion about the x-scale and the y-scale will be helpful here.)

c. Solve $1.5x + 6 = -2x + 15$ to get $x \approx 2.571$, $y \approx 9.857$.

d. Values of x that satisfy $1.5x + 6 < -2x + 15$ are those values of x such that $x < 2.571$. The graph of $y = 1.5x + 6$ is below the graph of $y = -2x + 15$ for values of $x < 2.571$, i.e., to the left of the line $x = 2.571$.

e. $1.5x + 6 > -2x + 15$ when $x > 2.571$. The graph of $y = 1.5x + 6$ is above the graph of $y = -2x + 15$ for values of $x > 2.571$, i.e., to the right of the line $x = 2.571$.

54. **a.** The coordinates of the points where this graph crosses the x-axis are $(0, 0)$ and $(9, 0)$.

b. Rewrite the equation in factored form as $y = x(x - 9)$. The desired points are those whose x-coordinates are the x-intercepts for the given equation (the values of x for which $y = 0$).

c. The values of x that satisfy $x^2 - 9x < 0$ are x such that $0 < x < 9$. The portion of the graph below the x-axis shows that.

d. The values of x that satisfy $x^2 - 9x > 0$ are x such that $x > 9$ or $x < 0$. The portion of the graph to the right of the line $x = 9$ or to the left of the line $x = 0$ show that.

e. The minimum value of y occurs when $x = 4.5$. That minimum value is -20.25.

55. **a.** $a = 1, b = -6$ and $c = 8$, so using the quadratic formula:

$$x = \frac{-(-6) \pm \sqrt{(-6)^2 - 4(1)(8)}}{2(1)}$$
$$x = \frac{6 \pm \sqrt{36 - 32}}{2}$$
$$x = \frac{6 \pm \sqrt{(4)}}{2} = \frac{6 \pm 2}{2}$$
$$x = 4 \text{ or } x = 2$$

b. $a = -1, b = -1$ and $c = 6$, so using the quadratic formula:

$$x = \frac{-(-1) \pm \sqrt{(-1)^2 - 4(-1)(6)}}{2(-1)}$$
$$x = \frac{1 \pm \sqrt{1 - (-24)}}{-2}$$
$$= \frac{1 \pm \sqrt{25}}{-2} = \frac{1 \pm 5}{-2}$$
$$x = -3 \text{ or } x = 2$$

c. $a = 1, b = -7$ and $c = 10$, so using the quadratic formula:

$$x = \frac{-(-7) \pm \sqrt{(-7)^2 - 4(1)(10)}}{2(1)}$$
$$x = \frac{7 \pm \sqrt{49 - 40}}{2}$$
$$x = \frac{7 \pm \sqrt{9}}{2} = \frac{7 \pm 3}{2}$$
$$x = 5 \text{ or } x = 2$$

d. $a = 4, b = -1$ and $c = 0$, so using the quadratic formula:

$$x = \frac{-(-1) \pm \sqrt{(-1)^2 - 4(4)(0)}}{2(4)}$$
$$x = \frac{1 \pm \sqrt{1 - 0}}{8}$$
$$x = \frac{1 \pm 1}{8}$$
$$x = 0 \text{ or } x = 0.25$$

e. $a = 2, b = -12$ and $c = 18$, so using the quadratic formula:

$$x = \frac{-(-12) \pm \sqrt{(-12)^2 - 4(2)(18)}}{2(2)}$$

$$x = \frac{12 \pm \sqrt{144 - 144}}{4} = \frac{12 \pm 0}{4}$$

$$x = 3$$

f. $a = 1, b = 3$ and $c = -4$, so using the quadratic formula:

$$x = \frac{-(3) \pm \sqrt{(3)^2 - 4(1)(-4)}}{2(1)}$$

$$x = \frac{-(3) \pm \sqrt{(9) + 16}}{2}$$

$$x = \frac{-(3) \pm \sqrt{25}}{2} = \frac{-(3) \pm 5}{2}$$

$$x = 1 \text{ or } x = -4$$

56.

$$\begin{aligned} x^2 + 5x + 7 &= 1 \\ x^2 + 5x + 7 - 1 &= 1 - 1 \\ x^2 + 5x + 6 &= 0 \\ (x + 2)(x + 3) &= 0 \\ x &= -2 \text{ or } x = -3 \end{aligned}$$

Check: If $x = -2$, then

$$\begin{aligned} (-2)^2 + 5(-2) + 7 &= 1 \\ 4 - 10 + 7 &= 1 \\ 1 &= 1 \end{aligned}$$

57.

$$\begin{aligned} x^2 + 6x + 15 &= 6 \\ x^2 + 6x + 15 - 6 &= 6 - 6 \\ x^2 + 6x + 9 &= 0 \\ (x + 3)(x + 3) &= 0 \\ x &= -3 \end{aligned}$$

Check: If $x = -3$, then

$$\begin{aligned} (-3)^2 + 6(-3) + 15 &= 6 \\ 9 - 18 + 15 &= 6 \\ 6 &= 6 \end{aligned}$$

Possible Answers to Mathematical Reflections

1. Linear equations can be solved by solving the equation to get x on one side and a constant on the other. The goal is to undo the operation on either side of the equation by adding, subtracting, multiplying, or dividing both sides by the same quantity. Some choices for proceeding are more helpful than others. Adding or subtracting first does not always lead to a simpler equation. When equations include parentheses, you want to replace the side of the equation with the parentheses with an equivalent expression that is expanded. Order of operations is used when you are simplifying expressions on one side of the equal sign. For example, you can use order of operations to solve the equation: $42 = 6 + 2(x + 5)$. You can either subtract 6 from both sides or you can simplify the right side and replace it with the expression $6 + 2x + 10$, getting $42 = 6 + 2x + 10$. Then you can replace the right side again with the expression $16 + 2x$, using the Commutative Property of Addition. Then you have $42 = 16 + 2x$. Subtracting 16 from both sides, you have $26 = 2x$, so $x = 13$. Alternatively, students can make a table to find the value of x for which the expressions on either side of the equation are equivalent, or they can graph the two related equations to find the solution.
2. You can make a table to find the value of x for which the expressions on either side of the equation are equivalent and a graph of the equation. You can also use graphs to find the solution to an equation. You may be able to factor the quadratic expression by applying the Distributive Property or by drawing an area model to find the factors and then setting each factor equal to 0 and solving for x. For example, in $x^2 + 5x + 6 = 0$, the Distributive Property helps you factor the expression to obtain $(x + 3)(x + 2) = 0$, so the solutions are $x = -3$ or $x = -2$.
3. The solution or roots of a linear equation $0 = mx + b$ are the x-intercepts of the graph of the associated linear equation, $y = mx + b$. Similarly the solutions, or roots, to a quadratic equation, $0 = ax^2 + bx + c$, are the x-intercepts of the graph of the associated graph of $y = ax^2 + bx + c$. To find the x-intercept of a linear equation or a quadratic equation you could substitute 0 for y and solve for x.

Investigation 4 Looking Back at Functions

Mathematical and Problem-Solving Goals

- Interpret rate of change for a linear equation from an equation that is not in $y = mx + b$ form
- Relate parts of an equation to context and to linear relationships
- Write and interpret equivalent expressions in context
- Use patterns of change to write linear, exponential, and quadratic relationships
- Interpret symbolic statements and expressions that contain parentheses and several terms (not in standard linear or quadratic form) within a given context
- Determine characteristics of a graph (patterns of change, intercepts, maxima and minima, shape, etc.) of an equation by looking at its symbolic representation
- Determine what information equivalent expressions offer about a function

In this investigation students interpret and generate symbolic equations or expressions within a given context to find answers to specific questions and to describe the underlying pattern of change represented by the symbolic statement.

Summary of Problems

Problem 4.1 Pumping Water

Problem 4.1 uses linear equations to represent the amount of water w in a pool that is emptied after t hours. Students use the equations to answer questions about the rate at which water is being pumped out each hour, as well as the amount of water at the beginning of the pumping and the number of hours that it takes to empty the pool.

Problem 4.2 Generating Patterns

Students write equations representing a linear, an exponential, and a quadratic function given two points on the graph of each function. This problem provides the opportunity to revisit situations from previous units, but more important to investigate how symbolic statements capture the patterns of change in these three functions.

Problem 4.3 Sorting Functions

Students learn to predict the type of relationship the equation of a function represents and the characteristics a graph of the function would have.

	Suggested Pacing	Materials for Students	Materials for Teachers	ACE Assignments
All	$3\frac{1}{2}$ days	Graphing calculators (optional), poster paper or, transparency (optional)		
4.1	1 day			1–4, 20–23, 40
4.2	1 day			5–7, 24–35, 41
4.3	1 day		Transparency 4.3	8–19, 36–39, 42–43
MR	$\frac{1}{2}$ day			

4.1 Pumping Water

Goals

- Interpret rate of change for a linear equation from an equation that is not in $y = mx + b$ form
- Relate parts of an equation to the context of pumping water and to linear relationships
- Write and interpret equivalent expressions in context

Launch 4.1

Describe the situation about water being pumped from a school pool. Write the equation on the board. Tell the class that they are to find some information about the amount of water and the rate at which it is being pumped.

Let students work in pairs on this problem.

Explore 4.1

Some students may write $(t - 5)(-250)$ as an equivalent expression for the amount of water. This is correct, but if it occurs, encourage them to find another expression for the amount of water.

Suggested Questions Ask:

- *Is there a way to write the equation in expanded form?*
- *Does the expanded form help you find the answers for Question A more easily?*

Summarize 4.1

For Questions A–D, ask different pairs to present their work. Ask the rest of the class if they agree and if they have any questions they want to ask the pair. The idea is to get the class to take charge of the learning rather than just wait for you to question the students.

For Question D, some students may have read the -450 as the rate per hour that the water is being pumped out, not knowing to distribute the -450 to the 2, the coefficient of x inside the parentheses. Tables and graphs will be helpful to see the constant rate of 2 times -450 (or -900) gallons per minute. Some may apply the Distributive Property to write $w = -900t + 3{,}150$.

Make sure that all students understand how to use the Distributive Property to write the equations in the form $y = mx + b$.

Suggested Questions Ask:

- *Which form of the equation, $w = -250(t - 5)$ or $w = -250t + 1250$, would an engineer most likely use to represent this situation? Why?* (Students should pick the second equation, as it makes the most sense for those people who need to estimate the time to empty the pool. It is possible some students may find plausible reasons for engineers to use the first equation, as it is easier to solve for $w = 0$ since the factor $t - 5$ would have to be 0 (so $t = 5$). We started with the first equation to see if students could recognize that this is a linear situation.)
- *Without making a graph, describe the shape of the graph of the equation. Is this relationship linear? Exponential? Quadratic? Why?*
- *In Questions A, part (1) and D, part (1), how is the information about the amount of water being pumped out related to the graph of the equation?* (It is the slope of the line that the equation represents. It represents the constant rate of change relating the two variables, amount of water and time. As time increases by 1 hour, the amount of water decreases by 250 gallons in A1 and 900 gallons in D1.)

4.1 Pumping Water

At a Glance

PACING 1 day

Mathematical Goals

- Interpret rate of change for a linear equation from an equation which is not in $y = mx + b$ form
- Relate parts of an equation to the context of pumping water and to linear relationships
- Write and interpret equivalent expressions in context

Launch

Describe the situation about water being pumped from a school pool. Write the equation $w = -250(t - 5)$ on the board. Tell the class that they are to find some information about the amount of water and the rate at which it is being pumped.

Let students work in pairs on this problem.

Explore

Some students may write $(t - 5)(-250)$ as an equivalent expression for the amount of water. This is correct, but if it occurs, encourage them to find another expression for the amount of water.

- *Is there a way to write the equation in expanded form?*
- *Does the expanded form help you find the answers for Question A more easily?*

Summarize

For Questions A–D, ask different pairs to present their work. Ask the rest of the class if they agree and if they have any questions they want to ask the pair.

For Question D, tables and graphs will be helpful to see the constant rate of 2 times -450 or -900 gallons per minute and not just the -450 in front of the parentheses. Some may apply the Distributive Property to write $w = -900t + 3{,}150$.

Make sure students understand how to use the Distributive Property to write the equations in the form $y = mx + b$. Ask:

- *Which form of the equation, $w = -250(t - 5)$ or $w = -250t - 1{,}250$, would an engineer most likely use to represent this situation? Why?*
- *Without making a graph, describe the shape of the graph of the equation. Is this relationship linear? Exponential? Quadratic? Why?*

In Questions A, part (1) and D, part (1), how is the information about the amount of water being pumped out related to the graph of the equation?

Materials

- Student notebooks

ACE Assignment Guide for Problem 4.1

Core 1–2, 21–23
Other *Applications* 3, 4; *Connections* 20; *Extensions* 40

Adapted For suggestions about adapting ACE exercises, see the CMP *Special Needs Handbook.*
Connecting to Prior Units 20: *Covering and Surrounding*; 21: *Covering and Surrounding* and *Filling and Wrapping*; 22: *Moving Straight Ahead*; 23: *Frogs, Fleas and Painted Cubes*

Answers to Problem 4.1

A. 1. 250 gallons are being pumped out each hour. Students may make a table and notice the constant rate of change, which is -250, or they may recognize that -250 is the coefficient of t in a linear relationship between w and t.

2. 5 hours. Students can find in their table the corresponding t value when w is 0 or they can find where the graph of $w = -250t + 1{,}250$ intersects the x-axis. If students look at the equation $w = -250t + 1{,}250$, they may solve the equation for $w = 0$, so t would equal 5.

3. 1,250 gallons. Answer can be found by looking at the equation or by looking at the table or graph.

B. 1. $-250t + 1{,}250$ or $1{,}250 - 250t$.

2. The -250 represents that there are 250 gallons of water being pumped out each hour. The 1,250 is the number of gallons of water in the tank at the start.

3. Answers will vary. The original expression tells us that the x-intercept is 5, since for w to equal 0 the factor $(t - 5)$ must equal 0, so $t = 5$. The y-intercept is harder to read in this expression. However, the rate of change is not hard to compute, since it is just -250 times 1. In this expression, $-250t + 1{,}250$, it is easier to read the amount of water at the start and to read the amount of water being pumped out each hour.

C. 1. The pattern of change is linear. For every change in time by one hour the amount of water in the pool decreases by a constant amount of 250 gallons.

2. The graph would have a y-intercept at $(0, 1{,}250)$ and slant down from left to right. It would cross the x-axis at $(5, 0)$.

D. 1. 900 gallons per hour. Students may make a table on a graphing calculator.

2. 3.5 hours. Students may use their table. They would have to use $\frac{1}{2}$-hour intervals of time to get the exact time in their table. There would be 0 gallons left in the pool between 3 and 4 hours. To check, students can substitute 3.5 hours into the equation for t and the result will be $w = -450[2(3.5) - 7] = -450(7 - 7) = 0$ gallons. Some students may use the guess and check method in the equation to begin with. Others may solve the equation: $w = -450(2t - 7)$ for t when $w = 0$, since $w = 0$ means that the amount of water in the pool is zero gallons. There are two different ways to solve the equation $0 = -450(2t - 7)$. You can use the Distributive Property on the right side, getting $0 = -900t + 3{,}150$; subtract 3,150 from both sides; and then divide by -900, getting 3.5. The other way is to look at the equation $-450(2t - 7) = 0$ and notice that in order for the product on the left hand side to equal zero, $2t - 7$ must equal 0, so $t = 3.5$ [NOTE: When two numbers are multiplied so that their product is 0, one or both of the factors must be zero, which is important in the next investigation.]

3. 3,150 gallons. This can be found in the table when time is zero or by solving the equation $w = -450(2t - 7)$ for w when $t = 0$, $w = -450(-7) = 3{,}150$.

4. Using the Distributive Property, the equation becomes $w = -900t + 3{,}150$, which is equivalent to the original equation. Some students may say that $(2t - 7)(-450)$ is an equivalent expression, which is correct since they have just used the Commutative Property. However, their new expression does not give any new information about the problem. The expanded form of this equation tells you that the tank started with 3,150 gallons and that the rate of change is -900 gallons per hour, so students may say that it is more useful.

4.2 Generating Patterns

Goal:

- Use patterns of change to write linear, exponential, and quadratic relationships

Launch 4.2

Explain to students that they will create their own linear, exponential, and quadratic patterns and write equations that represent their pattern.

Give the students the coordinates of two points on linear, quadratic, and exponential equations. Their task is to generate 4 more points that fit each pattern of change and to write an equation to represent the pattern of change.

Have students work in groups of 2–3.

Explore 4.2

As students are making their patterns you may want to ask them how they chose the pattern they did.

Suggested Question Ask:

- *How did you check whether your pattern was linear? Exponential? Quadratic?* (For linear, students may have taken differences of successive y-values and found a constant difference. For exponential, students may have taken quotients and looked for a constant quotient value. For quadratic, some students may try to use the symmetry of a parabola, second differences, or used the equation $y = x^2$ to generate values.)

When students are working on finding equations for their patterns, they should be able to find the equation of a line, given two points.

For the exponential pattern a few students may need prompting.

Suggested Question Ask:

- *What is an example of an exponential equation? What do exponential equations look like?* (You may want to remind students about the King of Montarek and the chessboard, or about rubas from *Growing, Growing, Growing,* in order to help them to remember what exponentials look like. Formally, exponential equations are of the form $y = a(b)^x$.)

For students that are working on the quadratic equation and struggling, you may need to remind them about the general form of a quadratic: $y = ax^2 + bx + c$. It is not necessary at this point that students are experts at writing equations for quadratics. With some help, most students should be able to write an equation. Some will find c by working backward. Some may have noted the relationship between the second difference and the coefficient a from *Frogs, Fleas, and Painted Cubes*. (The second difference is $2a$.) Some may guess and check values for a and b until it works.

For the summary, look for interesting strategies or places where students are struggling.

Summarize 4.2

For each function (linear, exponential, or quadratic), have students put up their patterns on the board or overhead. Have students explain why their relationship is linear, exponential, or quadratic.

The following table of patterns (Figure 1) includes the unique linear and exponential patterns and five possible examples of quadratic patterns. Be sure to have the class check whether the class patterns are correct. If the following quadratic functions do not come up, you can pose them as a further check on students' understanding of quadratic functions. The equation for Quad #1 is $y = x^2$. The pattern for #2 is *not quadratic*; the second difference is not a constant. The pattern for #3 is quadratic and its equation is $y = -0.5x^2 + 4.5x - 3$. The pattern in #4 *is not quadratic*, but the student used the symmetry of quadratics to write the pattern. Quad #5 is quadratic and its equation is $y = 0.5x^2 + 1.5x - 1$.

Be sure to have students explain how they got their equations. The following responses come from CMP classes:

Linear Functions

For the linear relationship, most students find the y-intercept for the linear pattern by working backwards in the table. They then use the y-intercept, -2, and the slope of 3 to write $y = -2 + 3x$.

One student begins with the first x-value in the table, one, and notices that the y-value "goes up by three each time". She uses this information to write $1 + 3x$. When she checks her work, she notices that the values in the x-column are shifted "one too high". She adjusts the equation and writes $y = 1 + 3(x - 1)$ which makes "it work." These two equations are equivalent.

Exponential Functions

There are several equivalent equations for the exponential relationship.

Some students write correct equations, either $y = 4^{x-1}$ or $y = 4^x \times 0.25$. In the latter equation, they find the y-intercept of 0.25 by working backward in the table, dividing 1 by 4 (using the growth rate of 4).

Some students write incorrect equations, the most popular being $y = 1 \times 4^x$. We assume this is the result of those students thinking that 1 is the y-intercept (since it is the first entry in the table). NOTE: $\frac{1}{4}(4^x) = 4^{-1}(4^x) = 4^{x-1}$.

Quadratic functions

Many students will write the simple function ($y = x^2$).

Some students may just write down a symmetric sequence of numbers such as 1, 4, 7, 9, 10, 9, 7, 4, 1. For these students, you may want to have them graph their points or raise the question of whether the pattern 1, 4, 10, 20, 30, 20, 10, 4, 1 is quadratic in order to see if they are using other criteria besides symmetry.

Suggested Questions Ask:

- *Is there a way to check whether your pattern is quadratic, as you did for linear and exponential?* (Checking for constant second differences is a way to check that a pattern is quadratic. Some may make a graph.)

Figure 1

	Linear	Exp.	Quad. Ex. 1	Quad. Ex. 2	Quad. Ex. 3	Quad. Ex. 4	Quad. Ex. 5
x	*y*	*y*	*y*	*y*	*y*	*y*	*y*
1	1	1	1	1	1	1	1
2	4	4	4	4	4	4	4
3	7	16	9	8	6	16	8
4	10	64	16	13	7	64	13
5	13	256	25	18	7	16	19
6	16	1024	36	23	6	4	26

- *I notice that there is only one example for the linear equation. Is there one that we didn't think of that is not equivalent to the one we got? Why or why not?* (No. Only one linear pattern can be produced given two points, since the two points determine what the constant rate of change is, or two points determine a straight line.)
- *What about exponential functions? Do you think there is another possible exponential pattern if you have to go through (1, 1) and (2, 4)? Why or why not?* (No. Only one exponential pattern can be drawn through two given points. Note that there are exactly two parameters (a and b) in the exponential equations $y = ab^x$. Also it takes only two points to uniquely determine the growth factor for exponential functions. In this case, it is 4.)
- *How many points do you need to determine a line?* (Two)
- *How many points do you need to determine an exponential function?* (Two)
- *What about quadratics? Can we think of another one that is not on the board?* (There are infinitely many quadratics that you can find passing through 2 points. See answers to problem below for an explanation. There are three parameters in the general quadratic equation, $y = ax^2 + bx + c$, so it takes three points to uniquely define a quadratic function.)

Have the class try to come up with another quadratic pattern.

- *What if I told you that the point (3, 9) had to be included in your table? How many different quadratics patterns could we find then?* [If (3, 9) was added, then there could be one pattern, since 3 points determine the second difference of 2 and the starting point of (0, 1), and thus determine the quadratic pattern. Students have talked about this in Investigation 1 when they were trying to find equivalent quadratic expressions. Two quadratic expressions are equivalent if they contain the same three points.]

Ask students to put up their equations for the linear and exponential equations. The quadratic equation is the hardest to come up with unless it is the simplest quadratic, $y = x^2$. There is an explanation in the answer to this problem about how to determine the quadratic equation. This is an advanced idea and you may want to go through it for your students if they are interested, or if they have already worked on it in the problem in Question C, part (1.)

4.2 Generating Patterns

At a Glance

PACING 1 day

Mathematical Goal

- Use patterns of change to write linear, exponential, and quadratic relationships

Launch

In this problem, students make their own linear, exponential, and quadratic patterns and write equations that represent these patterns.

Give the students the coordinates of two points on linear, quadratic, and exponential equations. Have them generate 4 more points that fit each pattern of change and write equations to represent the patterns of change.

Let students work in groups of 2–3.

Explore

Ask students how they chose the pattern they did.

- *How can you check if a pattern is linear? Exponential? Quadratic?*

For the exponential pattern, a few students may need prompting.

- *What is an example of an exponential equation? What do exponential equations look like?*

Remind students about the King of Montarek's chessboard and rubas from *Growing, Growing, Growing*, and the quadratic general form: $y = ax^2 + bx + c$.

Some students may be able to write an equation for the quadratic; however, this is not a goal for this problem. This is an advanced idea and is explained in the answer to this problem.

Summarize

For each function (linear, exponential and quadratic), have students put up their patterns on the board or overhead. Have students explain why their relationship is linear, exponential or quadratic.

- *Is there a way to check whether your pattern is quadratic like you did for linear and exponential?*
- *I notice that there is only one example for linear equation. Is there one that we didn't think of? Why or why not?*
- *What about exponential functions? Do you think there is another possible exponential pattern through (1, 1) and (2, 4)? Why or why not?*
- *How many points do you need to determine a line? How many points do you need to determine an exponential function?*
- *What about quadratics? Can we think of another one not on the board?*
- *If I told you that the point (3, 9) had to be included in your table, how many different quadratic patterns could we find then?*

Let the class check whether the patterns are correct.

Materials

- Student notebooks

ACE Assignment Guide for Problem 4.2

Core 5, 7, 26–29, 33–35

Other *Applications* 6; *Connections* 24, 25, 30–32; *Extensions* 41; unassigned choices from previous problems

Adapted For suggestions about adapting ACE exercises, see the CMP *Special Needs Handbook*.

Connecting to Prior Units 24, 33: *Frogs, Fleas and Painted Cubes;* 25, 35: *Growing, Growing, Growing*; 26–31: *Say it With Symbols*; 34: *Moving Straight Ahead*

Answers to Problem 4.2

A. There is only one possible linear pattern (given in Figure 1 on page 98) because once you have fixed two points, in this case 1 and 4 for the y-values, the constant rate of change is determined, in this case +3.

There is only one possible exponential pattern (given in the table). Once you have fixed two points, in this case 1 and 4 for the y-values, the growth factor of 4 is determined.

There are infinitely many patterns that students can generate for the quadratic; the table shows 3 possible patterns. Second differences must have a constant non-zero rate of change. The y-values for the points (1, 1) and (2, 4) determine a first difference of 3, but the second difference depends on what the student puts in for the third value. For example, if the student uses 9 for the value for 3, then the second difference is fixed (at 2 in this case). This is why if you are given three points of a quadratic pattern, the quadratic is fixed. NOTE: A common mistake that students make is to simply make a symmetrical pattern in the y column, (for example, 1, 4, 6, 7, 8, 7, 6, 4, 1) without checking second differences.

B. A linear relationship always has a constant rate of change. For every change of 1 in the x-values, there is a constant change of 3 in the y-values.

An exponential relationship has the same value (the growth factor) for the quotients between successive y-values. To find the y-value corresponding to consecutive x-values in an exponential relationship, multiply the previous y-value by the growth factor (in this case by 4). A quadratic relationship has a constant second difference. When you take the differences between successive y-values, then the differences of the differences, you get a constant rate of change.

C. **1.** The linear equation $y = 3x - 2$ is unique but equivalent to $y = 1 + 3(x - 1)$; the 3 is the rate of change, the -2 is the y-intercept. The exponential equation is $y = 4^{x-1}$ and is unique but equivalent to $y = (\frac{1}{4})(4^x)$. The 4 is the growth factor; the $\frac{1}{4}$ is the y-intercept. Quadratic 1 in Figure 1 is $y = x^2$. The other quadratic equations are more difficult to find. A description of how to find these equations is given below.

2. The linear and exponential equations should be the same, except for equivalent forms $y = 3x - 2$ or $y = 1 + 3(x - 1)$ and $y = 4^{x-1}$ or $y = (\frac{1}{4})(4^x)$. The quadratic equation (if students were able to find one) will vary. After looking at several tables of quadratic relationships in *Frogs, Fleas, and Painted Cubes*, some students have correctly conjectured that the coefficient of x^2 is always one half the value of the second difference if x increases by 1 each time in the table). Students can find the y-intercept by working backward in the table. Thus, one way to find the equation of a quadratic is to find the value for a and the y-intercept value c, plug them into the equation $y = ax^2 + bx + c$, and solve for b using any point (x, y) in their table. For example, for Quadratic 3, the second difference is -1, so $a = -\frac{1}{2}$. By extending the table back to $x = 0$, students can find that $c = -3$. The equation becomes $y = -\frac{1}{2}x^2 + bx - 3$. Substituting the point (1, 1) in the equation, we get $1 = -\frac{1}{2}(1)^2 + b(1) - 3 = -\frac{1}{2} + b - 3$, so $b = 4.5$. The equation is $y = -\frac{1}{2}x^2 + 4.5x - 3$. Quadratic 5 has an equation of $y = 0.5x^2 + 1.5x - 1$.

4.3 Sorting Functions

Goals

- Determine characteristics of a graph (patterns of change, intercepts, maxima and minima, shape, etc.) of an equation by looking at its symbolic representation
- Determine what information equivalent expressions offer about a function

Launch 4.3

In this problem, we will be sorting functions and seeing what family they belong to: linear, quadratic, or exponential. Also we will look at the equivalent forms of these functions and what information the forms give us.

Remind students of the decisions they have made over the course of this unit about which form of an expression to use.

Suggested Questions Ask:

- *Remember the equations $M = 16(10) + 7(2x) + 11(0.5x + 5)$ and $M = 215 + 19.5x$ from the walkathon in Investigation 2. Which equation would you choose to find the amount of money if the students traveled 10 kilometers, and why? Which equation gives more information about the context?*
- *If you were asked to solve the equation $x^2 + 4x + 4 = 0$ for x, which would you use, this form or the factored form $(x + 2)(x + 2) = 0$?*
- *Which form is easier to use, factored or expanded, when finding the y-intercept of the quadratic $y = x^2 + 7x + 10$, and why?*

You could put the 18 equations on cardboard in large lettering. This could be used in the summary for students to create equivalent families on the side walls.

Students can work in pairs.

Explore 4.3

Suggested Question Ask:

- *Are there any functions that are not linear, exponential, or quadratic? If so, which ones, and how do you know?* (Equations 4, 5, 8 and 16; Equation 4 has an exponent on x that is higher than two, as does equation 5 when it is multiplied out, Equations 8 and 16 are non-linear functions that do not have the patterns of change that exponential or quadratics have, which can be seen by using a table of values and taking quotients and second differences, respectively.)

For Question B, part (2), the goal is for students to predict the information using the symbols and algebraic reasoning. If students are using graphs and tables, encourage them to see if there is another way to find the maximum and minimum points or the x- and y-intercepts.

Suggested Questions Depending on the equation they are working on, you may want to ask students,:

- *Is there an equivalent equation that may be more helpful to find the information you are looking for?*
- *Does the parabola open up or down? How do you know?*
- *Which form is easier for finding the x-intercepts, the factored form or the expanded form?*

Summarize 4.3

Make a table on the board (or use Transparency 4.3) with four columns: Linear, Exponential, Quadratic, and Other, and have students share their ideas about which equations belong in which column.

For any repeated equation in different columns, have the students make arguments for each case until the class comes to a consensus for the final classification.

In each column, ask students to share which equations are equivalent and why they are equivalent. Arguments may include use of a graph, table, or substitution of two points for linear and exponential and three points for quadratic, and use of properties of number such as the Commutative or Distributive properties.

- *In which form was it easier to determine the x-intercepts?*
- *In which form was it easier to determine the y-intercept?*
- *How did you find the rate of change for Equation 14? For Equation 18?* (Students probably did some symbolic manipulation to get these equations in the form $y = mx + b$. If students only used tables to find this answer, you should have students try to find a solution that uses the Distributive and Commutative properties.)
- *Does the graph of Equation 9 cross the x-axis? How do you know?* [Yes; the graph crosses once since there is only one x-intercept $(-4, 0)$ which can be found by setting $y = 0$ and solving for x by setting each factor equal to zero.]
- *Does the graph of Equation 10 cross the x-axis? How do you know?* (Yes; the graph crosses twice since there are two x-intercepts $(\frac{3}{4}, 0)$ and $(-1, 0)$, which can be found by setting $y = 0$ and solving for x by setting each factor equal to zero.)

Ask students to share the problems that they devised that could be represented by the equation. Try to get one linear, one exponential, and one quadratic example. Ask the class if the student's problems fit the equations they gave.

4.3 Sorting Functions

At a Glance

PACING 1 day

Mathematical Goals

- Determine characteristics of a graph (patterns of change, intercepts, maxima and minima, shape, etc.) of an equation by looking at its symbolic representation
- Determine what information equivalent expressions offer about a function

Launch

In this problem we will be sorting functions and seeing which family they belong to: linear, quadratic, or exponential. Also, we will look at the equivalent forms of these functions and what information the forms give us.

- *Remember the equations $M = 16(10) + 7(2x) + 11(0.5x + 5)$ and $M = 215 + 19.5x$ from the walkathon in Investigation 2.*
- *Which equation would you choose to find the amount of money if the students traveled 10 kilometers, and why?*
- *Which equation gives more information about the context?*
- *If you were asked to solve the equation $x^2 + 4x + 4 = 0$ for x, which would you use, this form, or the factored form $(x + 2)(x + 2)=0$?*
- *Which form is easier to use, factored or expanded, when finding the y-intercept of the quadratic $y = x^2 + 7x + 10$, and why?*

Students can work in pairs.

Explore

- *Are there any functions that are not linear, exponential, or quadratic? If so which ones and how do you know?*

For Question B, part (2), if students are using graphs and tables, encourage them to find another way to predict maximum and minimum points or x- and y-intercepts. The goal is for students to predict from the symbols

Ask the following (depending on the equation they are working on):

- *Is there an equivalent equation that may be more helpful to find the information you are looking for?*
- *Does the parabola open up or down? How do you know? Which form is easier for finding the x-intercepts, factored or expanded?*

Summarize

Make a table on the board (or use Transparency 4.3) with four columns: Linear, Exponential, Quadratic, and Other and have students share ideas about which equations belong in which column.

In each column, ask students to share which equations are equivalent and why they are equivalent.

Materials

- Student notebooks
- Transparency 4.3

continued on next page

Summarize
continued

- *In which form was it easier to determine the x-intercepts? The y-intercept? How did you find the rate of change for Equation 14? Equation 18?*
- *Does the graph of Equation 9 cross the x-axis? How do you know? Does the graph of Equation 10 cross the x-axis?*

Ask students to share the problems that they devised that could be represented by the equation, and ask the class if the students' problems fit the equations they gave.

ACE Assignment Guide for Problem 4.3

Core 11–18, 36, 37

Other *Applications* 8–10, 19; *Connections* 38–39; *Extensions* 42–43; and unassigned choices from previous problems

Adapted For suggestions about adapting ACE exercises, see the CMP *Special Needs Handbook*.

Connecting to Prior Units 36–37: *Frogs, Fleas and Painted Cubes*; 38: *Looking for Pythagoras*; 39: *Filling and Wrapping*

Answers to Problem 4.3

A. **1.** Equations 3, 7, 14, 18

2. Equations 2, 6, 13

3. Equations 1, 9, 10, 11, 12, 15, 17

B. **1.** Equations 1 and 9; Equations 2 and 13; Equations 3 and 14; Equations 11 and 17

2. Equations 1 and 9: Quadratics pattern with y-intercept of 16 and x-intercept of -4. The minimum is $(-4, 0)$.

Equations 2 and 13: Exponential patterns with starting point $(0, \frac{1}{3})$ and a growth factor of 3.

Equations 3 and 14: Linear pattern, x-intercept is $(5, 0)$ and y-intercept is 10. The rate of change is -2. The line has a negative slope, so it falls left to right.

Equations 11 and 17: Quadratics pattern with y-intercept of $(0, 0)$ and x-intercepts of $(0, 0)$ and $(5, 0)$. The minimum is (2.5, 25).

C. Answers will vary. An example for Equation 2 is that the King of Montarek will put one ruba on the first square on a chessboard, 3 on the next square, 9 on the next square, and so on, multiplying by 3 for each successive square. Equation 2 represents the number of rubas on square x of the chessboard.

The student edition pages for this investigation begin on the next page.

STUDENT PAGE

Notes

Investigation 4

Looking Back at Functions

Throughout your work in algebra, you have identified patterns of change between variables as linear, exponential, and quadratic functions. You have used tables, graphs, and equations to represent and reason about these functions. In this unit, you have found that writing equivalent expressions for a quantity or variable can reveal new information about a situation. This investigation will help pull these ideas together.

4.1 Pumping Water

Every winter, Magnolia Middle School empties their pool for cleaning. Ms. Theodora's math class decides to collect data on the amount of water in the pool and how long it takes to empty it. They write an equation to represent the amount of water w (in gallons) in the pool after t hours.

$$w = -250(t - 5)$$

Problem 4.1 Looking at Patterns of Change

A. Answer the following questions. Explain your reasoning.

1. How many gallons of water are pumped out each hour?
2. How long will it take to empty the pool?
3. How many gallons of water are in the pool at the start?

B. 1. Write an expression for the amount of water in the tank after t hours that is equivalent to the original expression.

2. What information does this new expression tell you about the amount of water in the tank?
3. Which expression is more useful in this situation? Explain.

STUDENT PAGE

STUDENT PAGE

Notes

C. **1.** Describe the pattern of change in the relationship between the two variables w and t.

2. Without graphing the equation, describe the shape of the graph. Include as much information as you can.

D. Suppose the equation for the amount of water w (in gallons) in another pool after t hours is $w = -450(2t - 7)$.

1. How many gallons of water are pumped out each hour?

2. How long will it take to empty the pool?

3. How many gallons of water are in the pool at the start?

4. Write an expression that is equivalent to $-450(2t - 7)$. Which expression is more useful? Explain.

ACE **Homework starts on page 60.**

4.2 Generating Patterns

In this problem, you are given two data points for a linear, exponential, and quadratic relationship. You will use these points to find more data points. Then you will write an equation for each relationship.

STUDENT PAGE

Notes

Problem 4.2 Linear, Exponential, Quadratic

A. The first two rows in a table of numbers are given below. Write four more numbers in each column to make a linear relationship, an exponential relationship, and a quadratic relationship.

Data Points

x	Linear y	Exponential y	Quadratic y
1	1	1	1
2	4	4	4
3	■	■	■
4	■	■	■
5	■	■	■
6	■	■	■

B. Explain why the pattern in each column is correct.

C. 1. Write an equation for each relationship. Explain what information the variables and numbers represent.

2. Compare your equations with those of your classmates. Do you all have the same equations? Explain.

ACE Homework starts on page 60.

STUDENT PAGE

STUDENT PAGE

Notes

4.3 Sorting Functions

In the following problem, a set of equations relating x and y is given. Some of the expressions for y are in factored form, and some are in expanded form.

Which form is easier to use to determine whether a function is linear, exponential, quadratic, or none of these?

Which form is easier to use to determine the x- and y-intercepts, rates of change, and maximum or minimum points of the graph of the function?

Problem 4.3 Sorting Functions

Use the following equations for Questions A–C.

(1) $y = x^2 + 8x + 16$

(2) $y = \frac{1}{3}(3^x)$

(3) $y = 10 - 2x$

(4) $y = 2x^3 + 5$

(5) $y = (x^2 + 1)(x^2 + 3)$

(6) $y = 0.5^x$

(7) $y = 22 - 2x$

(8) $y = \frac{3}{x}$

(9) $y = (x + 4)(x + 4)$

(10) $y = (4x - 3)(x + 1)$

(11) $y = 20x - 4x^2$

(12) $y = x^2$

(13) $y = 3^{x - 1}$

(14) $y = 16 - 2(x + 3)$

(15) $y = 4x^2 - x - 3$

(16) $y = x + \frac{1}{x}$

(17) $y = 4x(5 - x)$

(18) $y = 2(x - 3) + 6(1 - x)$

A. Which equations represent functions that are

1. linear? **2.** exponential? **3.** quadratic?

B. **1.** For each function in Question A, find those equations that represent the same function.

2. Without graphing the equation, describe the shape of the graph of those equations in part (1). Give as much detail as possible, including patterns of change, intercepts, and maximum and minimum points.

C. Pick one linear, one quadratic, and one exponential equation. Describe a problem that could be represented by each equation.

ACE **Homework starts on page 60.**

Notes

Applications

Connections

Extensions

Applications

1. A pump is used to empty a swimming pool. The equation $w = -275t + 1{,}925$ represents the gallons of water w that remain in the pool t hours after pumping starts.
   a. How many gallons of water are pumped out each hour?
   b. How much water is in the pool at the start of pumping?
   c. Suppose there are 1,100 gallons of water left in the pool. How long has the pump been running?
   d. After how many hours will the pool be empty?
   e. Write an equation that is equivalent to $w = -275t + 1{,}925$. What information does it tell you about the situation?
   f. Without graphing, describe the shape of the graph of the relationship between w and t.

2. A new pump is used to empty the pool in Exercise 1. The equation $w = -275(2t - 7)$ represents the gallons of water w that remain in the pool t hours after pumping starts.
   a. How many gallons of water are pumped out each hour?
   b. How much water is in the pool at the start of pumping?
   c. Suppose there are 1,000 gallons of water left in the pool. How long has the pump been running?
   d. After how many hours will the pool be empty?
   e. Write an equation that is equivalent to $w = -275(2t - 7)$. What information does it tell you about the situation?

3. A truck has a broken fuel gauge. Luckily, the driver keeps a record of mileage and gas consumption. The driver uses the data to write an equation for the relationship between the number of gallons of gas in the tank g and the number of miles driven m since the last fill-up.

$$g = 25 - \frac{1}{15}m$$

   a. How many gallons of gasoline are in a full tank? Explain.
   b. Suppose the driver travels 50 miles after filling the tank. How much gas is left?

Notes

c. After filling the tank, how many miles can the driver travel before 5 gallons remain?

d. After filling the tank, how many miles can the driver travel before the tank is empty?

e. How many miles does the driver have to travel in order to use 1 gallon of gas? Explain.

f. In the equation, what do the numbers 25 and $\frac{1}{15}$ tell you about the situation?

4. A middle school pays $2,500 to print 400 copies of the yearbook. They give some free copies to the yearbook advisor and staff and sell the rest to students. The equation below tells how close the school is to paying for the printing bill.

$$y = 2{,}500 - 15(N - 8)$$

Describe what information the numbers and variables represent in this situation.

For: Help with Exercise 4
Web Code: ape-6404

5. The Department of Natural Resources is collecting data on three different species of animals. They find that these species show different patterns of population growth. They write the equations below to represent the population P of each species after x years.

Species 1	Species 2	Species 3
$P_1 = 10{,}000 + 100x$	$P_2 = 10(3^x)$	$P_3 = 800 + 10x^2$

a. Describe what information the numbers and variables represent in each equation.

b. Describe the pattern of growth for each species. Explain how the patterns differ.

c. Pick any two species. After how many years will the populations of the two species be equal? Explain how you got your answer.

Notes

6. The tables below represent the projected growth of certain species of deer. Use the three tables to answer parts (a)–(c).

Table 1

Year	Deer
2000	1,000
2001	1,030
2002	1,061
2003	1,093
2004	1,126

Table 2

Year	Deer
2000	1,000
2001	1,030
2002	1,060
2003	1,090
2004	1,120

Table 3

Year	Deer
2000	1,000
2001	3,000
2002	9,000
2003	27,000
2004	81,000

a. Describe the growth represented in each table. Are any of these patterns linear, exponential, or quadratic?

b. Write an equation for each linear, exponential, or quadratic pattern in part (a).

c. Does any table show a population of deer growing at a rate of 300% per year? Explain.

7. Suppose the figures shown are made with toothpicks.

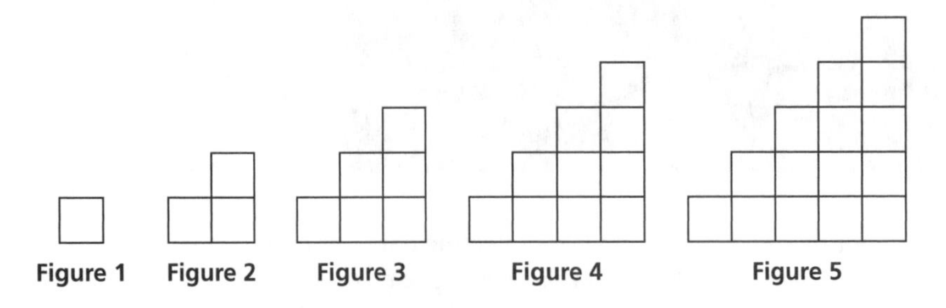

a. What patterns in the set of figures do you notice?

b. How many toothpicks do you need to make Figure 7?

c. Is the relationship between the perimeter and the figure number linear, quadratic, or exponential? Explain.

d. Is the relationship between the total number of toothpicks and the figure number linear, quadratic, or exponential?

Notes

e. Write an equation to represent the perimeter of Figure N. Explain your rule.

f. Write an equation to represent the total number of toothpicks needed to make Figure N. Explain your rule.

For Exercises 8–10, use the graphs below.

Graph 1

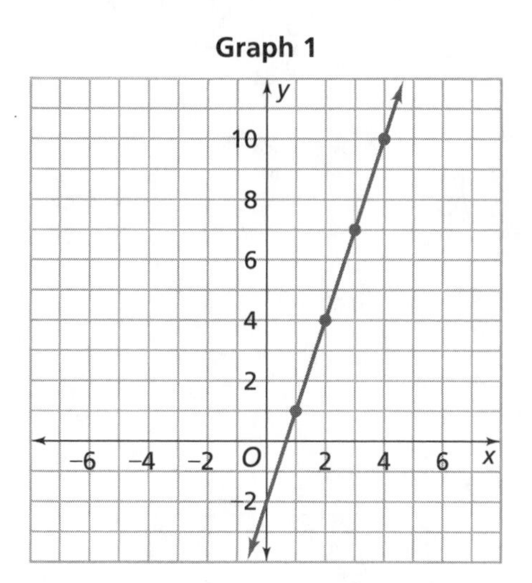

Graph 2

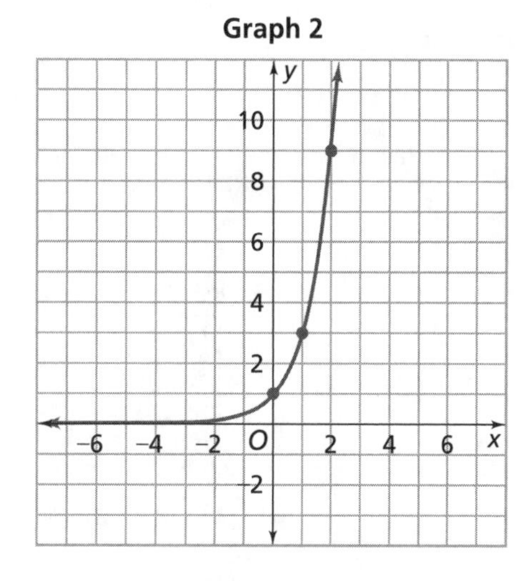

Graph 3

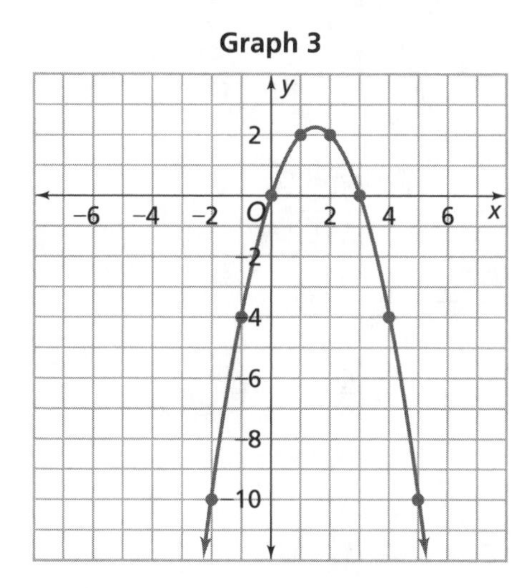

Graph 4

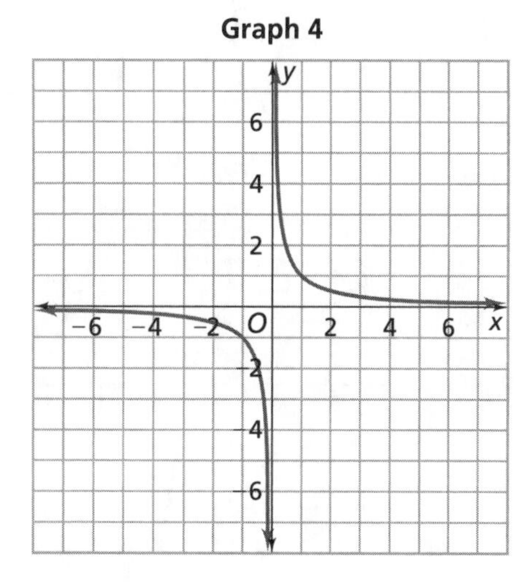

8. Which graphs represent linear, quadratic, or exponential functions?

9. Make a table of y-values for $x = 1, 2, 3, \ldots 6$ for each linear, quadratic, or exponential function.

10. Write an equation for each linear, quadratic, or exponential function. Describe your strategy.

Notes

For Exercises 11–17, match each equation with one of the graphs below.

Graph A

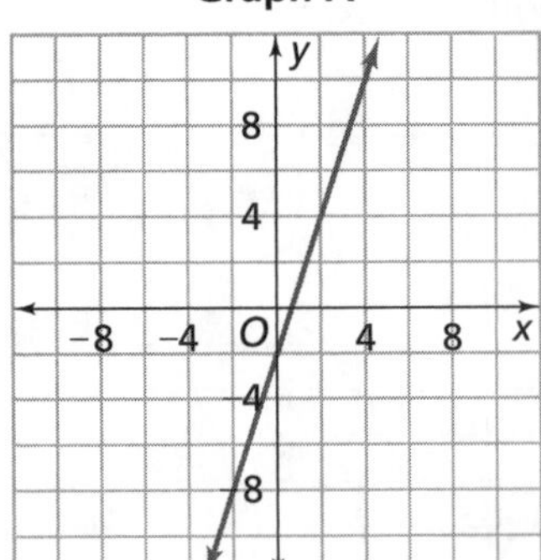

Graph B

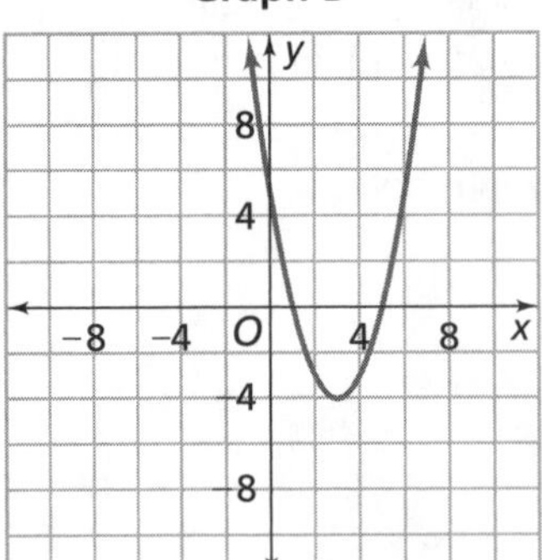

Graph C

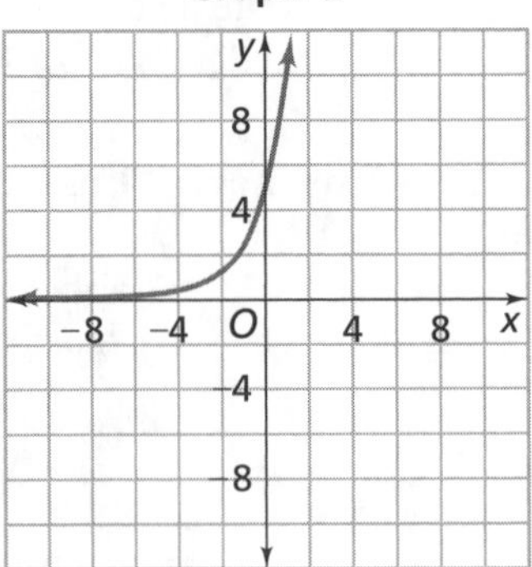

Graph D

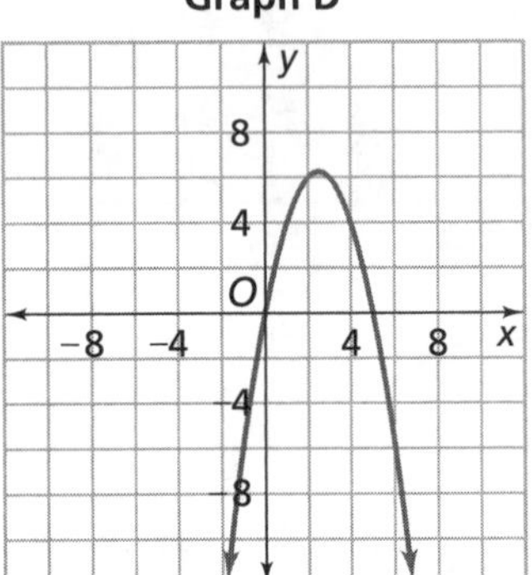

Graph E

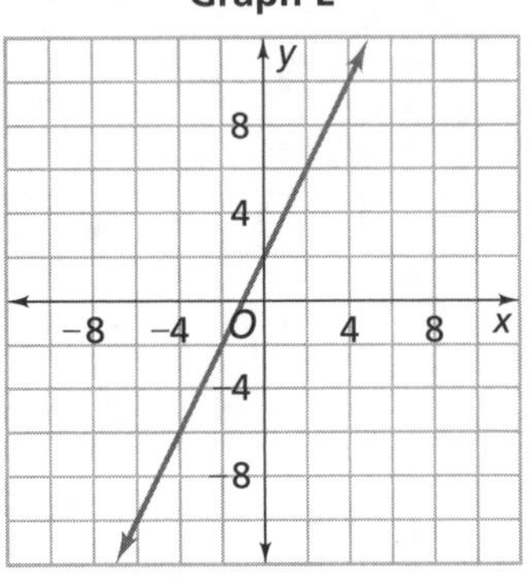

Graph F

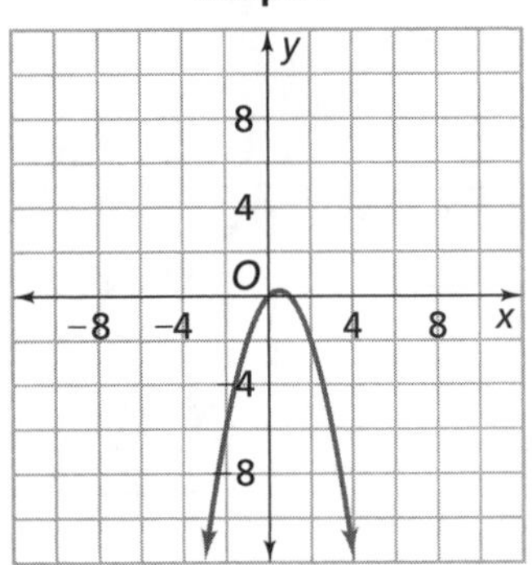

Graph G

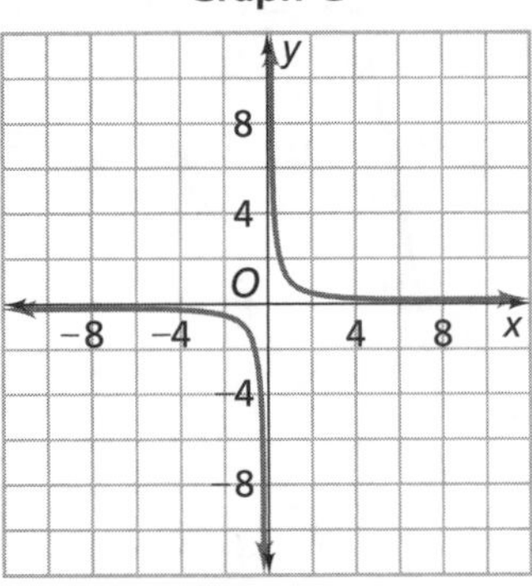

11. $y = \frac{1}{x}$

12. $y = x(5 - x)$

13. $y = (x - 1)(x - 5)$

14. $y = x(1 - x)$

15. $y = 2 + 2x$

16. $y = 5(2^x)$

17. $y = -2 + 3x$

Notes

18. For parts (a)–(c), use the set of equations below.

(1) $y = x^2 + 8x$ (4) $y = 2(x - 3) + 6$ (7) $y = 0.25^x$

(2) $y = 2x$ (5) $y = x(x + 8)$ (8) $y = 17 + x(x + 3)$

(3) $y = 4^{x-1}$ (6) $y = 0.25(4^x)$ (9) $y = (x + 1)(x + 17)$

a. Which equations represent linear, quadratic, or exponential functions?

b. Find any equations that represent the same function.

c. Without graphing the equation, describe the shape of the graph of each equation in part (b). Give as much detail as possible, including patterns of change, intercepts, and maximum and minimum points.

19. Pick a linear, quadratic, and exponential equation from Exercise 18. Describe a problem that can be represented by each equation.

Connections

20. Use the figure of the pool for parts (a)–(d). Drawing is not to scale.

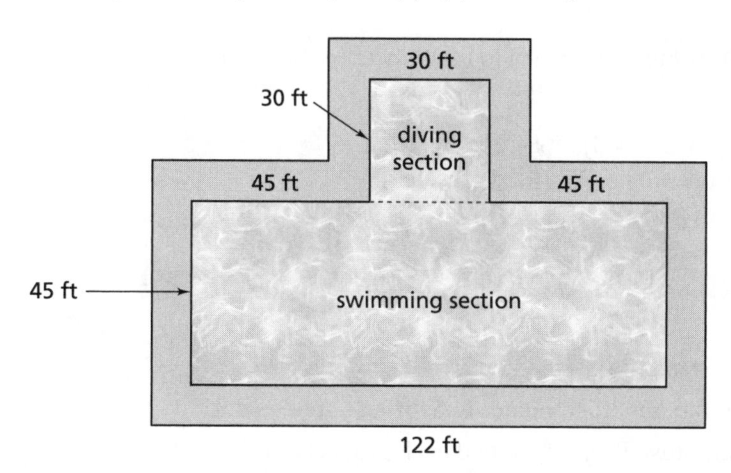

a. How many 1-foot square tiles do you need to build a border that is 1-tile wide around the pool?

b. What is the surface area of the water?

c. The swimming section is 4 feet deep. The diving section is 10 feet deep. What is the volume of the pool?

d. The pool is filled at a rate of 600 cubic feet per hour. How long does it take to fill the pool?

Applications Connections

STUDENT PAGE

STUDENT PAGE

Notes

21. **a.** Give the formula for the circumference of a circle with radius r.

b. Give the formula for the area of a circle with radius r.

c. Give the formula for the volume of a cylinder with a height of h and radius of r.

d. For parts (a)–(c), which equations are linear? Explain.

22. A line has a slope of 1.5 and goes through the point $(2, 5)$.

a. Find the coordinates of three other points that lie on the line.

b. Find the coordinates of the y-intercept.

c. Find the y-coordinate of the point whose x-coordinate is -4.

d. Write an equation for the line.

23. Sabrina uses an area model to find the product $(x + 2)(x + 3)$.

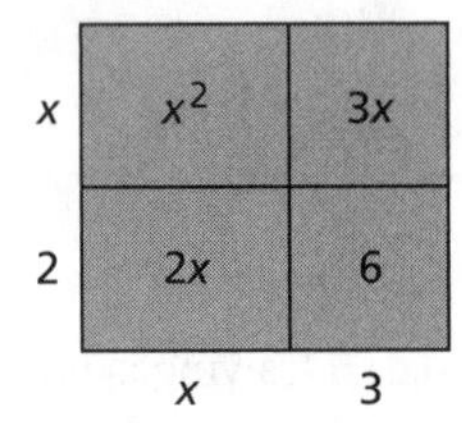

Tara uses the Distributive Property to multiply $(x + 2)(x + 3)$.

$$\begin{aligned}(x + 2)(x + 3) &= (x + 2)x + (x + 2)3 \\ &= x^2 + 2x + 3x + 6 \\ &= x^2 + x(2 + 3) + 6 \\ &= x^2 + 5x + 6\end{aligned}$$

a. Explain each step in Tara's method.

b. Explain how Tara's method relates to Sabrina's area model.

c. Use the Distributive Property to find each product.

i. $(x + 5)(x + 3)$ **ii.** $(x + 4)(x + 1)$ **iii.** $(x - 2)(x + 4)$

Notes

24. The equation $d = -16t^2 + 16t + 6.5$ represents the distance d in feet, from the ground to the top of a basketball player's head t seconds after the player jumps.

a. Find the distance to the top of the player's head after 0.1 second.

b. Find the distance to the top of the player's head after 0.3 second.

c. Find the distance to the top of the player's head after 1 second.

d. What operations did you perform to calculate your answers in parts (a)–(c)? In what order did you perform the operations?

25. A bacteria colony begins with 5,000 bacteria. The population doubles every hour. This pattern of exponential growth can be modeled by the equation $b = 5{,}000(2^t)$, where b is the number of bacteria and t is the number of hours.

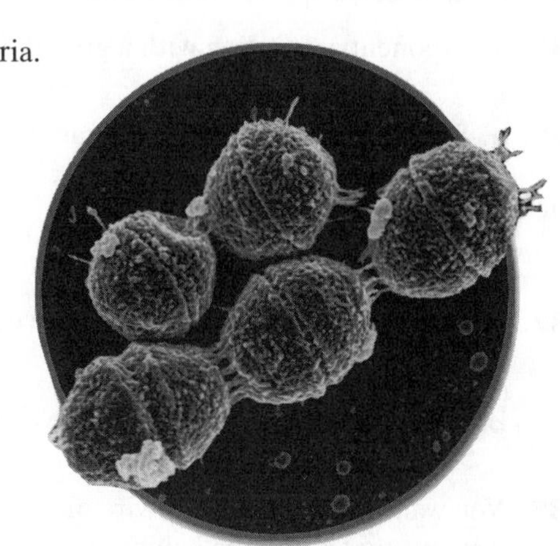

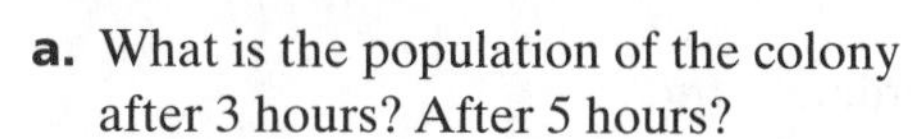

a. What is the population of the colony after 3 hours? After 5 hours?

b. What mathematical operations did you perform to calculate your answers in part (a)? In what order did you perform these operations?

Write an expression equivalent to the given expression.

26. $5 - 6(x + 10) - 4$

27. $-3(x - 4) - (x + 3)$

28. $x(x + 2) - 5x + 6$

29. $6x^2 + 5x(x - 10) + 10$

30. $\frac{1}{2}x^2 + \frac{1}{4}x^2 + x^2 + 3x$

31. $7x^2 - 3.5x + 0.75x - 8$

Go Online
PHSchool.com
For: Multiple-Choice Skills Practice
Web Code: apa-6454

Notes

32. Write an equation for

a. y in terms of z given $y = 6x + 10$ and $x = 2z - 7$

b. P in terms of n given $P = xn - 6n$, and $x = 12 - n$

c. A in terms of w given $A = \ell w$ and $\ell = 15 - w$

For Exercises 33–35, give an equation for each function.

33. a parabola with x-intercepts $(-3, 0)$ and $(2, 0)$

34. a line with a slope of -4 and an x-intercept of $(2, 0)$

35. an exponential function with a growth factor of 1.25

36. a. Sketch each equation on the same coordinate grid.

$y = 4x^2$ $\quad y = -4x^2$ $\quad y = \frac{1}{4}x^2$ $\quad y = -\frac{1}{4}x^2$

b. What is the effect of the variable a in the equation $y = ax^2$?

37. a. Sketch each equation on the same coordinate grid.

$y = 4x^2 + 5$ $\quad y = 4x^2 - 5$ $\quad y = 4x^2 + 3$ $\quad y = 4x^2 - 3$

b. What is the effect of the variable c in the equation $y = 4x^2 + c$?

38. You want to tie the anchor wire of a flagpole to the ground at a distance that is half the height of the pole. What is the height of the tallest flagpole you can support with a 60-foot anchor wire?

39. The figures show cones inside cylinders with the same radius and height. Which cone has a volume of $3\pi x^2$ cubic units? Explain.

Cone 1

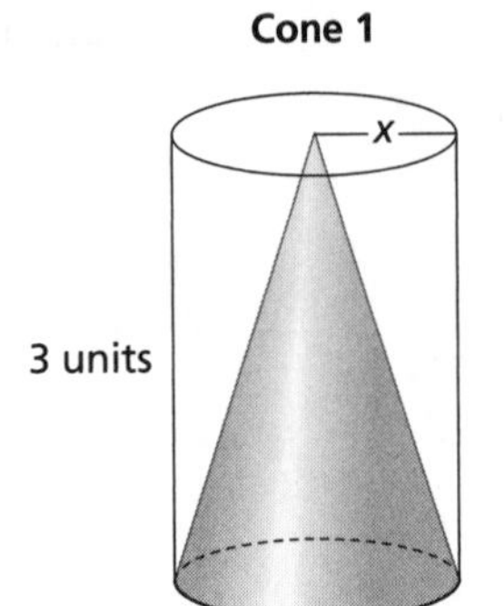

Cone 2

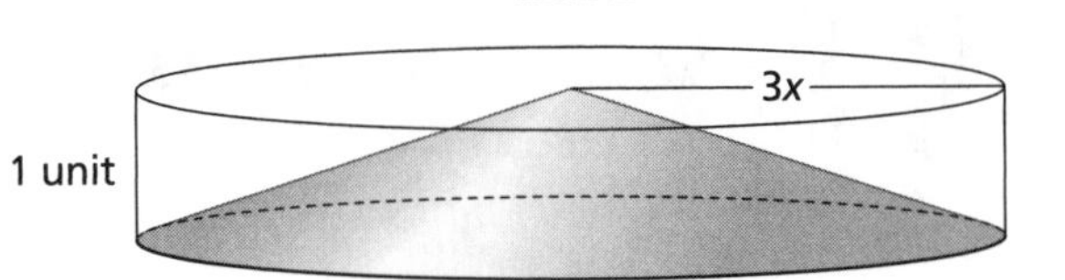

Notes

Extensions

40. Caley's cell phone company offers two different monthly billing options for local phone service.

Plan I: \$25 for up to 100 minutes, plus \$0.50 for each extra minute.

Plan II: \$50 for an unlimited number of minutes.

a. Suppose Caley uses about 200 minutes each month. What is the best option for her? Explain.

b. For what number of minutes are the costs of the two plans equal? Explain.

c. Write an equation for each plan. Describe how the variables and numbers represent the growth patterns of the plans.

d. Graph each equation on the same coordinate grid. Describe how the graphs describe the growth patterns of the phone plans.

41. The equation below represents the space s in feet between cars that is considered safe given the average velocity v in feet per second on a busy street.

$$s = \frac{v^2}{32} + v + 18$$

a. Suppose a car travels at a rate of 44 feet per second. How far should it be from the car ahead of it in order to be safe?

b. What is 44 feet per second in miles per hour?

c. Suppose a taxi is 100 feet behind a car. At what velocity is it safe for the taxi to be traveling in feet per second? In miles per hour?

Notes

42. **a.** Graph $y = x^2 + 4$. Is it possible to find x when $y = 0$? Explain.

b. Give two examples of a quadratic equation ($ax^2 + bx + c = 0$, where a, b, and c are real numbers) with no solution.

c. Give two examples of a quadratic equation with 1 solution.

d. Give two examples of a quadratic equation with 2 solutions.

43. Below is the graph of $y = (x + 2)(x - 1)(x - 5)$. The scale on the x-axis is 1. The scale on the y-axis is 5.

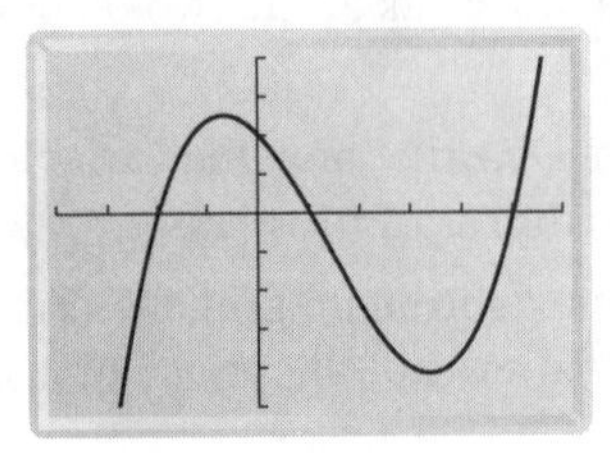

a. What are the solutions to $(x + 2)(x - 1)(x - 5) = 0$? How are the solutions shown on the graph?

b. What values of x satisfy the inequality $(x + 2)(x - 1)(x - 5) < 0$? How is your answer shown on the graph?

c. How can you find the answer to part (b) without using the graph?

STUDENT PAGE

STUDENT PAGE

Notes

Mathematical Reflections 4

In this investigation, you studied equations that represent linear, exponential, or quadratic functions. You also used expanded or factored expressions for *y* to make predictions about the shape of the graph of these functions. These questions will help you summarize what you have learned.

Think about your answers to these questions. Discuss your ideas with other students and your teacher. Then write a summary of your findings in your notebook.

1. Describe how you can tell whether an equation is a linear, exponential, or quadratic function. Include the factored or expanded form of the expression for y.
2. Describe how you can determine specific features of the graph of a function from its equation. Include its shape, x- and y-intercepts, maximum and minimum points, and patterns of change.

Notes ______________________________

Investigation 4

ACE Assignment Choices

Problem 4.1

Core 1–2, 21–23
Other *Applications* 3, 4; *Connections* 20; *Extensions* 40

Problem 4.2

Core 5, 7, 26–29, 33–35
Other *Applications* 6; *Connections* 24, 25, 30–32; *Extensions* 41; and unassigned choices from previous problems

Problem 4.3

Core 11–18, 36, 37
Other *Applications* 8–10, 19; *Connections* 38–39; *Extensions* 42–43; and unassigned choices from previous problems

Adapted For suggestions about adapting ACE exercises, see the CMP *Special Needs Handbook*.
Connecting to Prior Units 20: *Covering and Surrounding*; 21: *Covering and Surrounding* and *Filling and Wrapping*; 22, 34: *Moving Straight Ahead*; 23–24, 33, 36–37: *Frogs, Fleas and Painted Cubes;* 25, 35: *Growing, Growing, Growing*; 26–31: *Say it With Symbols*, Investigation 1; 32: *Say it With Symbols*, Investigation 2; 38: *Looking for Pythagoras*; 39: *Filling and Wrapping*

Applications

1. a. 275 gallons are being pumped out each hour; Students may make a table and notice the constant rate of change, which is -275, or they may recognize that -275 is the coefficient of t in a linear relationship between w and t.

   b. 1,925 gallons. This can be found using a table and finding the value for and when $t = 0$ or by substituting into the equation $t = 0$, then solving for w.

   c. 3 hours. Students can find in their table the corresponding t value when w is 1,100 or they can solve the equation $w = -275t + 1{,}925$ for t if $w = 1{,}100$.

   d. 7 hours. Students can find in their table the corresponding t value when w is 0 or they can solve the equation $w = -275t + 1{,}925$ when $w = 0$.

   e. $w = -275(t - 7)$. The original equation tells us that before the pump started working, there were 1,925 gallons of water in the pool, and that every hour the pump emptied the pool of 275 gallons of water. In this equation it is easy to see that when $t = 7$, the amount of water is 0, or the tank is empty.

   f. The relationship is a linear relationship because there is a constant rate of change.

2. a. 550 gallons. Students may use a table and notice the constant rate of change which is -550, after multiplying -275 by 2 or they may recognize that -550 is the coefficient of t in a linear relationship between w and t.
   $w = -275(2t - 7)$
   $w = -550t + 1{,}925$

   b. 1,925 gallons of water were in the pool when the pump started; This can be found using a table and finding the value for w when $t = 0$ or by substituting into the equation $t = 0$ and solving for w.

   c. 1.68 hours or 1 hour, 41 minutes. Students can estimate from their table the corresponding t value when w is 1,000; they can solve the equation $w = -275(2t - 7)$ for t if $w = 1{,}000$ by applying the Distributive Property and then solving for t:

$$\begin{aligned} 1{,}000 &= -550t + 1{,}925 \\ 1{,}000 - 1{,}925 &= -550t \\ \frac{-925t}{-550} &= \frac{-550t}{-550} \\ 1.68 &\approx t \end{aligned}$$

   The pump has been running for about 1.68 hours.

ACE ANSWERS 4

d. 3.5 hours; Students can find in their table the corresponding t value when w is 0, or they can solve the equation $w = -275(2t - 7)$ for t when $w = 0$.

$$0 = -550t + 1{,}925$$
$$-1{,}925 = -550t$$
$$\frac{-1{,}925}{-550} = \frac{-550t}{-550}$$
$$3.5 = t$$

The pool will be empty in 3.5 hours.

e. $w = -550t + 1{,}925$. This equation tells us that before the pump started working there were 1,925 gallons of water in the pool, and that every hour the pump emptied the pool of 550 gallons of water.

3. a. 25 gallons. Let $m = 0$, as 0 miles have been driven since the last fill-up. From the equation, $g = 25$, meaning the tank holds 25 gallons of gas.

b. 21.7 gallons. $g = 25 - \frac{50}{15} = 21.7$ gallons

c. Substituting into the equation, $5 = 25 - \frac{1}{15}m$, so $m = 300$ miles. (NOTE: A graph and a table would also show that 5 gallons remain after 300 miles.)

d. 375 miles. Students may use their table to find the value of m that corresponds to $g = 0$ or solve the equation $g = 25 - \frac{1}{15}m$ for m when g equals zero. Since m has a coefficient of $-\frac{1}{15}$, students may have a difficult time deciding how to apply the properties of equality. They may multiply by 15 (or they could also divide by $\frac{1}{15}$).

e. The tank holds 25 gallons, so $g = 25 - 1 = 24$ when 1 gallon has been used. Therefore, solving $24 = 25 - \frac{1}{15}m$, $m = 15$. The driver would have to travel 15 miles to use 1 gallon of gas.

f. 25 is the number of gallons of fuel in the tank after a fill-up, and $\frac{1}{15}$ indicates that the truck uses $\frac{1}{15}$ gallon of gas every 1 mile.

4. The variable y represents how much money they still need to pay for the printing bill, depending on the number of books sold. N represents the number of books sold or given away; 2,500 is the amount they owe for printing at the start of the project; 15 is the price they charge for each book; and 8 represents the free copies they gave to the yearbook advisor and staff.

5. a. For Species 1, the 10,000 is the starting population. The 100 is the rate at which the population grows every year. So every year the population increases by 100 animals. The P_1 is the total population after x years.

For Species 2, the 10 is the starting population, and the 3^x means that the population triples every year. The P_2 is the total population after x years.

For Species 3, the 800 is the starting population. The P_3 is the total population after x years.

b. The pattern of growth for Species 1 is linear. The pattern of growth for Species 2 is exponential. The pattern of growth for Species 3 is quadratic. After a certain time Species 2 will surpass both, since exponential growth patterns increase at an increasing rate.

c. Answers will vary, however, any two populations will be the same at some value for x.

Species 1 and 2 are the same when x is between 6.3 and 6.4.

Species 2 and 3 are the same when x is between 4.1 and 4.2.

Species 3 and 1 are the same when x is about 35.74 and -25.74.

One way to find these values for x is to use a graphing calculator. If you use the table function and set the increments to 0.1 or 0.01, you can get close estimates for the values for which the equations are equal.

6. a. **Table 1** is quadratic with a second difference of 1. **Table 2** is linear with a constant rate of change of 30. **Table 3** is exponential with a growth factor of 3.

b. Possible answers: **Table 2:** Let N be the number of deer and y be the year. Then $N = 1{,}000 + 30(y - 2{,}000)$. Let N be the number of deer and x be the number of years after 2000 (so when $x = 1$ the year is 2001); then the equation is $N = 1{,}000 + 30x$.

Table 3: Let N be the number of deer and y be the year. Then $N = 1000(3)^{y-2000}$. Or if N is the number of deer and x is the number of years after 2000 (so $x = 1$ represents the year 2001), then the equation is $N = 1000(3)^x$.

c. Table 3 shows the deer population growing at a rate of 300% per year.

7. a. Answers will vary.

b. 70. Students may draw the next two figures and count the number of toothpicks. OR Make a table of values and use the pattern in the table to find the number of toothpicks in the 7th figure.

Figure	Toothpicks
1	4
2	10
3	18
4	28
5	40
6	54
7	70

c. Linear. Possible answer: The figure number times 4 equals the perimeter. The figure number equals the number of the toothpicks on the bottom and the number of toothpicks going up (height). If you double the figure number, you get the number of toothpicks that make up the "stairs" on the left side of the figure giving $n + n + 2n = 4n$. This pattern shows that the data will go up at a constant rate. The graph will be a straight line with a slope of 4.

d. Quadratic. Possible answer: In the data table, as x increases by 1, the y-value has a second difference of 2.

e. $P = 4N$. To find the perimeter you take the figure number and multiply it by 4.

f. Possible answers:
$T = N^2 + 3N$, where T is total number of toothpicks and N is the figure number. If you work back on the table, you find that the y-intercept is 0. This means that in the quadratic equation form of $y = ax^2 + bx + c$, $c = 0$. Because the second difference is 2, the value of $a = 1$

(a = Half of the second difference). So far, we know that our equation is $y = 1x^2 + bx + 0 = x^2 + bx$. A table can be used to find b. See below.

Figure Number	x^2	bx	Total Toothpicks
0	0	+ 0 (3 × 0)	0
1	1	+ 3 (3 × 1)	4
2	4	+ 6 (3 × 2)	10
3	9	+ 9 (3 × 3)	18
4	16	+ 12 (3 × 4)	28
x	x^2	$3x$	$x^2 + 3x$

$T = N(N + 3)$, where T is total number of toothpicks and N is figure number.

Figure (N)	$N + 3$	Total Toothpicks $N(N + 3)$
1	4	4
2	5	10
3	6	18
4	7	28

If you divide the total toothpicks by the figure number, the result is the second column of numbers. This number is the figure number plus 3. To get the total number of toothpicks, you multiply the $N + 3$ and the figure number.

8. Graph 1 is linear since it is a straight line with a constant rate of change of 3. Graph 2 is exponential since it has an increasing graph with a growth factor of 3. Graph 3 is quadratic since it has an upside down U-shape and a second difference of −2. Graph 4 is none of the above. Graph 4 was studied in *Thinking With Mathematical Models* and is an inverse variation graph.

9.

Graph 1	
X	Y
1	1
2	4
3	7
4	10
5	13
6	16

Graph 2	
X	Y
1	3
2	9
3	27
4	81
5	243
6	729

Graph 3	
X	Y
1	2
2	2
3	0
4	−4
5	−10
6	−18

10. **Graph 1:** $y = 3x - 2$. To find this equation you need to find the y-intercept and the slope or rate of change. Students may use the formula $m = \frac{\Delta y}{\Delta x}$, i.e. $m = \frac{y_2 - y_1}{x_2 - x_1}$, to find slope by using two of their points in the table. They may look at the constant rate of change, which is 3. To find the y-intercept, they may look at the graph and see that it is -2.

Graph 2: $y = 3^x$. To find this equation students need the starting point and the growth factor. By looking at the table it is easy to see that each y-value increases by a growth factor of 3. The starting point can be found by dividing the y-value for $x = 1$ by 3 in order to get the y-value associated with $x = 0$. Doing this, you get (0, 1) for the starting point. So the equation is $y = 1(3)^x$ or $y = 3^x$.

Graph 3: Since the x-intercepts are zero and 3, the factors could be $x(3 - x)$, and the equation may be $y = x(3 - x)$. By checking the point (1, 2) in this equation, we see that this is correct, since three points [the x-intercepts and the point (1, 2)] determine a parabola. NOTE: The equation for Graph 4 is $y = \frac{1}{x}$ or equivalently $xy = 1$.

11. G
12. D
13. B
14. F
15. E
16. C
17. A
18. a. Linear: Equations 2 and 4.
Quadratic: Equations 1, 5, 8 and 9.
Exponential: Equations 3, 6, and 7.
b. Equations 2 and 4 represent the same function, Equations 1 and 5 represent the same function and Equations 3 and 6 represent the same function.
c. The graph of equations 2 and 4 is a line with a starting point of (0, 0), a rate of change of 2, and an increasing pattern from left to right. The graph of equations 1 and 5 is a parabola that opens up with a y-intercept of (0, 0), x-intercepts of (0, 0) and $(-8, 0)$ and a minimum point at $(-4, -16)$. The graphs of Equations 3 and 6 are increasing curves with y-intercept (0, 0.25) and a growth factor of 4.
19. Answers will vary. Possible answer for the linear equation: $y = 2x$. You get 2 dollars for every kilometer you walk where x is the number of kilometers walked and y is the total amount of money collected. Possible answer for the quadratic equation: $y = x^2 + 8x$. This represents the number of handshakes between two teams if one team has x members and the other team has $x + 8$ members. Possible answer for the exponential equation: $y = 4^{x-1}$. y is the number of rubas on the xth square of a checkerboard if the King puts 1 on the first square, 4 on the second, and 16 on the third and then continues to quadruple the number of rubas for each successive square.

Connections

20. a. 394 tiles. Students will calculate this in various ways, for example:
$6(45) + 4(30) + 4$, or
$4(45 + 1) + 2(45) + 4(30)$, or
$4(45) + (45 + 30 + 45) + 4 + 3(30)$.
b. 6,300 ft^2. Students will calculate this in various ways, for example:
$2(45^2) + 30(30 + 45)$, or
$2(45^2) + 30^2 + 30(45)$, or
$45(45 + 30 + 45) + 30^2$.

c. 30,600 ft^3. Students will calculate this in various ways, for example:
$4(2)(45^2) + 4(45)(30) + 10(30^2)$, or
$4(45^2) + 4(45)(30) + 4(45^2) + 10(30^2)$ or
$4(45)(45 + 30 + 45) + 10(30^2)$.

d. 51 hours. It will take 30,600 $ft^3 \div 600$ ft^3/h = 51 hours to fill the pool.

21. a. $C = 2\pi r$

b. $A = \pi r^2$

c. $V = \pi r^2 h$

d. The equation in part (a) is a linear relationship between C and r. If students are confused about what the variables are, remind them that π is a constant.

22. A line has a slope of 1.5 and goes through the point (2, 5).

a. Possible answers include points that satisfy the equation $y = 1.5x + 2$. For example, (0, 2), (1, 3.5), and (−1, 0.5). Students may make a graph with the given conditions or a table like the one shown below, starting from the point (2, 5) and using the constant rate of change to find y-values for x-values greater than and less than 2.

X	Y
1	3.5
2	5
3	6.5
4	8
5	9.5

Another way students may solve this problem is by finding the equation of the line right away. The equation of a line that has a slope of 1.5 and that passes through the point (2, 5) would be $y = 1.5x + 2$.

b. (0, 2). The y-intercept can be found by subtracting the rate of change of 1.5 from 5 twice to get the value of 2 for y when $x = 0$ or by solving the equation $5 = 1.5(2) + b$ for b.

c. −4. Solving the equation $y = 1.5(-4) + 2$ for y gives −4.

d. $y = 1.5x + 2$

23. a. First Tara distributed $(x + 2)$ to x and to 3. Second she distributed x to x and to 2. Third she distributed 3 to x and to 2. Then she applied the Distributive Property when she said that $2x + 3x = x(2 + 3)$. To get the term $5x$, the Commutative Property was used: $x(2 + 3) = (2 + 3)x = 5x$.

b. Finding the area of the left-hand column of the table, which is $(x + 2)x$, and adding it to the right hand column area $(x + 2)3$, is the same as her first step. Her second step is just expressing the two column's areas as a sum of the parts that make them up. The last two steps are just to combine the two x-terms and are not represented in the area model.

c. i. $x^2 + 8x + 15$
$(x + 5)(x + 3) =$
$(x + 5)x + (x + 5)3 =$
$x^2 + 5x + 3x + 15 =$
$x^2 + x(5 + 3) + 15 = x^2 + 8x + 15$

ii. $x^2 + 5x + 4$
$(x + 4)(x + 1) = (x + 4)x + (x + 4)1 =$
$x^2 + 4x + x + 4 =$
$x^2 + x(4 + 1) + 4 = x^2 + 5x + 4$

iii. $x^2 + 2x - 8$
$(x - 2)(x + 4) = (x - 2)x + (x - 2)4 =$
$x^2 - 2x + 4x - 8 =$
$x^2 + x(-2 + 4) - 8 = x^2 + 2x - 8$

24. a. 7.94 feet;
$d = -16(0.1^2) + 16(0.1) + 6.5 = 7.94$

b. 9.86 feet;
$d = -16(0.3^2) + 16(0.3) + 6.5 = 9.86$

c. 6.5 feet; $d = -16(1^2) + 16(1) + 6.5 = 6.5$

d. The operations are exponentiation, multiplication, and addition; the exponentiation is done first, then the multiplication and then the addition. (NOTE: the multiplication of numbers not involving exponents could be done before the exponentiation.)

25.a. 40,000 and 160,000; To find the population after 3 hours, substitute 3 into the equation $b = 5000(2^t)$ for t. Then $b = 5{,}000(8) = 40{,}000$. To find the population after 5 hours, substitute 5 into the equation for t. Then $b = 5000(32) = 160{,}000$.

b. First perform the repeated multiplication defined by the 2^t in the parentheses; then take this product and multiply it by 5,000.

26. Possible answers: $-59 - 6x$, $1 - 6x - 60$, or $5 - 6x - 60 - 4$.

27. Possible answers: $-4x + 9$;
$-3x + 12 - (x + 3)$; $-3x + 12 - x - 3$;
$-3(x - 4) - x - 3$; $-4x + 12 - 3$;
$-3x + 9 - x$

28. Possible answers: $x^2 + 2x - 5x + 6$;
$x^2 - 3x + 6$;

29. Possible answers:
$6x^2 + 5x^2 - 50x + 10$
$11x^2 - 50x + 10$

30. Possible answers:

$\frac{3}{4}x^2 + x^2 + 3x$;

$\frac{7}{4}x^2 + 3x$

$x(\frac{7}{4}x + 3)$

$\frac{7}{4}x\,(x + \frac{12}{7})$

31. Possible answers:
$7x^2 - 2.75x - 8$;
$3.5x(2x - 1) + 0.25(3x - 32)$

32. a. $y = 6(2z - 7) + 10$ or equivalently $y = 12z - 42 + 10$ or $y = 12z - 32$

b. $P = (12 - n)n - 6n$ or equivalently $P = 12n - n^2 - 6n$ or $P = 6n - n^2$ or $P = n(6 - n)$

c. $A = (15 - w)w$ or equivalently $A = 15w - w^2$.

33. Possible answer:
$y = (x + 3)(x - 2) = x^2 + x - 6$. Some students may have equations that are quadratics with a factored form of $a(x + 3)(x - 2)$, where a is a non-zero real number. As long as the linear factors have -3 and 2 as their solutions for x when the factor is set equal to zero, the answer is valid. Also, equations which are not of the form $a(x + 3)(x - 2)$ may work, too. For example, $3(\frac{4}{3}x + 4)(x - 2)$, which expands to $y = 4x^2 + 4x - 24$, is a possible answer.

34. $y = -4x + 8$ is the only possible equation unless the student writes another equation that is equivalent to this.

35. Possible answers: $y = 1.25^x$, $y = a(1.25)^x$, where a is a real number.

36. a.

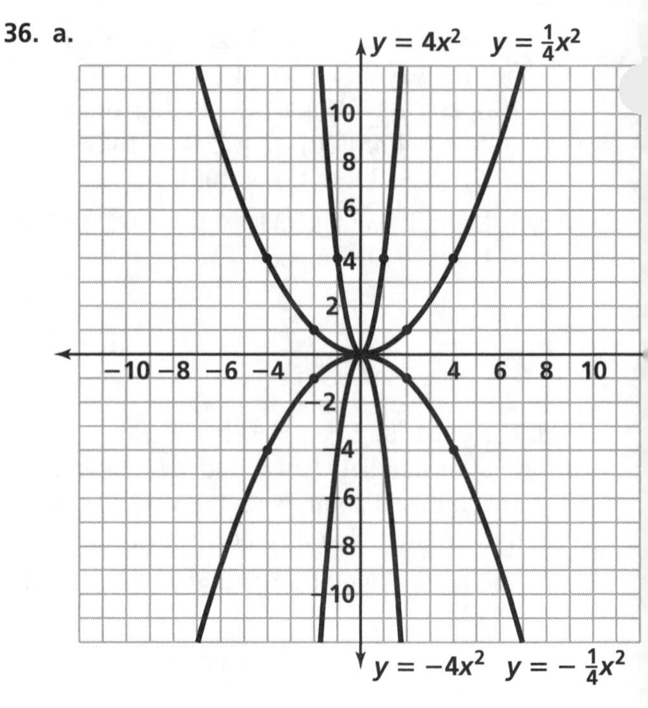

b. If a is positive, then the parabola opens up and if a is negative, then the parabola opens down. As $|a|$ increases the parabola becomes thinner and as $|a|$ decreases the parabola becomes wider.

37. a.

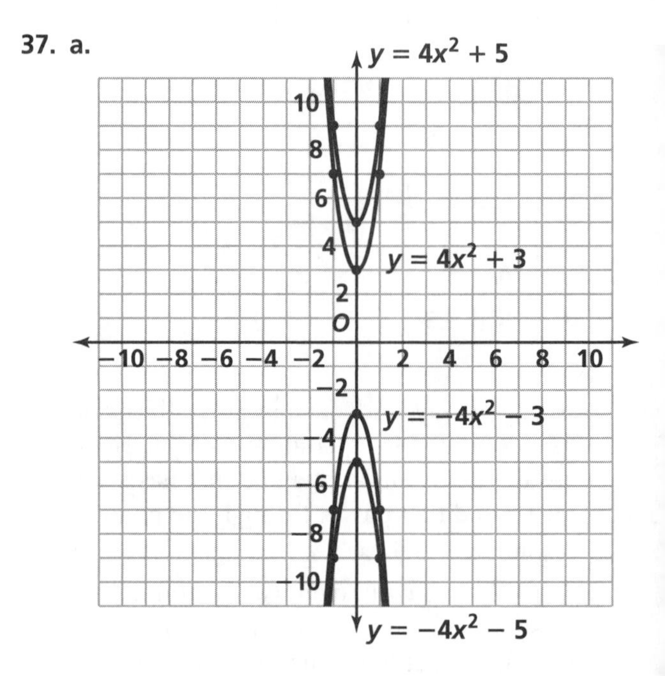

b. The c-value is the y-intercept so changes in the c-value move the parabola up or down. So if c is 0, the y-intercept is at the origin, and when c increases, the parabola moves up, since the y-intercept value is increasing. As c decreases, the parabola moves down, since the y-intercept value is decreasing.

38. About 53.67 feet. To find h in the diagram below using the Pythagorean theorem, we need to solve the equation $h^2 + (\frac{1}{2}h)^2 = 60^2$, which is the same as solving the equation $h^2 + \frac{1}{4}h^2 = 3{,}600$, or $\frac{5}{4}h^2 = 3{,}600$. Students may either divide both sides by $\frac{5}{4}$ and obtain the equation $h^2 = 2{,}880$, or they may look at the table of $y = \frac{5}{4}h^2$ in the graphing calculator and find h when $y = 3{,}600$.

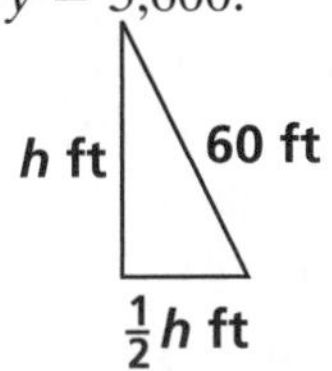

39. Cone 2. The base area of the first cylinder is πx^2. The volume of cylinder 1 is $\pi x^2(3)$, so the volume of cone 1 is a third of that, or πx^2. The base area of cylinder 2 is $\pi(3x)^2 = 9\pi x^2$, so the volume of this cylinder is $9\pi x^2(1)$ and the volume of cone 2 is a third of that, or $3\pi x^2$ cubic units.

Extensions

40. a. Plan II. If Caley uses Plan 1, she will owe $25 + 0.50 \times 100 = \$75$. If she uses Plan II, she will owe \$50. So Plan II is the better choice.

b. The equations are the same when you use 150 minutes. In order to pay fifty dollars for Plan I, you would pay 25 for up to 100 minutes and then 25 dollars more for 50 more minutes for a total of $100 + 50 =$ 150 minutes.

c. Suppose that M_1 and M_2 are the monthly bill amounts and n is the number of minutes used. Plan I's equation is $M_1 = 25$ when n is from 0 to 100 minutes and $M_1 = 25 + (100 - n)0.5$ for more than 100 minutes. Plan II's equation is $M_2 = 50$. The growth pattern for M_2 is linear and M_1 is linear in pieces.

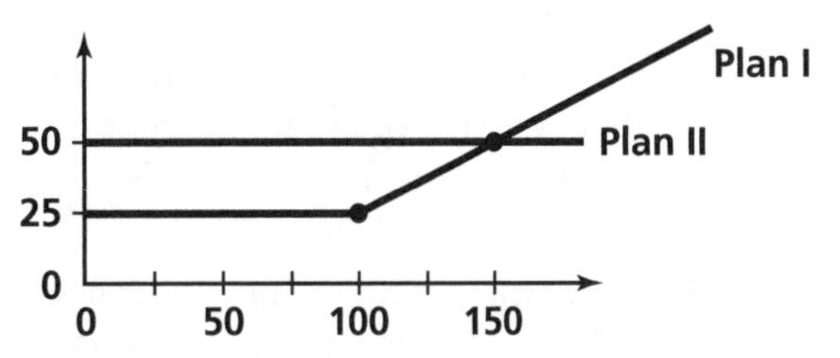

d. Plan I is a horizontal line, and then after 100 minutes it has a positive slope. Plan II remains a horizontal line no matter how many minutes you talk. So Plan I will always cost more money if you talk more than 150 minutes.

41. a. 122.5 feet; A car should be $S = \frac{44^2}{32} + 44 + 18$ or 122.5 feet away.

b. 30 mph; 44 ft/sec is $44 \times 60 = 2{,}640$ feet per minute and $2{,}640 \times 60 = 158{,}400$ feet per hour. Then $158{,}400/5{,}260 \approx 30$ miles per hour

c. About 37.5 or 38 ft/sec (25.57 or 25.9 miles/hr). If a car is trailing 100 feet behind a car, its safe speed would be 37.5 or 38 feet per second, which is about 25.57 or 25.9 miles per hour. Students can find these values by putting the equation $S = \frac{v^2}{32} + v + 18$ into a graphing calculator and going to the table to find the value for v when S is 100.

42. a. Graph $y = x^2 + 4$. It is not possible to find x when y is zero, since there are no x-intercepts. Also, solving the equation $0 = x^2 + 4$ means finding a number that when you square it and add 4 gives you zero, which is impossible, since any real number whether negative or positive squared is positive, and adding four results in a positive number. Therefore the result cannot be zero.

b. Answers will vary. Some possible answers: $y = x^2 + 4$, $y = x^2 + 1x + 8$. For the teacher: Any answer $y = ax^2 + bx + c$ in which the value of $b^2 - 4ac$ is a negative number is a possible answer. This is because in the quadratic formula given in the Did You Know? in the SE after Problem 3.4, if $b^2 - 4ac$ is negative, the result is a negative value under the radical in the formula. This results in roots that are not in the real number system. When this happens the parabola does not cross the x-axis in the coordinate (real) plane.

c. Answers will vary. Some possible answers: $x^2 + 4x + 4$, $x^2 + 8x + 16$; any quadratic that can be factored into something of the form $a(yx + z)^2$ where a, y, and z are real numbers.

d. Answers will vary. Some possible answers: $x^2 - 4$, $x^2 + 6x + 8$.

43. a. Solutions of $(x + 2)(x - 1)(x - 5) = 0$ are $x = -2$, $x = 1$, or $x = 5$. Those solutions are shown on the graph by the points where the graph crosses the x-axis.

b. The values of x that satisfy $(x + 2)(x - 1)(x - 5) < 0$ are those such that $x < -2$ or $1 < x < 5$. That can be seen on the graph when portions of it are below the x-axis.

c. Using only the equation and answers to part (a), one can find answers to part (b) by "plugging in" a number for x that is less than 2 into the expression $(x + 2)(x - 1)(x - 5)$ and asking if the result is positive or negative. Repeat the process for a number between -2 and 1, for a number between 1 and 5, and for a number greater than 5. When the result is a negative number for the chosen interval, the x-values in that interval satisfy the given inequality $(x + 2)(x - 1)(x - 5) < 0$.

Possible Answers to Mathematical Reflections

1. If an equation can be put in the form $y = mx + b$, then it is linear. You may have to apply the Distributive or Commutative properties in order to get the equation in this form. The highest exponent of the independent and dependent variable is 1. If an equation is of the form, $y = a(b)^x$ or is equivalent to an equation of this form then it is exponential. If an equation can be written in the form $y = ax^2 + bx + c$ for real numbers a, b, and c, the highest exponent of the independent variable is 2, and the exponent of the dependent variable is 1, then it is quadratic. In factored form, a quadratic will have exactly two linear factors and both factors must contain x^1. For example, the quadratic expression $3(x + 3)(2x - 1)$ has exactly two linear factors $x + 3$ and $2x - 1$, each containing x^1.

2. Looking at a linear equation $y = mx + b$, the value of b gives the y-intercept , the value of m gives the slope and tells you whether it is rising from left to right (when m is positive) or falling (when m is negative). The m also tells you how steep the slope is.

Looking at an exponential equation $y = a(b)^x$ the a tells you the y-intercept and the b tells you how fast the exponential will grow; it is the growth factor for the function.

Looking at the quadratic equation $y = ax^2 + bx + c$, the c tells you the y-intercept and the a tells you whether the parabola opens up (a is positive) or down (a is negative) and that the constant second difference is $2a$. The factored form of a quadratic expression makes it easier to see the x-intercepts. For example, if the quadratic equation is $y = (x + 3)(x - 1)$ the x-intercepts are the values for x that make each factor equal to 0 so they are -3 and 1. The value for x between these two x-intercepts is the x-value of the maximum or minimum of the parabola. In the case of $y = (x + 3)(x - 1)$ the point $(-1, -4)$ is a minimum since the parabola opens up [the a will be positive when the equation $y = (x + 3)(x - 1)$ is expanded].

Investigation 5 Reasoning With Symbols

Mathematical and Problem-Solving Goal

- Translate verbal statements into algebraic statements
- Write a series of equivalent expressions to show why a particular number trick works
- Write conjectures about numbers as symbolic statements
- Use the properties of numbers and algebra to confirm a conjecture such as the sum of an even number and an odd number is odd
- Write a series of equivalent expressions to show why a particular conjecture about squaring odd numbers works

All of these goals are aspects of modeling with symbolic statements—displaying relationships, generalizations, or conjectures. In addition to modeling situations, students will find that writing equivalent expressions can help them confirm or prove a conjecture. Sometimes, also, the symbolic statements can reveal additional patterns in the situation.

Summary of Problems

Problem 5.1 Using Algebra to Solve a Puzzle

Students explore why a familiar number trick works. Students use symbolic statements and properties of equality and numbers to show why the trick works.

Problem 5.2 Odd and Even Revisited

Students explore algebraic expressions that represent even and odd integers. They use these expressions to examine the sums and products of two evens, two odds, or an even and an odd. This conjecture was first explored in *Prime Time*.

Problem 5.3 Squaring Odd Numbers

Students explore the patterns that emerge from squaring an odd number and then subtracting one. An interesting connection back to triangular numbers (or the number of handshakes) from *Frogs, Fleas, and Painted Cubes* is found in the pattern.

	Suggested Pacing	Materials for Students	Materials for Teachers	ACE Assignments
All	$3\frac{1}{2}$ days	Graphing calculators (optional), grid paper, student notebooks	Transparency markers	
5.1	1 day			1–3, 12–18, 39
5.2	1 day		Transparency 5.2	4–8, 19–31, 40
5.3	1 day		Summary Transparencies 5.3A, 5.3B	9–11, 32–38, 41–43
MR	$\frac{1}{2}$ day			

5.1 Using Algebra to Solve a Puzzle

Goals

- Translate verbal statements into algebraic statements
- Write a series of equivalent expressions to show why a particular number trick works

Launch 5.1

Briefly tell the story about the e-mail message that Elizabeth (or you) received. Ask the students to pick a number from 1 to 10 and perform the steps as you read them.

Suggested Question At the end, ask:

- *You should have a three-digit number. What is your three-digit number?* (Call on different students to give you their number. As they tell you the number, tell them what number they picked and what their age is. Repeat this for a few more students.)

Ask the class to use their algebraic knowledge to figure out the puzzle using Questions B and C.

Explore 5.1

Suggested Questions If students are having trouble, ask:

- *How can you indicate multiplication of the number n by 2?* ($2n$)
- *How can you indicate the addition of 5 to this expression?* ($2n + 5$)
- *How can you indicate multiplying this expression by 50?* [$50(2n + 5)$ or $100n + 250$]

Continue.

Summarize 5.1

Ask one or two students to show their work.

Suggested Question You might want to explore:

- *How does the current year figure into the series of statements?* (The ending expression is $100n + 250 + 1{,}756 - 1{,}993$ or $100n +$ age in 2006. The age is obtained by subtracting the birth date from the present year. If this is year 2006 and you were born in 1993, then you would subtract the two to get 13. To disguise this obvious calculation, $2006 - 1993$, the trick splits 2006 into $250 + 1{,}756$ and then further disguises it by combining 250 with $100n$ to get $50(2n + 5)$. So if we adjust the trick to fit a new year, then we have to adjust 1,756 by adding the number of years difference between the present year and the year 2006.)

Use one of the number tricks in ACE Exercises 1 or 2 to reinforce the use of symbolic statements to illustrate how a number trick works.

5.1 Using Algebra to Solve a Puzzle

At a Glance

PACING 1 day

Mathematical Goals

- Translate verbal statements into algebraic statements
- Write a series of equivalent expressions to show why a particular number trick works

Launch

Briefly tell the story about the e-mail message that Elizabeth (or you) received. Ask the students to pick a number from 1 to 10 and perform the steps as you read them.

At the end ask:

- *You should have a three-digit number. What is your three-digit number?*

Call on different students to give you their number.

As they tell you the number, tell them what number they picked and what their age is. Repeat this for a few more students.

Ask the class to use their algebraic knowledge to figure out the puzzle using Questions B and C.

Explore

If students are having trouble, ask:

- *How can you indicate multiplication of the number n by 2?*
- *How can you indicate the addition of 5 to this expression?*
- *How can you indicate multiplying this expression by 50?*

Summarize

Ask one or two students to show their work.

You might want to explore:

- *How does the current year figure into the series of statements?*

Use one of the number tricks in ACE 1 or 2 to reinforce the use of symbolic statements to illustrate how a number trick works.

Materials

- Student notebooks

ACE Assignment Guide for Problem 5.1

Core 1–3
Other *Connections* 12–18, *Extensions* 39

Adapted For suggestions about adapting Exercise 1–3 and other ACE exercises, see the CMP *Special Needs Handbook*.
Connecting to Prior Units 12: *Moving Straight Ahead*; 13–14: *Frogs, Fleas and Painted Cubes*; 15–18: *Say it With Symbols*, Investigation 3

Answers to Problem 5.1

A. 1. Check students' work.

2. The first number is your choice, and the last two represent your age in the year 2006.

B. 1. Let n be the number chosen in the first step and x be your age in 2006. Then, assuming you have already had your birthday this year, we can write the symbolic statement $50(2n + 5) + 1{,}756 - (2006 - x) =$ $100n + 250 + 1{,}756 - 2006 + x = 100n + x$. So it makes sense that the hundreds digit is the initial value chosen and that the last two digits represent one's age in 2006. If the number 1,755 were added instead, then the age would be one less, which makes sense since the person would not have had a birthday yet in the year 2006.

2. The puzzle is for 2006. To adjust for the current year, subtract 250 from the current year and add this result in step 5 instead of 1,756 for those who have had their birthday in the current year. For those who have not had their birthday in the current year, subtract 251 from the current year and add this result in step 5 instead of 1,755.

5.2 Odd and Even Revisited

Goals

- Write conjectures about numbers as symbolic statements
- Use the properties of numbers and algebra to confirm a conjecture such as the sum of an even number and an odd number is odd

Launch 5.2

Suggested Questions Ask:

- *In an earlier unit you investigated even and odd numbers. What can you say about an even number? An odd number?*
- *If we add two even numbers, is the sum even or odd?*
- *If we add two odd numbers, is the sum even or odd?*
- *If we add an even and an odd number, is the sum even or odd?*
- *What about the product of two numbers?*
- *How can we show that our conjectures are true?* (Students may say to try many examples. You can counter by saying, what happens if somewhere out there we can find two numbers for which our conjecture is not true. We must find another way.)

Pose the questions in the Getting Ready.

- *Daphne claims that you can represent an even number with the expression $2n$, where n is any integer. Is this true? Why?* (Yes; the number $2n$ has a factor of 2, so it must be even. If $n = -2, -1, 0, 1, 2, 3$, etc, then we get $-4, -2, 0, 2, 4, 6, \ldots$)
- *Write an algebraic expression that will generate all odd numbers. Explain why it works.* ($2n + 1$ represents an odd number. 2 is not a factor of 1, so it is not a factor of $2n + 1$. If it were, we would be able to factor out a 2 and write $2n + 1$ as 2 times an integer.)

You might want to do Question A as a whole class discussion. If so, then assign Question B and discuss it before assigning Question C.

Let the class work in pairs.

Explore 5.2

If students are having trouble with Question B, give them some square tiles or cut some out to show them how even and odd numbers are represented. This was done in the *Prime Time* unit in 6th grade.

For Question C, some students may want to write $2n$ and $2n + 1$ for an even and an odd. You may have to use examples for n to show that these two will not randomly represent an even and odd number, because once the n is picked, then both the even and the odd are determined. That is, they will be consecutive integers. The odd number should not depend on the even number.

Summarize 5.2

Go over Question B and then give the class time to work on Question C. Some may choose to use a geometric argument for C. Encourage the class to try both methods.

The product of an even and odd number (or two odds) is a direct application of multiplying two binomials: $2n(2m + 1) = 4nm + 2n$. A 2 can be factored out to write $2(2mn + n)$. So now we have an even number, since it is the product of 2 and the number $2mn + n$.

There are some interesting applications about divisibility rules that can be proven using algebraic reasoning. Some of these rules appear in the ACE.

5.2 Odd and Even Revisited

At a Glance

PACING 1 day

Mathematical Goals

- Write conjectures about numbers as symbolic statements
- Use the properties of numbers and algebra to confirm a conjecture such as the sum of an even number and an odd number is odd.

Launch

Ask:

- *In an earlier unit you investigated even and odd numbers. What can you say about an even number? An odd number?*
- *If we add two even numbers, is the sum even or odd?*
- *If we add two odd numbers, is the sum even or odd?*
- *If we add an even number and an odd number, is the sum even or odd?*
- *What about the product of two numbers?*
- *How can we show that our conjectures are true?*

Students may say to try many examples. You can counter by saying what happens if somewhere out there we can find two numbers for which our conjecture is not true; we must find another way.

Pose the questions in the Getting Ready.

- *Daphne claims that you can represent an even number with the expression 2n where n is any whole number. Is this true? Why?*
- *Write an algebraic expression that will generate all odd numbers. Explain why it works.*

You might want to do Question A as a whole class discussion. If so, then assign Question B and then discuss it before assigning Question C.

Let the class work in pairs.

Explore

If students are having trouble with Question B, give them some square tiles or cut some out to show them how even and odd numbers are represented. This was done in the *Prime Time* unit in 6th grade.

Some students may want to write $2n$ and $2n + 1$ for an even and an odd. You may have to use examples for n to show that these two will not randomly represent an even and odd number, because once the n is picked then both the even and the odd are determined. That is they will be consecutive integers. The odd number should not depend on the even number.

Summarize

Go over Question B and then give the class time to work on Question C. Some may choose to use a geometric argument for C. Encourage the class to try both methods.

The product of an even number and an odd number (or two odds) is a direct application of multiplying two binomials: $2n(2m + 1) = 4nm + 2n$. A 2 can be factored out to write $2(2mn + n)$. So now we have an even number, since it is the product of 2 and the number $2mn + n$.

Materials
- Student notebooks
- Transparency 5.2

ACE Assignment Guide for Problem 5.2

Core 4–7, 19–28
Other *Applications* 8, *Connections* 29–31, *Extensions* 40; and unassigned choices from previous problems

Adapted For suggestions about adapting ACE exercises, see the CMP *Special Needs Handbook*.
Connecting to Prior Units 19–28: *Say it With Symbols*, Investigation 3; 29: *Frogs, Fleas and Painted Cubes*; 30–31: *Say it With Symbols*, Investigation 1

Answers to Problem 5.2

A. Student reasoning will vary. Students may have trouble with the idea that $2(n + m)$ is an even integer. One way to think about it is that $n + m$ is "some integer number" and $2(n + m)$ is "some integer number" multiplied by two, which is the characteristic of an even number.

B. Yes; Bianca's argument confirms the conjecture because $2n + 2m$ can be written as a rectangular array with one dimension equal to 2 and the other dimension equal to $n + m$.

C. **1.** Students may use different things to represent odd numbers: $2n + 1$ or $2n - 1$, for example. One possible argument: Let n and m represent any two integers. Then $2n$ is even and $2m + 1$ is odd. $2n + 2m + 1$ is the sum of an even and an odd and $2n + 2m + 1 = 2(n + m) + 1$. $2(n + m) + 1$ is an odd number
Thus the sum of an even and an odd is odd.

2. Let n and m represent any integer. Then $2n$ is even and $2m + 1$ is odd. $2n(2m + 1)$ is the product of an even and an odd. $2n(2m + 1) = 4nm + 2n = 2(2nm + n)$. $2(2nm + n)$ is an even number. Thus the product of an even and an odd is even.

5.3 Squaring Odd Numbers

Goals

- Translate verbal statements into algebraic statements
- Write a series of equivalent expressions to show why a particular conjecture about squaring odd numbers works

Launch 5.3

Pick an odd number, square it, and then subtract 1. Have the class do the same for several odd numbers. Then look for patterns, explain why the patterns work, and make conjectures.

All of the class will be able to organize their work in a table for the first few odd numbers and to observe patterns. They may even be able to give verbal explanations for why their conjectures work.

Have students work in pairs.

Explore 5.3

Look for interesting patterns and conjectures.

Encourage those who are ready for writing a general expression for an odd number to carry out the procedure. It should be obvious that 4 is a factor of the final expression. To get the factor of 8, one needs to multiply the numerator and denominator by 2. This shows that 8 is a factor or multiple of the number. The other factor is the expression for triangular numbers, which was explored in *Frogs, Fleas, and Painted Cubes*.

Summarize 5.3

Let students share their work. You can also use the summary transparency to show students' work.

Some may use a table:

n	1	3	5	7
$n^2 - 1$	0	8	24	48
Pattern	8 × 0	8 × 1	8 × 3	8 × 6

Some may use algebraic reasoning:

To prove this, students might provide the following argument:

Let $2n + 1$ represent an odd number.

$$(2n + 1)^2 - 1 = 4n^2 + 4n + 1 - 1$$
$$= 4n^2 + 4n$$
$$= 4n(n + 1)$$

At this point we have 4 times a number $n(n + 1)$. Since $n(n + 1) = 2\left[\frac{n(n + 1)}{2}\right]$, it is twice a trangular number. Then, multiply $4n(n + 1)$ by $\frac{2}{2}$ to get $\frac{8n(n + 1)}{2}$.

We have shown that squaring an odd number and subtracting one yields a number that is 8 times a triangular number. The first part of this problem, observing patterns and making conjectures, is accessible to all students. Whether you want to help students develop a symbolic argument at this time is a decision you can make based on your students.

This is a situation in which writing an equivalent expression for $4n(n + 1)$ as $\frac{8n(n + 1)}{2}$ reveals some interesting new information. It is worth pointing out the geometric arrangements of dots on the summary transparency to show the eight triangular numbers in an n-by-n array of dots.

5.3 Squaring Odd Numbers

At a Glance

PACING 1 day

Mathematical Goals

- Translate verbal statements into algebraic statements
- Write a series of equivalent expressions to show why a particular conjecture about squaring odd numbers works

Launch

Pick an odd number, square it, and then subtract 1. Have the class do the same for several odd numbers. Then look for patterns, explain why the patterns work, and make conjectures.

Some students may be able to give verbal explanations for why their conjectures work.

Have students work in pairs.

Explore

Look for interesting patterns and conjectures.

Encourage those who are ready to write a general expression for an odd number to carry out the procedure.

It should be obvious that 4 is a factor of the final expression. To get the factor of 8, one needs to multiply the numerator and denominator by 2. This shows that 8 is a factor or multiple of the number. The other factor is the expression for triangular numbers, which was explored in *Frogs, Fleas, and Painted Cubes.*

Summarize

Let students share their work. You can also use the summary transparency to show student work.

Some may use a table and some may use algebraic reasoning.

The first part of this problem, observing patterns and making conjectures, is accessible to all students. Whether you want to help students develop a symbolic argument at this time is a decision you can make based on your students.

It is worth pointing out the geometric arrangements of dots on the summary transparency to show the eight triangular numbers in an n-by-n array of dots.

Materials

- Student notebooks
- Summary Transparencies 5.3A, 5.3B

ACE Assignment Guide for Problem 5.3

Core 9–11, 32–37
Other *Connections* 38, *Extensions* 41–43; and unassigned choices from previous problems

Adapted For suggestions about adapting ACE exercises, see the CMP *Special Needs Handbook*.
Connecting to Prior Units 32–33: *Moving Straight Ahead*; 34: *Growing, Growing, Growing*; 36: *Frogs, Fleas and Painted Cubes*; 37: *Say It With Symbols*, Investigation 1; 38: *Say It With Symbols*, Investigation 4

Answers to Problem 5.3

A.

x	x^2	$x^2 - 1$
1	1	0
3	9	8
5	25	24
7	49	48
9	81	80
11	121	120
13	169	168
15	225	224

B. Answers will vary. Some possible patterns include: The numbers in the last column are multiples of 4; they are multiples of 8; they are even.

C. Answers will vary. See Summary Transparency 5.3 for some conjectures and proofs.

The student edition pages for this investigation begin on the next page.

Notes

Investigation 5

Reasoning With Symbols

You have looked at patterns and made conjectures and predictions. You have given informal arguments to support your conjectures. In this investigation, you will look at how algebra can help you further justify some of your conjectures by providing evidence or proof.

5.1 Using Algebra to Solve a Puzzle

People receive a lot of information by email. Some emails are useful, while others are for fun. A puzzle similar to the following appeared in several emails in 2003.

Problem 5.1 Using Algebra to Solve a Puzzle

On February 1, 2006, Elizabeth shared the following puzzle with her classmates.

- Pick a number from 1 to 9.
- Multiply this number by 2.
- Add 5.
- Multiply by 50.
- If you already had your birthday this year, add 1,756. If not, add 1,755.
- Subtract the four-digit year in which you were born.

A. **1.** Suppose the year is 2006. Work through the steps using today's month and day.

2. You should have a three-digit number. Look at the first digit and the last two digits. What information do these numbers represent?

Notes

B. Let n represent the number you choose in the first step. Repeat the steps with n. Use mathematical statements to explain why the puzzle works.

C. Will the puzzle work for the current year? If not, how can you change the steps to make it work?

ACE **Homework starts on page 76.**

5.2 Odd and Even Revisited

In *Prime Time,* you looked at factors and multiples. You explored several conjectures about even and odd whole numbers, including:

- The sum of two even whole numbers is even.
- The sum of an even whole number and odd whole number is odd.

How might you convince a friend that these conjectures are true?

Are these conjectures true for odd and even integers?

Getting Ready for Problem 5.2

Daphne claims that the algebraic expression $2n$, where n is any integer, will produce all even integers.

- Is Daphne correct? Explain.
- Write a symbolic expression that will produce all odd integers. Explain why it works.

Notes

Problem 5.2 Odd and Even Revisited

Rachel offers the following argument for showing that the sum of two even integers is even.

- Let n and m represent any integer.
- Then $2n$ and $2m$ are two even integers.
- $2n + 2m$ is the sum of two even integers.
- But $2n + 2m = 2(n + m)$.
- $2(n + m)$ is an even integer.
- So the sum of two even integers is even.

A. Study Rachel's argument. Provide reasons for each step. Does her argument prove the conjecture that the sum of any two even integers is an even integer? Explain.

B. Bianca offers the following argument:

- You can represent even numbers as a rectangular array with one dimension equal to 2. The following pictures represent the sum of two even numbers.

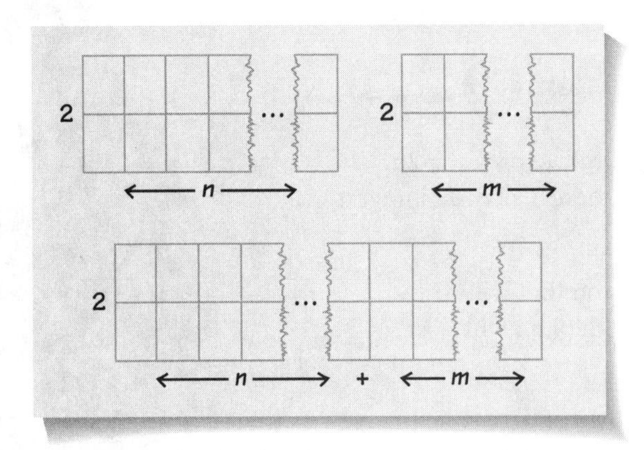

Does Bianca's argument prove the conjecture about the sum of two even numbers? Explain.

Notes

C. Use a method similar to those in Questions A and B to show that the following conjectures are true.

1. The sum of an odd integer and an even integer is an odd integer.
2. The product of an even and an odd integer is even.

ACE Homework starts on page 76.

5.3 Squaring Odd Numbers

In this problem, you will operate on odd numbers and look for patterns.

Problem 5.3 Squaring Odd Numbers

A. Perform the following operations on the first eight odd numbers. Record your information in a table.

- Pick an odd number.
- Square it.
- Subtract 1.

B. What patterns do you see in the resulting numbers?

C. Make conjectures about these numbers. Explain why your conjectures are true for any odd number.

ACE Homework starts on page 76.

Notes

Applications

Connections

Extensions

ACE

Applications

Maria presents several number puzzles to her friends. She asks them to think of a number and to perform various operations on it. She then predicts the result. For Exercises 1 and 2, show why the puzzles work.

1.

Puzzle 1

- Pick a number.
- Double it.
- Add 6.
- Divide by 2.
- Subtract the number you thought of.

Maria claims the result is 3.

2.

Puzzle 2

- Think of a number.
- Add 4.
- Multiply by 2.
- Subtract 6.
- Divide by 2.
- Subtract the number you thought of.

Maria claims the result is 1.

3. **a.** Design a puzzle similar to Maria's puzzles.

b. Try it on a friend.

c. Explain why your puzzle works.

Notes

For Exercises 4–6, show that the following conjectures are true.

4. The sum of two odd integers is even.
5. The product of two even integers is even.
6. The product of two odd integers is odd.

7. Look at the product of three consecutive whole numbers. For example:

   $1 \times 2 \times 3$ $\quad$ $2 \times 3 \times 4$ $\quad$ $3 \times 4 \times 5$

   a. What patterns do you observe?
   b. Make a conjecture about the product of three consecutive whole numbers. Explain why your conjecture is correct.

Homework Help Online
PHSchool.com
For: Help with Exercise 7
Web Code: ape-6507

8. Look at the product of four consecutive whole numbers.
   a. What patterns do you observe?
   b. Make a conjecture about the product of four consecutive whole numbers. Explain why your conjecture is correct.

9. a. Are the following numbers divisible by 2? Explain.

   10,034 $\quad$ 69,883

   b. What patterns among these numbers do you notice that can help you determine whether a number is divisible by 2?
   c. Explain your conclusion.

10. a. Look at several numbers that are divisible by 4.
    b. What patterns among these numbers do you notice that can help you determine whether a number is divisible by 4?
    c. Explain your conclusion.

11. a. Look at several numbers that are divisible by 5.
    b. What patterns among these numbers do you notice that can help you determine whether a number is divisible by 5?
    c. Explain your conclusion.

Notes

Connections

12. Study the sequence of cube buildings below.

- What pattern do you notice?
- Use the pattern to construct the next building in the sequence.
- Think about your steps as you construct your building. The labels below show one way you might think about the pattern.

1 cube

1 cube in the center and
5 arms with 1 cube each

1 cube in the center and
5 arms with 2 cubes each

a. Describe a pattern you see in the cube buildings.

b. Use your pattern to write an expression for the number of cubes in the nth building, where n is an integer.

c. Use your expression to find the number of cubes in the fifth building.

d. Use the Distributive and Commutative properties to write an expression equivalent to the one in part (b). Does this expression suggest another pattern in the cube buildings? Explain.

e. Look for a different pattern in the buildings. Describe the pattern and use it to write a different expression for the number of cubes in the nth building.

Notes ______

For Exercises 13 and 14, suppose a chess tournament has *n* participants. Each participant plays each of the other participants twice.

13. a. Find the total number of games played for tournaments with 2, 3, 4, 5, and 6 participants.

b. Look for a pattern in your data. Use the pattern to write an expression for the number of games played in a tournament with *n* participants.

14. Gina used a table to answer Exercise 13. Make a table like the one below to record wins (W) and losses (L) for a tournament with *n* participants.

Game 1 (columns), **Game 2** (rows)

	P_1	P_2	P_3	...	P_n
P_1					
P_2					
P_3					
...					
P_n					

a. How many cells should your table have?

b. How many cells in the table will not be used? Explain.

c. Use your answers from parts (a) and (b) to write an expression for the total number of games played.

d. Compare your expressions for the total number of games played in Exercises 13(b) and 14(c).

Connections

Notes

For Exercises 15–18, answer parts (a) and (b) below.

a. Write an equation to represent each situation.

b. Write a problem that can be solved by substituting a value into the equation. Then solve your problem.

15. Suppose you go on an 8-hour car trip. You travel at an average rate of r miles per hour for the first 6 hours on the highway and at an average rate of 30 mph slower for the last 2 hours in the city. Find the distance traveled.

16. Suppose a bag contains only dimes and quarters. The bag has 1,000 coins. Find the amount of money in the bag.

17. Suppose the length of a rectangular pool is 4 feet longer than twice the width. Find the area of the pool.

18. Suppose that for a concert, there are x reserved seats that cost $15 per seat and $(4{,}000 - x)$ unreserved seats that cost $9 per seat. The concert sells out. Find the amount of money collected for the concert.

Solve each equation for x without using a table or a graph.

19. $(x - 4)(x + 3) = 0$

20. $x^2 + 4x = 0$

21. $x^2 + 9x + 20 = 0$

22. $x^2 + 7x - 8 = 0$

23. $x^2 - 11x + 10 = 0$

24. $x^2 - 6x - 27 = 0$

25. $x^2 - 25 = 0$

26. $x^2 - 100 = 0$

27. $2x^2 + 3x + 1 = 0$

28. $3x^2 + 10x + 8 = 0$

Go Online
PHSchool.com
For: Multiple-Choice Skills Practice
Web Code: apa-6554

STUDENT PAGE

Notes

29. The height of a ball (in feet) t seconds after it is thrown is $h = -16t^2 + 48t$. Find each without using a table or graph.

a. the height of the ball after 2 seconds

b. the maximum height of the ball

c. the total time the ball is in the air

d. How could you use a table or graph to answer parts (a)–(c)? Explain.

Connections

For Exercises 30 and 31, write an equation of the form $y =$ *expression* for each expression. Show whether the two expressions are or are not equivalent

(a) with a table and graph.

(b) without a table or graph.

30. $9x - 5(x - 3) - 20$ and $5 - 4x$

31. $(10x - 5) - (4x + 2)$ and $10x - 5 - 4x + 2$

For Exercises 32–36, complete each table without using a calculator. Decide whether the relationship is linear, quadratic, exponential, or none of these.

32.

x	5	−5	−3	−7
$y = 4(x - 7) + 6$	■	■	■	■

33.

x	5	−5	−3	−7
$y = -3 - 7(x + 9)$	■	■	■	■

34.

x	5	−5	−3	−7
$y = 2(3)^x$	■	■	■	■

35.

x	5	−5	−3	−7
$y = 3x^2 - x - 1$	■	■	■	■

36.

x	5	−5	−3	−7
$y = 5(x - 2)(x + 3)$	■	■	■	■

37. For Exercises 32 and 33, write an equivalent expression for y that would make the calculations easier.

Notes

38. Study the pattern in each table. Write an equation for those that are linear, exponential, or quadratic. Otherwise, write *none of these*.

Table 1

x	y
−2	15
0	9
2	3
3	0
4	−3

Table 2

x	y
0	−16
1	−15
2	−12
3	−7
4	0

Table 3

x	y
−2	2
−1	1
0	0
1	1
2	2

Table 4

x	y
0	3
1	12
2	48
3	192
4	768

Table 5

x	y
1	4
2	2
3	$\frac{4}{3}$
4	1
5	$\frac{4}{5}$

Extensions

39. a. Find the next statement for the following pattern.

$1^2 + 2^2 = 3^2 - 2^2$

$2^2 + 3^2 = 7^2 - 6^2$

$3^2 + 4^2 = 13^2 - 12^2$

$4^2 + 5^2 = 21^2 - 20^2$

b. Make a conjecture about these statements.

c. Show that your conjecture is correct.

Notes

40. For many years, mathematicians have been looking for a way to generate prime numbers. One of their proposed rules follows.

$$P = n^2 - n + 41$$

The rule suggests that if n is a whole number, then $n^2 - n + 41$ is a prime number.

George claims the rule is not true because he tested it for several values of n and found one that did not yield a prime number.

a. Test the rule for several values of n. Is each result prime?

b. Is George correct? Explain.

41. **a.** Look at several numbers that are divisible by 3.

b. What patterns among these numbers do you notice that can help you determine whether a number is divisible by 3?

c. Explain why your method works.

42. **a.** Look at several numbers that are divisible by 6.

b. What patterns among these numbers do you notice that can help you determine whether a number is divisible by 6?

c. Explain why your method works.

43. Judy thinks she knows a quick way to square any number whose last digit is 5. (Example: 25)

- Look at the digit to the left of 5. Multiply it by the number that is one greater than this number. (Example: $2 \times 3 = 6$)
- Write the product followed by 25. This is the square of the number. (Example: 625 is the square of 25.)

a. Try this squaring method on two other numbers that end in 5.

b. Explain why this method works.

Notes ______________________________

Mathematical Reflections 5

In this investigation, you made conjectures about patterns that you observed and represented these conjectures in symbolic statements. You also found ways to show that your conjectures were valid.

Think about your answers to this question. Discuss your ideas with other students and your teacher. Then write a summary of your findings in your notebook.

1. Describe how and why you could use symbolic statements to show relationships or generalizations.
2. Describe how you can show that your generalizations are correct.

Notes

Investigation 5

ACE Assignment Choices

Differentiated Instruction
Solutions for All Learners

Problem 5.1

Core 1–3
Other *Connections* 12–18, *Extensions* 39

Problem 5.2

Core 4–7, 19–28
Other *Applications* 8, *Connections* 29–31, *Extensions* 40; and unassigned choices from previous problems

Problem 5.3

Core 9–11, 32–37
Other *Connections* 38, *Extensions* 41–43; and unassigned choices from previous problems

Adapted For suggestions about adapting Exercise 1 and other ACE exercises, see the CMP *Special Needs Handbook*.
Connecting to Prior Units 12, 32–33: *Moving Straight Ahead*; 13–14, 29, 36: *Frogs, Fleas and Painted Cubes*; 15–28: *Say It With Symbols*, Investigation 3; 30–31, 37: *Say It With Symbols*, Investigation 1; 34: *Growing, Growing, Growing*; 38: *Say It With Symbols*, Investigation 4

Applications

1. The students may explain the result using an equation such as $(2x + 6) \div 2 - x$, where x is the number picked. In order to simplify this equation, students will need to make sense of $(2x + 6) \div 2$. They need to divide $2x + 6 = x + x + 3 + 3$ in two parts, with the result that $(2x + 6) \div 2 = x + 3$. Thus $(2x + 6) \div 2 - x = x + 3 - x = 3$ for any number x a student picks.
2. The students may explain the result using an equation such as $(2(x + 4) - 6) \div 2 - x = 1$. In order to simplify this equation, students will need to make sense of $(2(x + 4) - 6) \div 2$ which equals $(2x + 2) \div 2$. Since $2x + 2 = x + x + 1 + 1$, divide $x + x + 1 + 1$ in two parts, getting that $[2(x + 4) - 6] \div 2 = (2x + 2) \div 2 = x + 1$. Thus $[(2(x + 4) - 6) \div 2] - x = x + 1 - x = 1$ for any x a student picks.
3. Answers will vary.
4. Answers may vary among students, but they should make logical sense and a possible argument is as follows:

   Let n and m represent any integers. Then $2n + 1$ and $2m + 1$ are two odd numbers. But $(2n + 1) + (2m + 1) = 2n + 2m + 2 = 2(n + m + 1)$, and $2(n + m + 1)$ is an even number because it is a multiple of 2. So the sum of two odd integers is even.
5. Again answers may vary among students; one possible argument: Let n and m represent any integers. Then $2n$ and $2m$ are two even numbers. $(2n)(2m) = 4nm = 2(2nm)$, and $2(2nm)$ is an even integer. So the product of two even numbers must be even.
6. Answers may vary between students; a possible argument: Let n and m represent any integers. Then $(2n + 1)$ and $(2m + 1)$ are odd numbers. $(2n + 1)(2m + 1) = 4nm + 2n + 2m + 1 = 2(2nm + n + m) + 1$, and $2(2nm + n + m) + 1$ is an odd number since it is 1 more than a multiple of 2. So the product of two odd integers is odd.
7. **a.** Possible answers: The product of three consecutive whole numbers always will yield an even number. The product of three consecutive whole numbers is always a multiple of 6.

   b. The product of three consecutive whole numbers is even. There are two cases for a set of 3 consecutive numbers. Case 1: Two evens and an odd. Using the facts from Exercise 5 and Problem 2.2, (even × odd) × even = even × even = even. Case 2: Two odds and an even, (odd × even) × odd = even × odd = even. The product of three consecutive whole numbers is a multiple of 6 since there is a least one even (multiple of 2) and at least one multiple of 3 (there are 3 numbers so one must be a multiple of 3) so the product must be a multiple of 6.

8. a. The product of four consecutive whole numbers will always be even.

b. In a set of four consecutive whole numbers, there will be two odd whole numbers and two even whole numbers. This is symbolically shown with E = any even whole number and O = any odd whole number:
O × E × O × E; since O × E = E,
O × E × O × E = E × E = E

9. a. 10,034 is divisible by 2; 69,883 is not. Students may reason that they could tell because 4 is divisible by 2, however 3 is not.

b. Answers will vary. Some students may suggest that as long as the last digit is even, then the number is divisible by two, using the reasoning of long division.

c. One explanation is that any digit except the last represents a multiple of 10, which is clearly divisible by 2, and thus the only important digit to check is the ones digit.

10. a. Students' responses may vary, but they should note that the last two digits must be divisible by 4. For example, 4,516 is divisible by 4 whereas 4,519 is not, because 16 is divisible by 4, whereas 19 is not.

b. One pattern is given in part (a), however this is not easy to see. Since all powers of 10 *greater than* 10 (100, 10,000, etc.) are divisible by 4, you only have to check the last two digits.

c. See above.

11. a–c. Students' responses may vary, but they should note that the last digit must be 0 or 5, and this is true because the other digit is a multiple of 10, and thus is divisible by 5. The ones digit is the only important one to check.

Connections

12. a. Answers will vary. Some possibilities are below. The buildings are composed of a central cube and 5 arms that contain 0 cubes, then 1 cube, then 2 cubes, then 3 cubes, and so on. (This pattern is described in the SE.) The buildings are composed of a central tower that contains 1 cube, then 2 cubes, and so on. Each new building is the previous building with 5 cubes added.

b. There are many possible equivalent expressions for the number of cubes in the nth building. Some examples:
$1 + 5(n - 1); n + 4(n - 1); 5n - 4$.

c. The fifth building contains 21 cubes, which can be found by substituting 5 into any of the above equations or other correct equations.

d. Answer depends on what the students had for part (b) and students' answers will vary. However, the expression $5n - 4$ is the simplest form of the expression possible. This expression can be thought of as representing an addition of five blocks for every new tower and a starting "0" tower of -4 blocks.

e. Students may either find a different pattern that relates to one of the previous expressions, or they may find a new expression altogether. Other possibilities include rewriting $n + 4(n - 1)$ as $n + 4n - 4$.

13. a. Students may list all the combinations or make a table. For 2 participants, 2 games must be played; for 3 participants, 6 games must be played; for 4 participants, 12 games must be played; for 5 participants, 20 games must be played; and for 6 participants, 30 games must be played.

b. The expression for the number of games played, g, in relation the number of participants in the league, n, is $(n)(n - 1) = g$ or $n^2 - n = g$.

14. a. n^2, where n is the number of participants in the league

b. n, The diagonal is not filled in because participants do not play themselves.

c. Students should combine the two equations to create a new expression $n^2 - n$, but some students may recognize that this is the same as $(n)(n - 1)$ and use this as their expression.

d. Depending on which expressions students used for parts (a) and (b) their answers may vary. They should note that, regardless, the expressions are equivalent.

15. a. $6r + 2(r - 30) = 8r - 60 =$ distance traveled

b. Possible question: How many miles are traveled if the rate is 70 miles per hour? Substitute 70 for r, the rate of speed, in the simplest expression and get $8(70) - 60 = 560 - 60 = 500$ miles.

16. a. If x is the number of dimes, then $0.10x + 0.25(1{,}000 - x) = 0.10x + 250 - 0.25x = 250 - 0.15x =$ amount of money in dollars.

b. If the amount of money in the bag is \$10, how many of each coin are in the bag? Set \$10 equal to your expression and solve for the number of coins:

$$10 = 250 - 0.15x$$
$$10 - 250 = 250 - 250 - 0.15x$$
$$-240 = -0.15x$$
$$\frac{-240}{-0.15} = \frac{-0.15x}{-0.15}$$
$$1{,}600 = x$$

So theoretically there are 1,600 dimes and −600 quarters. Teacher note: Students may recognize that this answer doesn't make sense since the number of dimes and quarters each should be greater than or equal to zero. So x should be less than or equal to 1,000 and greater than or equal to zero, since we want to account for only a non-negative number of coins.

To check, when we put the values into the equation we get:
$0.10x + 0.25(1{,}000 - x) =$
$0.10(1{,}600) + 0.25(1{,}000 - 1{,}600) =$
$160 - 150 = 10$, which is the amount of money in dollars in the bag.

17. a. $A = w(2w + 4) = 2w^2 + 4w$

b. Find the dimension of the rectangle if the area is 48. Set the equation equal to 48 and solve for w.

$$2w^2 + 4w = 48$$
$$w^2 + 2w = 24$$
$$w^2 + 2w - 24 = 0$$
$$(w + 6)(w - 4) = 0$$
$$w = -6 \text{ or } w = 4$$

Only 4 makes sense here, so the width is 4 and the length is 12.

18. a. $15x + 9(4{,}000 - x) = 15x + 36{,}000 - 9x = 6x + 36{,}000 = 6(x + 6{,}000)$

b. If the total amount of money collected at a concert was \$60,000, find the number of reserved and unreserved seats. Set 60,000 equal to your simplest expression and solve for the number of tickets.

$$60{,}000 = 6x + 36{,}000$$
$$60{,}000 - 36{,}000 = 6x$$
$$24{,}000 = 6x$$
$$\frac{24{,}000}{6} = \frac{6x}{6}$$
$$4{,}000 = x$$

The number of reserved seats was 4,000 and the number of unreserved seats was 4,000 – 4,000 or 0.

19. 4 and −3; $(x - 4)(x + 3) = 0$, so $x = 4$ or $x = -3$

20. 0 and −4; $x^2 + 4x = x(x + 4) = 0$, so $x = 0$ or $x + 4 = 0$ and thus $x = 0$ or $x = -4$

21. −4 and −5; $x^2 + 9x + 20 = (x + 4)(x + 5) = 0$, so $(x + 4) = 0$ or $(x + 5) = 0$, and thus $x = -4$ or $x = -5$

22. −8 and 1; $x^2 + 7x - 8 = (x + 8)(x - 1) = 0$, so $(x + 8) = 0$ or $(x - 1) = 0$ and thus $x = -8$ or $x = 1$

23. 10 and 1; $x^2 - 11x + 10 = (x - 10)(x - 1) = 0$, so $(x - 10) = 0$ or $(x - 1) = 0$ and thus $x = 10$ or $x = 1$

24. 9 and −3; $x^2 - 6x - 27 = (x - 9)(x + 3) = 0$, so $(x - 9) = 0$ or $(x + 3) = 0$ and thus $x = 9$ or $x = -3$

25. 5 and -5; $x^2 - 25 = (x + 5)(x - 5) = 0$, so $x = -5$ or $x = 5$

26. 10 and -10; $x^2 - 100 = (x + 10)(x - 10) = 0$, so $x = -10$ or $x = 10$

27. -0.5 and -1; $2x^2 + 3x + 1 = (2x + 1)(x + 1) = 0$, so $x = -0.5$ or $x = -1$

28. $-\frac{4}{3}$ and -2; $3x^2 + 10x + 8 = (3x + 4)(x + 2) = 0$, so $x = -\frac{4}{3}$ or $x = -2$

29. a. 32 feet. Students may substitute in the value 2 into the equation for t and get 32.

b. 36 feet. To find the maximum height, students would first find the x-intercepts [see part (c)]. Then the maximum height occurs between the two intercepts, so it is at $t = \frac{3}{2}$. When $t = \frac{3}{2}$, $h = -16(\frac{3}{2})^2 + 48(\frac{3}{2}) = 36$.

c. 3 seconds; Students can use the equation, $h = -16t^2 + 48t$ and the factored form $h = -16t(t - 3)$, or $h = 16t(-t + 3)$, and find the x-intercepts which are 0 and 3. The intercepts are the points where the height is 0 so between them is the time that the ball is in the air.

d. Answers will vary; students who use a graph may see the highest point on the graph as the maximum height and use the x-intercept to find the total time the ball was in the air. The students who use a table will look for the highest y-value on the table for part (b)and the x-values for y is 0 for part (c).

30–31. a. The two expressions in both Exercises 30 and 31 are not equivalent. For part (a), students should make a graph or table and find that the two equations have either the same table and graph or that they are different, in which case they are not equivalent.

b. They can simplify the expressions using the Distributive Property and/or Commutative Property to see if the expressions are equivalent. For Exercise 30, the first expression simplifies to $4x - 5$, and for Exercise 31, the first expression simplifies to $6x - 7$, and the second expression to $6x - 3$. To show that they are not equivalent, students can show that a value for x when substituted into both expressions yields different answers.

32. The expression is linear.

x	5	-5	-3	-7
$y = 4(x - 7) + 6$	-2	-42	-34	-50

33. The expression is linear.

x	5	-5	-3	-7
$y = -3 - 7(x + 9)$	-101	-31	-45	-17

34. The expression is exponential. The values for y in the table are approximations.

x	5	-5	-3	-7
$y = 2(3)^x$	486	0.008	0.074	0.001

35. The expression is quadratic.

x	5	-5	-3	-7
$y = 3x^2 - x - 1)$	69	79	29	153

36. The expression is quadratic.

x	5	-5	-3	-7
$y = 5(x - 2)(x + 3)$	120	70	0	180

37. $4x - 28 + 6$ or $4x - 22$ (Exercise 32) and $-3 - 7x - 63$ or $-66 - 7x$ (Exercise 33)

38. Table 1: linear, $y = -3x + 9$

Table 2: quadratic, $y = x^2 - 16$

Table 3: none of these

Table 4: exponential, $3(4^x)$

Table 5: none of these (this is an inverse variations equation of the form $y = \frac{4}{x}$)

Extensions

39. a. $5^2 + 6^2 = 31^2 - 30^2$.

b–c. Let a be the first number; the second number must be $a + 1$. Then the following statement is true: $a^2 + (a + 1)^2 = (a(a + 1) + 1)^2 - (a(a + 1))^2$. When creating a proof for this statement, one should begin with the right-hand side of the equation and attempt to show that it is in fact equal to the left-hand side. The right-hand side $= (a(a + 1) + 1)^2 - (a(a + 1))^2 = (a^2 + a + 1)^2 - (a^2 + a)^2$ by the Distributive Property.
$(a^2 + a + 1)^2 - (a^2 + a)^2 =$
$(a^2 + a + 1)(a^2 + a + 1) -$
$(a^2 + a)(a^2 + a) =$
$(a^4 + 2a^3 + 3a^2 + 2a + 1) -$
$(a^4 + 2a^3 - a^2)$ by expansion using the Distributive Property.
$(a^4 + 2a^3 + 3a^2 + 2a + 1) -$
$(a^4 + 2a^3 - a^2) = 2a^2 + 2a + 1$ by combining like terms. The left-hand side, $a^2 + (a + 1)^2$, also equals $2a^2 + 2a + 1$. Since the left-hand side and the right-hand side of the equation are both equal, the conjecture is correct.

40. a. Students' answers may vary depending on their choice for n.

b. George is correct. All it takes is one counter example to disprove a conjecture. Thus even if many examples seem to work, it is not sufficient proof. This conjecture fails when n is 41, for example.

41. a–b. If the sum of the digits of a number is divisible by 3, then the number must also be divisible by 3. Also if a number is divisible by 3, then the sum of the digits is divisible by 3.

c. The following proofs are written symbolically, but this is not something that students are necessarily expected to come up with on their own. Students may talk informally about parts of the proof without the symbols. Let's look at the case: If the sum of the digits is divisible by 3, then the number is divisible by 3. Suppose n is a three-digit number that has the sum of its digits divisible by 3. Then $n = a(100) + b(10) + c$, where a, b, c are the digits of n.

Rewriting, $n = 99a + a + 9b + b + c$ and so, using the Commutative Property, we have that $n = (99a + 9b) + (a + b + c)$. Since $(99a + 9b)$ is divisible by 3, in order for the entire number n to be divisible by 3, $(a + b + c)$ must also be divisible by 3. For example, for $n = 651$:

$n = 6 \times 100 + 5 \times 10 + 1$
$= (6 \times 99) + (6 \times 1) + (5 \times 9) + (5 \times 1) + 1$
$= (6 \times 99) + (5 \times 9) + (6 \times 1) + (5 \times 1) + 1$
$= (99 \times 6 + 9 \times 5) + (6 \times 1 + 5 \times 1 + 1)$
$= 3(33 \times 6 + 3 \times 5) + (6 + 5 + 1)$
$= 3(33 \times 6 + 15) + (12)$
$= 3(198 + 15 + 4)$

So n is divisible by 3, since $6 + 5 + 1 = 12$ is divisible by 3.
Now let's look at another case: if a number is divisible by 3, then the sum of its digits is divisible by three. Say a number n is divisible by 3, then we can write $n = 3k$ where k is an integer. Thus $n = a(100) + b(10) + c = 3k$ Again we have that $n = 99a + 9b + a + b + c = 3k$, so dividing both sides by 3 we get that $k = 33a + 3b + \frac{a + b + c}{3}$. But since k is an integer, then $\frac{a + b + c}{3}$ must be an integer, so $a + b + c$ (the sum of the digits of n) must be divisible by 3.

42. a–b. If the sum of its digits is divisible by 3 and it is even then the number is divisible by 6.

c. Suppose n is an even number whose digits when summed are divisible by 3. Then it must be divisible by 2, since it is even. It must also be divisible by 3, by Exercise 41. By the Fundamental Theorem of Arithmetic (the prime factorization of) n must be of the form $n = 2 \times 3 \times \ldots$ If we rewrite this, we get $n = 6 \times \ldots$ Thus n is divisible by 6.

43. a. Answers will vary.

b. Students may find it easiest to explain why this method works by forming an equation to represent the value of any number ending in five, such as $(10x + 5)$, where x can be any whole number. Then a student taking the square of this value they will get $(10x + 5)(10x + 5) = (100x^2 + 100x + 25) = 100(x^2 + x) + 25 = 100(x)(x + 1) + 25$. This equation represents Judy's method of finding the square.

Possible Answers to Mathematical Reflections

1. Answers will vary. They should include things such as: symbolic statements are efficient ways to represent a conjecture or pattern.
2. The properties of number and equality can be applied to an equation to reveal information about the situation or to confirm a conjecture. Symbolic statements can also be used to analyze a given situation.

Looking Back and Looking Ahead

1. **a.** Lead group: $E = (5t + 15{,}000)$; second group $E = (1.5t + 1{,}500)$; third group: $E = 1{,}250$

   b. $E = (5t + 15{,}000) + (1.5t + 2{,}750)$

   c. $E = 6.5t + 17{,}750$

2. **a.** $I = 25x + 30y + 40z$

   b. $28.27

   c. $V = \frac{25x + 30y + 40z}{t}$

3. **a.** $T = n^2 + n$ or $T = n(n + 1)$. The first equation represents the geometric pattern of adding the tiles needed to make the nth square to the number of tiles needed to make the n-by-1 rectangle. The second equation could represent the number of tiles in each column, n times the number of columns, $n + 1$. Each column is a 1-by-n rectangle. There may be other expressions that students find.

   b. Apply the Distributive Property to the expression $n(n + 1)$: $n(n + 1) = n^2 + n$

   c. $P = 6n$

   d. It is the twentieth figure with a 20-by-20 square and 20 tiles in the arm. Its perimeter is 120 units.

   e. The relationship in part (a) is quadratic. The relationship in part (c) is linear and has a rate of change of 6, so as the value of n increases by 1, the value of P increases by 6.

Explaining Your Reasoning

4. Different equivalent expressions for a situation may tell you something about the geometric interpretation of the problem. For example, in Problem 1.1 the expression $4(s + 1)$ implied that students counted the side rectangle plus one corner piece four times, and $4s + 4$ implied that students counted the four corners plus the four side rectangles. Often it is easier to evaluate an expression that has fewer terms. The expressions $4s + 10 + 3(s - 1 + 4s)$ and $11s + 7$ are equivalent, but substituting 9 into the expression $11s + 7$ to find its value would probably be quicker. It is usually easier to tell the pattern of change of an expression when it is in a certain form.
5. Solving a linear equation can help answer a variety of questions about a situation. If the value of one variable is known, the value of the other variable can be found by solving the equation.

   Solving a quadratic equation can help answer questions about a situation. The quadratic equation for $y = 0$ can be solved in order to find the x-intercepts, and this information can be used to find the maximum or minimum values of the equation
6. Symbolic statements such as the ones used in Investigation 5, such as $2n + 1$ and $2n$, can be used to support conjectures. These expressions can be manipulated and then combined to find equivalent expressions that reveal different patterns and properties about a situation.

Guide to the Unit Project

Assigning the Unit Project

The unit project can be used as the final assessment to *Say It With Symbols*. The project allows students to apply what they have learned about writing algebraic expressions to describe patterns they observe and about verifying the equivalence to those expressions.

Materials

- Cuisenaire™ rods for each student:
  4 to 6 rods in each of three colors
  3 to 4 unit rods

Have a set of rods available so that students can see and stack examples like the picture in the Unit Project shown in the Student Edition.

Hold up one of the colored rods and ask students:

- *How long is this rod?*

Pass out the rods. If you decide to let students experiment in pairs, then each pair of students may share a set of rods.

You may want to have students begin the project in class so that they are able to share their results for rods of length 2–10 (Part 1, Questions 5 and 6). If you do not begin in class, make sure that students get a chance to share their equations with each other. There will be more than one way to find an expression for, say, the green rods. Encourage students to compare their symbolic expressions with other groups. Remind students to include and discuss examples of equivalent expressions for a given rod length in their final write up of this project.

Grading the Unit Project

The answers for the project are given below. Examine students' reasoning behind their equations and the equivalence among their expressions.

Answers to the Unit Project

1&4. Students will choose different rods, so answers will vary from 2 by 1 by 1 to 10 by 1 by 1.

2&4.

Length 2

Number of Rods	Surface Area
1	10
2	18
3	26
4	34
5	42

Length 3

Number of Rods	Surface Area
1	14
2	24
3	34
4	44
5	54

Length 4

Number of Rods	Surface Area
1	18
2	30
3	42
4	54
5	66

Length 5

Number of Rods	Surface Area
1	22
2	36
3	50
4	64
5	78

Length 6

Number of Rods	Surface Area
1	26
2	42
3	58
4	74
5	90

Length 7

Number of Rods	Surface Area
1	30
2	48
3	66
4	84
5	102

Length 8

Number of Rods	Surface Area
1	34
2	54
3	74
4	94
5	114

Length 9

Number of Rods	Surface Area
1	38
2	60
3	82
4	104
5	126

Length 10

Number of Rods	Surface Area
1	42
2	66
3	90
4	114
5	138

For every set of rods, each additional rod adds the same amount to the surface area.

For each additional rod of length:	The surface area increases by:
2	8
3	10
4	12
5	14
6	16
7	18
8	20
9	22
10	24

3&4.

Length (cm)	Equation in the Form $y = mx + b$
2	$A = 8n + 2$
3	$A = 10n + 4$
4	$A = 12n + 6$
5	$A = 14n + 8$
6	$A = 16n + 10$
7	$A = 18n + 12$
8	$A = 20n + 14$
9	$A = 22n + 16$
10	$A = 24n + 18$

Some strategies students may use are given. NOTE: All of the examples use a rod of length 4 (the purple rod).

Strategy 1 Students may make a table and recognize the pattern as linear. Since an increase of 1 in the number of rods is related to an increase of 12 in the surface area, an equation is $A = 12n + 6$.

Length 4

Number of Rods	Surface Area
1	18
2	30
3	42
4	54
5	66
n	$12n + 6$

Strategy 2 Students may reason as follows: For one rod, the surface area is 18. For two rods, it is $18 + 12$. For three rods, it is $18 + 12 + 12$. For four rods, it is $18 + 12 + 12 + 12$. Thus, the surface area is always 18 plus $(n - 1)$ multiplied by 12, or $A = 18 + 12(n - 1)$.

Strategy 3 Students may analyze the number of surfaces with an area of 4 and the number of surfaces with an area of 1. The top and the front surfaces together have a surface area of $4(n + 1)$, and the right sides of the rods have a surface area of n. To account for the back, the bottom and the left sides, double the areas: $2[4(n + 1) + n]$. The number of additional surfaces with an area of 1, created by the staggering of the rods, is $2(n - 1)$. The total area is $2[4(n + 1) + n] + 2(n - 1)$.

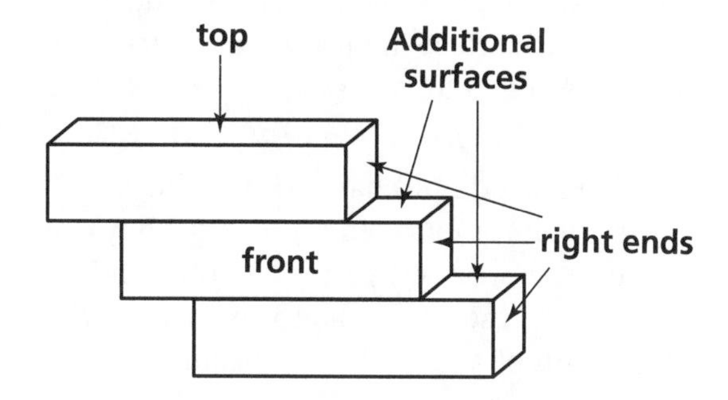

Strategy 4 Students may analyze the number of surfaces with an area of 4 and the number of surfaces with an area of 1 in a different way. The number of surfaces with an area of 4 is $2n + 2$: n in the front, n in the back, and 1 on the top and the bottom. This is a total surface area of $4(2n + 2)$. The number of surfaces with an area of 1 is $2n + 2(n - 1)$: each rod has 2 ends, for $2n$ surfaces, plus the $n - 1$ surfaces uncovered by the staggering on each end of the stack, for $2(n - 1)$. This expression is multiplied by 1 to get the surface area. The total surface area is thus $4(2n + 2) + 2n + 2(n - 1)$.

Strategy 5 Students might see a pattern in the number of surfaces with certain areas by making a table. Reasoning about the pattern leads to the equation
$A = [2 + 4(n - 1)](1) + [4 + 2(n - 1)](4)$
or to the equation
$A = (4n - 2)(1) + (2n + 2)(4)$. (Figure 1)

Strategy 6 Some students may form the rods into a rectangular prism. For rods of length 4, this prism has dimensions n, 4, and 1. The surface area of the prism, $2(4n + n + 4)$, is then adjusted for the number of faces with a surface area of 1 that are hidden in the arrangement, a total of $2(n - 1)$.

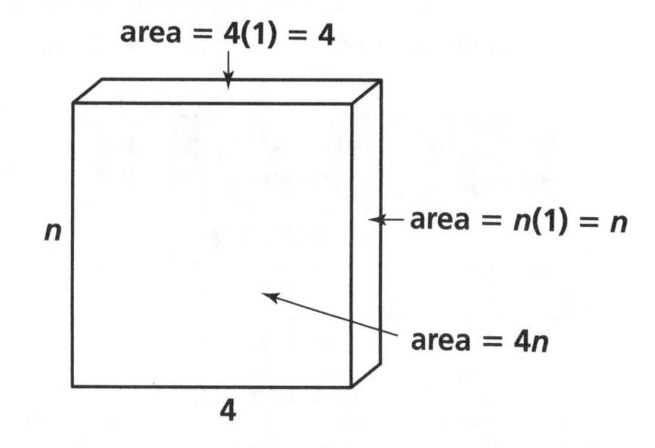

The area of each face of the prism plus the lost area is $2[4(n) + 1(n) + 4(1)] + 2(n - 1)$, or $2[4(n + 1) + n] + 2(n - 1)$.

Figure 1

Number of Rods	Faces With an Area of 1	Faces With an Area of 4	Total Surface Area
1	2	4	$2(1) + 4(4) = 18$
2	6	6	$6(1) + 6(4) = 30$
3	10	8	$10(1) + 8(4) = 42$
4	14	10	$14(1) + 10(4) = 54$
n	$2 + 4(n - 1)$ or $4n - 2$	$4 + 2(n - 1)$ or $2n + 2$	$[2 + 4(n - 1)](1) + [4 + 2(n - 1)](4)$ or $(4n - 2)(1) + (2n + 2)(4)$

Strategy 7 Some students may analyze the surface area of the figure as seen from the front, the right side, and the top; add the three numbers; and then multiply the sum by 2 to account for the back, the left side, and the bottom.

For rods of length 4, they might then produce the table below, which leads to the equation $A = 2[4n + n + 4 + (n - 1)]$ or to $A = 2(4n + n + n + 3)$, or $A = 2(6n + 3)$ (Figure 2)

5. Students' expressions should be equivalent. Explanations will vary.
6. a. Students are asked to compare their equations with classmates. The simplified equations are given in the table below.

Length (cm)	Equation in the Form $y = mx + b$
2	$A = 8n + 2$
3	$A = 10n + 4$
4	$A = 12n + 6$
5	$A = 14n + 8$
6	$A = 16n + 10$
7	$A = 18n + 12$
8	$A = 20n + 14$
9	$A = 22n + 16$
10	$A = 24n + 18$

b. The expressions are all linear equations; the variable n is raised to the 1st power. Each equation has a graph which is a straight line and that has a constant rate of change. However, the slope and y-intercepts are different for all the equations. The slopes (and y-intercepts) are all multiples of 2. The slopes (and y-intercepts) increase by 2 as the rod length increases by 2.

c. Students are asked to write an equation for the surface area, A, of any stack of n rods of length ℓ. $A = 2[\ell(n + 1) + 1(n)] + 2(n - 1)$, or $(2\ell + 4)n + 2\ell - 2$.

Students do not have to start from scratch for each length of rod. They can use the strategy for the "4" rods and replace the "4" in the formula with the length of a new rod. For example:

Using Strategy 6 to make a compact rectangle that is 4 long, n high, and 1 wide, would lead eventually to the formula $A = 2[4(n + 1) + 1(n)] + 2(n - 1)$. Replacing the "4" that represents the length of the rod we get $A = 2[1(n + 1) + 1(n)] + 2(n - 1)$ for "1" rods,

$A = 2[3(n + 1) + 1(n)] + 2(n - 1)$ for "3" rods,

$A = 2[5(n + 1) + 1(n)] + 2(n - 1)$ for "5" rods, and so on. In general,

$A = 2[\ell(n + 1) + 1(n)] + 2(n - 1)$ or $(2\ell + 4)n + 2\ell - 2$ for any length of rod ℓ.

Figure 2

Number of Rods	Surface area from front	Surface area from right side	Surface area from top	Total Surface Area
1	4	1	4	$2(4 + 1 + 4) = 18$
2	8	2	5	$2(8 + 2 + 5) = 30$
3	12	3	6	$2(12 + 3 + 6) = 42$
4	16	4	7	$2(16 + 4 + 7) = 54$
n	$4n$	n	$4 + (n - 1)$ or $n + 3$	$2[4n + n + 4 + (n - 1)]$ or $2(4n + n + n + 3) = 2(6n + 3)$

d. Students are asked to find the surface area of a stack of 50 rods each of length 10. Using the equation $A = 2[\ell(n + 1) + 1(n)] + 2(n - 1)$ for $\ell = 10$ and $n = 50$ we get that $A = 2[10(50 + 1) + 1(50)] + 2(50 - 1) = 1{,}218$ square units.

UNIT PROJECT

Part 2

NOTE: Answers are given below regarding the rectangular prism.

7. The dimensions are n, n, and 4.

8. An expression for the surface area is $2n^2 + 2(4n) + 2(4n)$, or $2n^2 + 8n + 8n$, or $2n^2 + 16n$.

9. The surface area of a prism that is 10 rods high and 10 rods wide is $2(10)^2 + 16(10) = 360$ square units.

10. To change the expression if the rod length were something other than 4, one would replace the 4 in the expression. If the length were x, the expression would be $2n^2 + 2(xn) + 2(xn)$.

11. The relationship is quadratic. In the equation, the highest power of the variable is 2. The graph has the shape of a parabola.

Unit Project

Finding the Surface Area of Rod Stacks

In this unit project, you will find different ways to find the surface area of colored rod stacks.

Part 1: Staircase Stacks

1. Choose a rod length to use to make a staircase stack. Use one of the unit rods to determine the dimensions of your chosen rod.
2. Stack several rods of this length as shown. Each rod is one unit high and one unit wide and is staggered one unit.

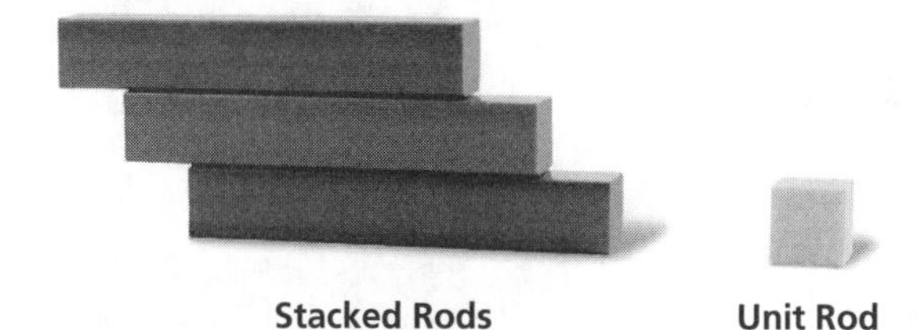

Stacked Rods **Unit Rod**

Find the surface area of one rod, a stack of two rods, a stack of three rods, and so on. Describe a pattern that you see in the surface areas of the stacks you made.

3. Write an equation that shows the relationship between the surface area A and the number of rods n in the stack. Explain.
4. Repeat Exercises 1–3 for two other rod lengths.
5. Find a student who used rods of the same length for Exercises 1–3 and whose expression from Exercise 3 looks different from yours. Are your expressions equivalent? Explain.

STUDENT PAGE

Notes

6. a. Make a table with columns for rod length and surface area equation. Complete the table for rod lengths 2 through 10. You will need to find students who used rods that you didn't use.

   b. Do the equations in your table represent linear, quadratic, or exponential relationships? Explain.

   c. Write an equation for the surface area A of any stack of n rods of length ℓ.

   d. Use your equation from part (c) to find the surface area of a stack of 50 rods of length 10.

Part 2: Finding the Surface Area of a Rectangular Prism

Suppose rods of length 4 are stacked to form a rectangular prism as shown at the right.

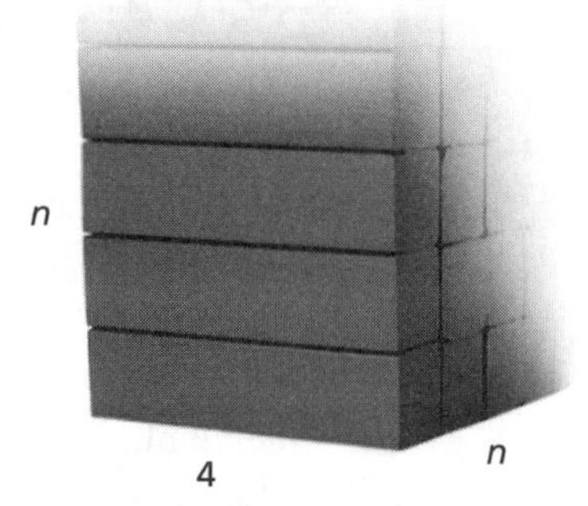

7. What are the dimensions of the prism?

8. Find an equation for the surface area of the prism.

9. Suppose the prism is 10 rods high and 10 rods wide. What is the surface area of the prism?

10. How would the equation change if the rod length were something other than 4?

11. Is the relationship between the surface area and the number of rods in a prism stack linear, quadratic, exponential, or none of these? Explain.

Write a report about the results you found for rod stacks and rod prisms. Explain how you found the equations for surface area in each case. Use diagrams to show what you did and what you found.

Notes

Looking Back and Looking Ahead

Unit Review

In this unit, you learned and practiced the standard rules for using symbolic expressions in algebra. You used properties of numbers and operations to write algebraic expressions in equivalent forms and to solve linear and quadratic equations with algebraic reasoning.

For: Vocabulary Review Puzzle
Web Code: apj-6051

Use Your Understanding: Symbols

Test your understanding and skill in the use of algebraic notation and reasoning by solving these problems about managing a concert tour.

The promoter pays appearance fees to each group on the concert program. Some groups also get a portion of the ticket sales.

- The lead group earns $15,000, plus $5 for every ticket sold.
- Another group earns $1,500, plus $1.50 for every ticket sold.
- The third group earns a flat fee of $1,250.

1. For parts (a)–(c), use E for the promoter's expenses and t for the number of tickets sold.

a. Write an equation to show payments to each separate group.

b. Write an equation to show payment to the lead group and the combined payments to the other groups.

c. Write an equivalent equation different from parts (a) and (b) to show the simplest calculation of the total amount paid to the performers.

2. Tickets cost $25, $30, and $40.

a. Write an equation that shows how the promoter's income from ticket sales I depends on the number of each type of ticket sold x, y, and z.

b. The promoter sells 5,000 tickets at $25, 3,000 tickets at $30, and 950 tickets at $40. Find the average income per ticket.

c. Write an equation that shows how the average income per ticket sold V depends on the variables x, y, z, and t.

Notes

3. Square tiles were used to make the pattern below.

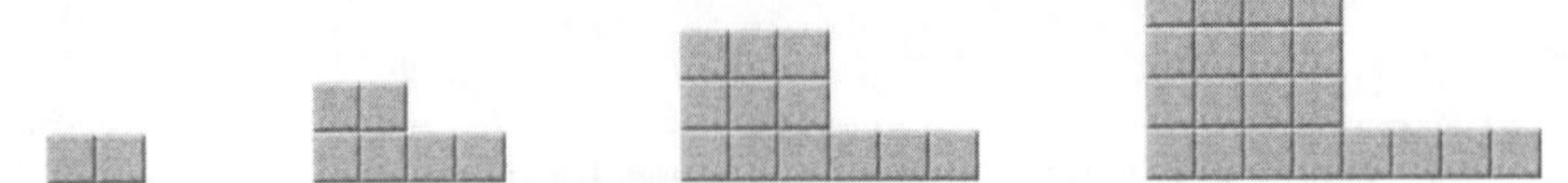

a. Write an equation for the number of tiles T needed to make the nth figure. Explain.

b. Find an equivalent expression for the number of tiles in part (a). Explain why they are equivalent.

c. Write an equation for the perimeter P of the nth figure.

d. Identify and describe the figure in this pattern that can be made with exactly 420 tiles.

e. Describe the relationship represented by the equations in parts (a) and (c).

Explain Your Reasoning

When you solve problems by writing and operating on symbolic expressions, you should be able to explain your reasoning.

4. How can writing two different equivalent expressions or equations for a situation be helpful?

5. How can solving a linear or quadratic equation be helpful?

6. How can a symbolic statement be helpful in expressing a general relationship or conjecture?

Look Ahead

The algebraic ideas and techniques you have used in this unit will be applied and extended in future mathematics courses and in science and business problems.

In later mathematics courses you will explore more techniques for solving quadratic and polynomial equations. You will also learn how to write equivalent expressions using more properties of real numbers.

STUDENT PAGE

Notes

English / Spanish Glossary

Commutative Property of Addition A mathematical property that states that the order in which quantities are added does not matter. It states that $a + b = b + a$ for any two real numbers a and b. For example, $5 + 7 = 7 + 5$ and $2x + 4 = 4 + 2x$.

propiedad conmutativa de la suma Una propiedad matemática que dice que el orden en que se suman las cantidades no tiene importancia. Para cualquieres números reales a y b, $a + b = b + a$. Por ejemplo, $5 + 7 = 7 + 5$ y $2x + 4 = 4 + 2x$.

Commutative Property of Multiplication A mathematical property that states that the order in which quantities are multiplied does not matter. It states that $ab = ba$ for any two real numbers a and b. For example, $5 \times 7 = 7 \times 5$ and $2x(4) = (4)2x$.

propiedad conmutativa de la multiplicación Una propiedad matemática que dice que el orden en que se multiplican los factores no tiene importancia. Para cualquieres números reales, $ab = ba$. Por ejemplo, $5 \times 7 = 7 \times 5$ y $2x(4) = (4)2x$.

Distributive Property A mathematical property used to rewrite expressions involving addition and multiplication. The Distributive Property states that for any three real numbers a, b, and c, $a(b + c) = ab + ac$. If an expression is written as a factor multiplied by a sum, you can use the Distributive Property to *multiply* the factor by each term in the sum.

$$4(5 + x) = 4(5) + 4(x) = 20 + 4x$$

If an expression is written as a sum of terms and the terms have a common factor, you can use the Distributive Property to rewrite the expression as the common factor multiplied by a sum. This process is called *factoring*.

$$20 + 4x = 4(5) + 4(x) = 4(5 + x)$$

propiedad distributiva Una propiedad matemática usada para reescribir expresiones que incluyen la suma y la multiplicación. La propiedad distributiva se establece para cualquieres números reales a, b, y c, $a(b + c) = ab + ac$. Si una expresión se escribe como la multiplicación de un factor por una suma, la propiedad distributiva puede usarse para multiplicar el factor por cada término de la suma.

$$4(5 + x) = 4(5) + 4(x) = 20 + 4x$$

Si una expresión se escribe como la suma de los términos y los términos tienen un factor común, la propiedad distributiva puede usarse para reescribir o descomponer en factores la expresión como la multiplicación del factor común por una suma.

$$20 + 4x = 4(5) + 4(x) = 4(5 + x)$$

Notes

equivalent expressions Expressions that represent the same quantity. For example, $2 + 5$, $3 + 4$, and 7 are equivalent expressions. You can apply the Distributive Property to $2(x + 3)$ to write the equivalent expression $2x + 6$. You can apply the Commutative Property to $2x + 6$ to write the equivalent expression $6 + 2x$.

expresiones equivalentes Expresiones que representan la misma cantidad, como por ejemplo $2 + 5$, $3 + 4$ y 7. Puedes aplicar la propiedad distributive a $2(x + 3)$ para escribir la expresión equivalente $2x + 6$. Puedes aplicar la propiedad conmutativa a $2x + 6$ para escribir la expresión equivalente $6 + 2x$.

expanded form The form of an expression made up of sums or differences of terms rather than products of factors. The expressions $x^2 + 7x + 12$ and $x^2 + 2x$ are in expanded form.

forma desarrollada La forma de una expresión compuesta de sumas o diferencias de términos en vez de productos de factores. Las expresiones $x^2 + 7x + 12$ y $x^2 + 2x$ están representadas en forma desarrollada.

factored form The form of an expression made up of products of factors rather than sums or differences of terms. The expressions $(x + 3)(x + 4)$ and $x(x - 2)$ are in factored form.

forma de factores La forma de una expresión compuesta de productos de factores en vez de sumas o diferencias de términos. Las expresiones $(x + 3)(x + 4)$ y $x(x - 2)$ están representadas en forma de factores.

P

parabola The graph of a quadratic function. A parabola has a line of symmetry that passes through the maximum point if the graph opens downward or through the minimum point if the graph opens upward.

parábola La gráfica de una función cuadrática. Una parábola tiene un eje de simetría que pasa por el punto máximo si la gráfica se abre hacia abajo o por el punto mínimo si la gráfica se abre hacia arriba.

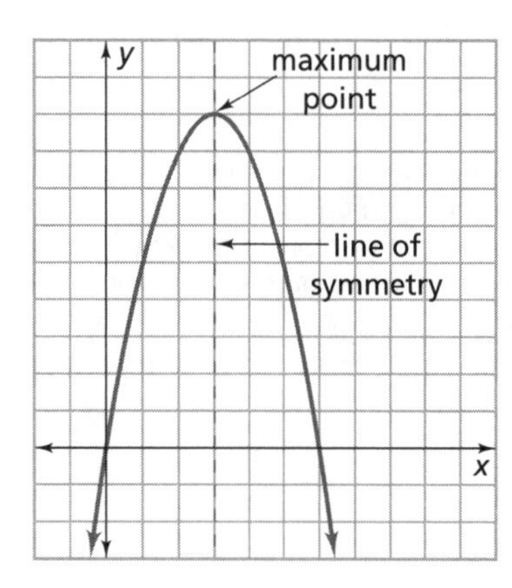

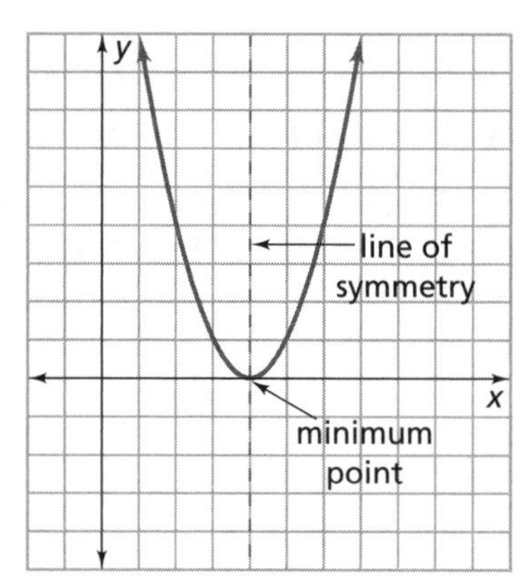

Notes

properties of equality The properties of equality state that if you add or subtract both sides of an equation by the same number, the two sides of the equation remain equal. If you multiply or divide both sides of an equation by the same non-zero number, the two sides of the equation remain equal.

propiedades de igualdad Las propiedades de igualdad establecen que si se suma o resta el mismo número a ambos lados de una ecuación, los dos lados de la ecuación se mantienen iguales. Si ambos lados de una ecuación se multiplican o dividen por el mismo número distinto de cero, los dos lados de la ecuación se mantienen iguales.

roots The roots of an equation are the values of x that make y equal 0. For example, the roots of $y = x^2 + 5x$ are -5 and 0 because $(-5)^2 + 5(-5) = 0$ and $0^2 + 5(0) = 0$. The roots of $y = x^2 + 5x$ are the solutions to the equation $0 = x^2 + 5x$. The roots of an equation are the x-intercepts of its graph.

raíces Las raíces de una ecuación son los valores de x que hacen que y equivalga a 0. Por ejemplo, las raíces de $y = x^2 + 5x$ son -5 y 0 porque $(-5)^2 + 5(-5) = 0$ y $0^2 + 5(0) = 0$. Las raíces de $y = x^2 + 5x$ son las soluciones de la ecuación $0 = x^2 + 5x$. Las raíces de una ecuación son los puntos de intersección del eje de las x de la gráfica de esa ecuación.

term An expression with numbers and/or variables multiplied together. In the expression $3x^2 - 2x + 10$, $3x^2$, $-2x$, and 10 are terms.

término Una expresión con números y/o variables multiplicados entre sí. En la expresión $3x^2 - 2x + 10$, $3x^2$, $-2x$, y 10 son términos.

Notes

Academic Vocabulary

Academic vocabulary words are words that you see in textbooks and on tests. These are not math vocabulary terms, but knowing them will help you succeed in mathematics.

Las palabras de vocabulario académico son palabras que ves en los libros de texto y en las pruebas. Éstos no son términos de vocabulario de matemáticas, pero conocerlos te ayudará a tener éxito en matemática.

D

describe To explain or tell in detail. A written description can contain facts and other information needed to communicate your answer. A diagram or a graph may also be included.

related terms: express, explain, illustrate

Sample: Without graphing, describe the shape of the graph of the equation $y = 2x^2 + 1$.

> The equation is quadratic so the graph is a parabola. The graph opens upward because 2 is positive. It is narrower than the graph of $y = x^2$ because the absolute value of 2 is greater than 1.

describir Explicar o decir con detalle. Una descripción escrita puede contener hechos y otra información necesaria para comunicar tu respuesta. También se puede incluir un diagrama o una gráfica.

términos relacionados: expresar, explicar, ilustrar

Ejemplo: Sin hacer la gráfica, describe la forma de la gráfica de la ecuación $y = 2x^2 + 1$.

> La ecuación es cuadrática así que la gráfica es una parábola. La gráfica se abre hacia arriba porque 2 es positivo. Es más estrecha que la gráfica de $y = x^2$ porque el valor absoluto de 2 es mayor que 1.

E

estimate To find an approximate answer.

related terms: guess, predict

Sample: Estimate the lateral surface area of the net of the cone below.

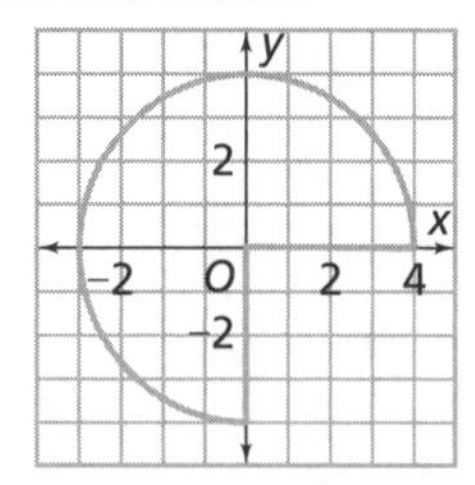

> I can count the number of unit squares. The net of the cone has 3 equal sections. I estimate one of the sections to be 13 square units, so the total is about 39 square units.

estimar Hallar una respuesta aproximada.

términos relacionados: conjeturar, predecir

Ejemplo: Estima el área lateral de la plantilla del cono que sigue.

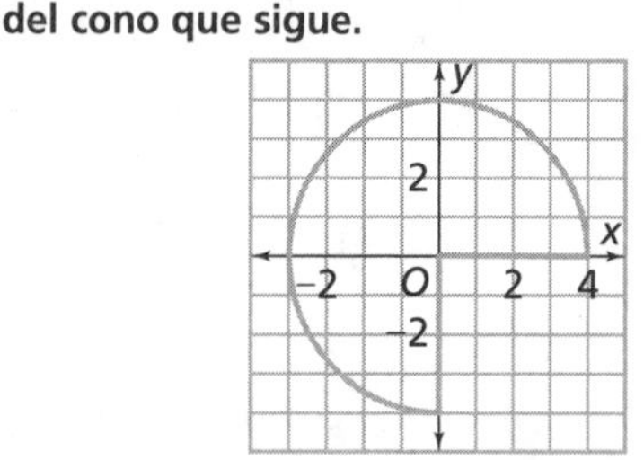

> Puedo contar el número de unidades cuadradas. La plantilla del cono tiene 3 secciones iguales. Estimo que una de las secciones tiene 13 unidades cuadradas, por tanto el total es aproximadamente 39 unidades cuadradas.

Notes

explain To give facts and details that make an idea easier to understand. Explaining can involve a written summary supported by a diagram, chart, table, or a combination of these.
related terms: analyze, clarify, describe, justify, tell

Sample: The equation shows the relationship between the number of gallons *g* of water in a tank and the number of minutes *m* a shower is on.

$$g = 50 - 2.5m$$

How many gallons of water are in a full tank before the shower begins? Explain.

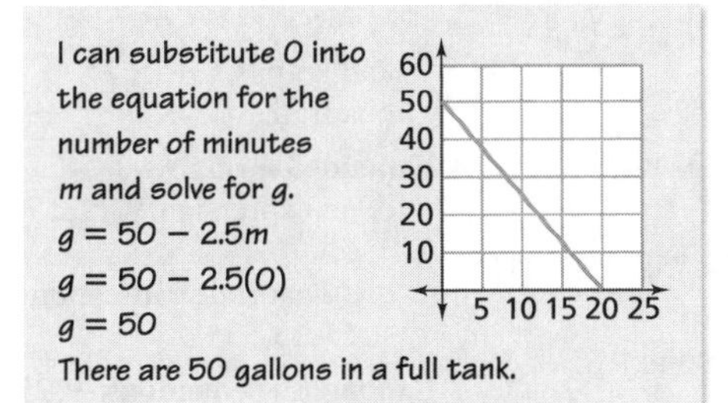

explicar Dar hechos y detalles que hacen que una idea sea más fácil de comprender. Explicar puede implicar un resumen escrito apoyado por un diagrama, una gráfica, una tabla o una combinación de éstos.
términos relacionados: analizar, aclarar, describir, justificar, decir

Ejemplo: La ecuación muestra la relación entre el número de galones *g* de agua en un tanque y el número de minutos *m* que ha estado funcionando una ducha.

$$g = 50 - 2.5m$$

¿Cuántos galones de agua hay en un tanque lleno antes que comience la ducha? Explica tu respuesta.

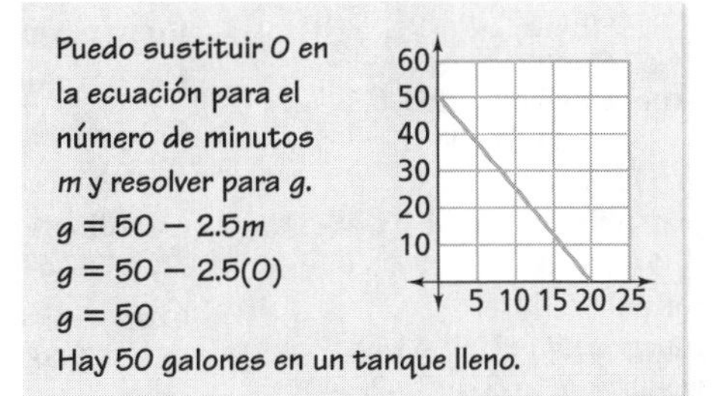

S

solve To determine the value or values that make a given statement true. Several methods and strategies can be used to solve a problem including estimating, isolating the variable, drawing a graph, or using a table of values.
related terms: find, graph

Sample: Solve the equation for *x*.
$0 = x^2 + 6x - 7$.

The equation is quadratic. I can solve the equation by factoring the right side of the equation into two factors and setting each factor equal to zero.

$0 = x^2 + 6x - 7$

$0 = (x + 7)(x - 1)$

$x + 7 = 0$ or $x - 1 = 0$

$x = -7$ or $x = 1$

I can also solve the quadratic by graphing and identifying the x-intercepts at $(-7, 0)$ and $(1, 0)$.

(-7, 0) (1, 0)

resolver Determinar el valor o valores que hacen cierto un enunciado dado. Pueden usarse varios métodos y estrategias para resolver un problema incluyendo estimar, despejar la variable, dibujar una gráfica o usar una tabla de valores.
términos relacionados hallar, hacer una gráfica

Ejemplo: Resuelve la ecuación para *x*.
$0 = x^2 + 6x - 7$.

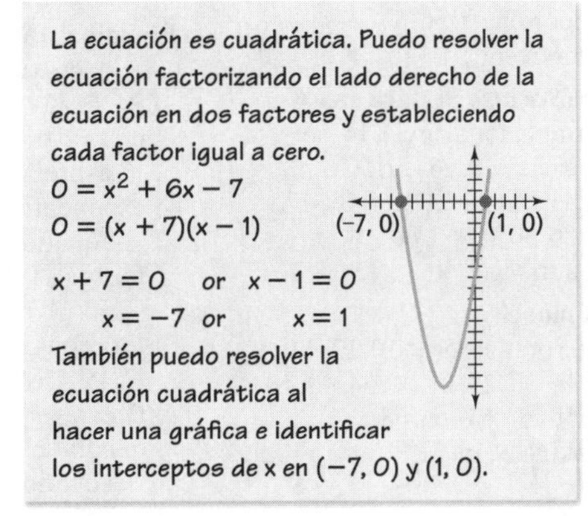

Notes

Index

STUDENT PAGE

Notes

STUDENT PAGE

Index

STUDENT PAGE

Notes

STUDENT PAGE

Notes

Acknowledgments

Team Credits

The people who made up the **Connected Mathematics 2** team —representing editorial, editorial services, design services, and production services— are listed below. Bold type denotes core team members.

Leora Adler, Judith Buice, Kerry Cashman, Patrick Culleton, Sheila DeFazio, Richard Heater, **Barbara Hollingdale, Jayne Holman,** Karen Holtzman, **Etta Jacobs,** Christine Lee, Carolyn Lock, Catherine Maglio, **Dotti Marshall,** Rich McMahon, Eve Melnechuk, Kristin Mingrone, Terri Mitchell, **Marsha Novak,** Irene Rubin, Donna Russo, Robin Samper, Siri Schwartzman, **Nancy Smith,** Emily Soltanoff, **Mark Tricca,** Paula Vergith, Roberta Warshaw, Helen Young

Additional Credits

Diana Bonfilio, Mairead Reddin, Michael Torocsik, nSight, Inc.

Technical Illustration

WestWords, Inc.

Cover Design

tom white.images

Photos

2, Tom Carter/PhotoEdit; **3,** Elio Ciol/Corbis; **5,** Ryan McVay/PictureQuest; **10,** Photodisc/Getty Images, Inc.; **14,** Tim Kiusalaas/Masterfile; **17,** Jeff Greenberg/AGE Fotostock; **19,** Jules Frazier/PictureQuest; **21,** Richard Haynes; **23,** Michael Mancuso/Omni-Photo Communications, Inc.; **26,** Jeff Greenberg/Omni-Photo Communications, Inc.; **27,** Photodisc/Getty Images, Inc.; **29,** Stephen Simpson/Getty Images, Inc.; **30,** Terry W. Eggers/Corbis; **33,** Syracuse Newspapers/The Image Works; **35,** Jeff Greenberg/The Image Works; **41,** Richard Haynes; **43,** Dennis MacDonald/PhotoEdit; **44,** Francois Viete (1540–1603) (engraving) (b/w photo), French School, (19th century)/Private Collection, Lauros/Giraudon/www.bridgeman.co.uk; **47,** Tom Carter/PhotoEdit; **52,** Syracuse Newspapers/Al Campanie/The Image Works; **58,** David Young-Wolff/PhotoEdit; **61,** Lester Lefkowitz/Getty Images, Inc.; **62,** Tom Brakefield/Corbis; **67,** Dr. Gary Gaugler/Photo Researchers, Inc.; **69,** Spencer Platt/Getty Images, Inc.; **73,** Richard Haynes; **79,** Esbin/Anderson/Omni-Photo Communications, Inc.; **83,** Richard Haynes; **85,** Russ Lappa; **86,** Russ Lappa

Note: Every effort has been made to locate the copyright owner of the material reprinted in this book. Omissions brought to our attention will be corrected in subsequent editions.

STUDENT PAGE

STUDENT PAGE

Notes ______________________________

Name ________________________ Date ____________ Class ____________

Labsheet 1.1

Pool Problem

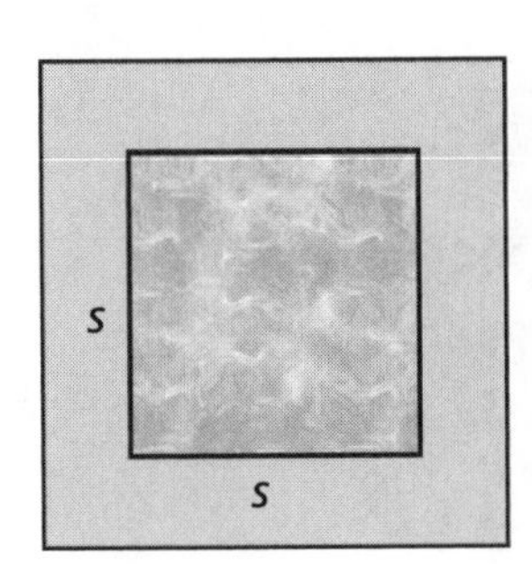

1 ft
1 ft
border tile

Expression ________________

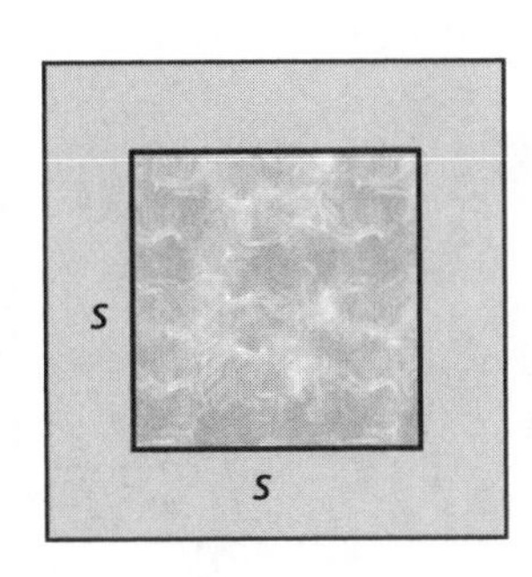

1 ft
1 ft
border tile

Expression ________________

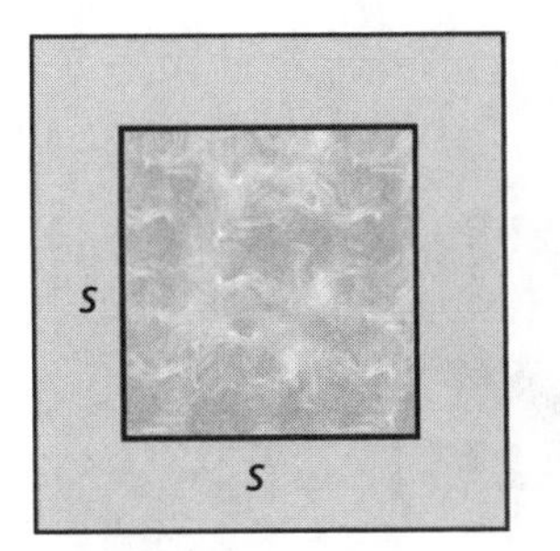

1 ft
1 ft
border tile

Expression ________________

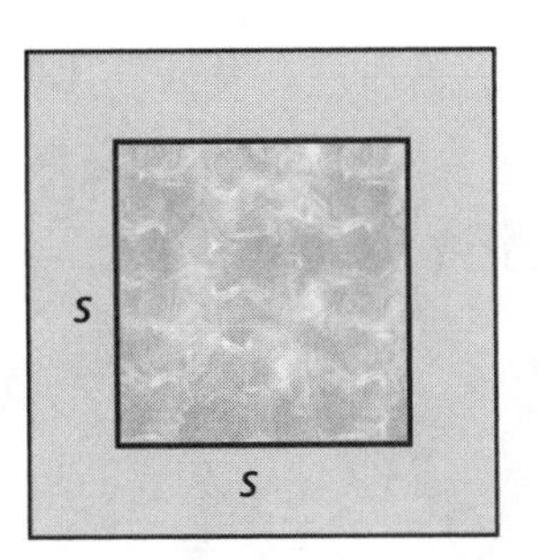

1 ft
1 ft
border tile

Expression ________________

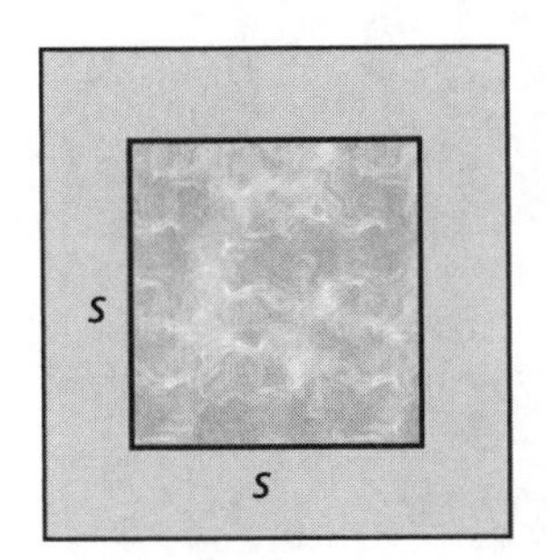

1 ft
1 ft
border tile

Expression ________________

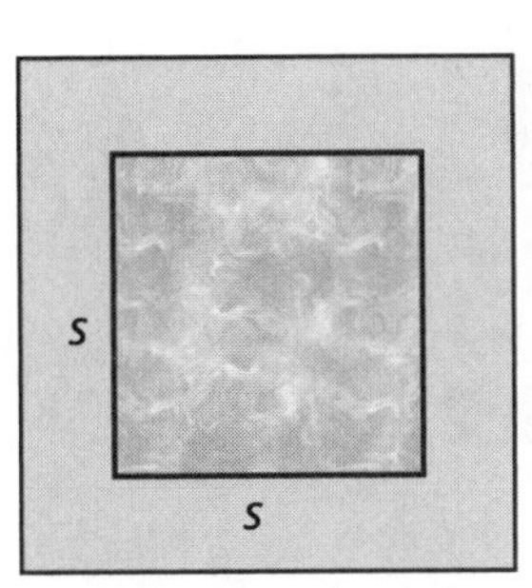

1 ft
1 ft
border tile

Expression ________________

Name ______________________ Date ____________ Class ____________

Labsheet 1.3

The Community Pool Problem

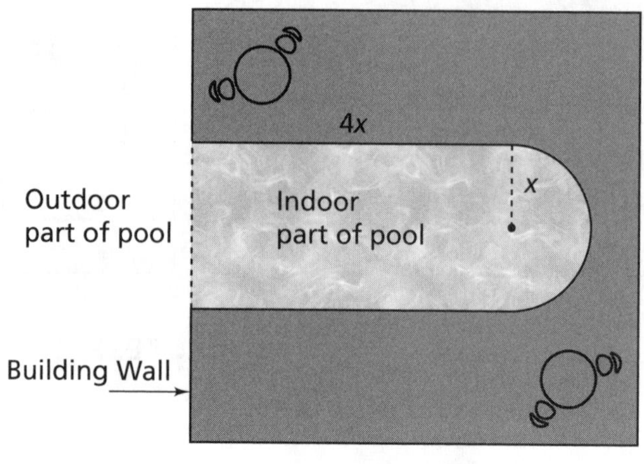

$$A = x^2 + \frac{\pi x^2}{2} + 8x^2 + \frac{\pi x^2}{4}$$

Sketch 1

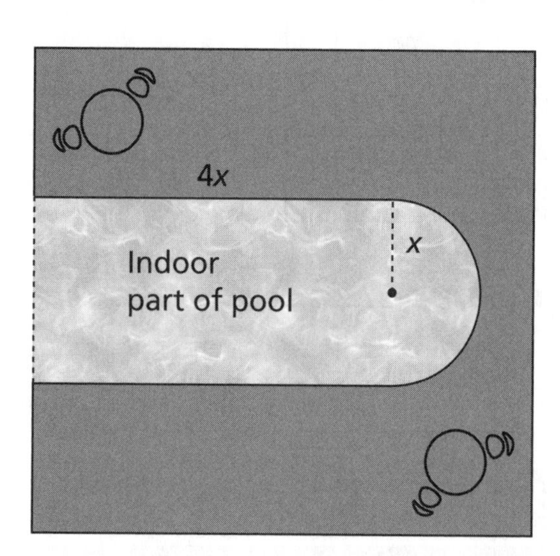

Sketch 2

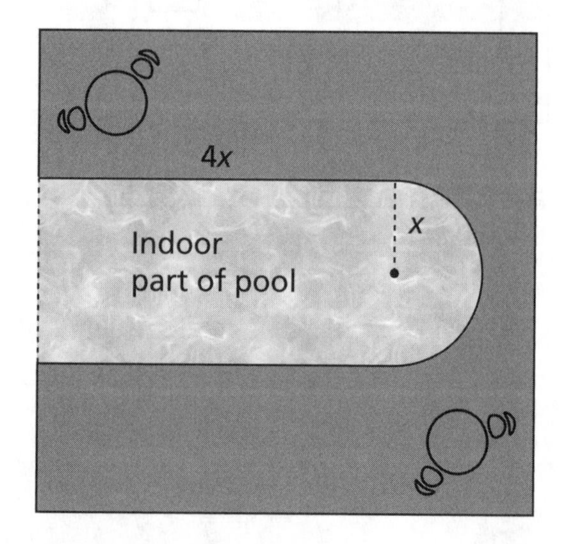

At a Glance

PACING: ________

Mathematical Goals

Launch

Materials

Explore

Materials

Summarize

Materials

Glossary

C

Commutative Property of Addition A mathematical property that states that the order in which quantities are added does not matter. It states that $a + b = b + a$ for any two real numbers a and b. For example, $5 + 7 = 7 + 5$ and $2x + 4 = 4 + 2x$.

Commutative Property of Multiplication A mathematical property that states that the order in which quantities are multiplied does not matter. It states that $ab = ba$ for any two real numbers a and b. For example, $5 \times 7 = 7 \times 5$ and $2x(4) = (4)2x$.

D

Distributive Property A mathematical property used to rewrite expressions involving addition and multiplication. The Distributive Property states that for any three real numbers a, b, and c, $a(b + c) = ab + ac$. If an expression is written as a factor multiplied by a sum, you can use the Distributive Property to *multiply* the factor by each term in the sum.

$$4(5 + x) = 4(5) + 4(x) = 20 + 4x$$

If an expression is written as a sum of terms and the terms have a common factor, you can use the Distributive Property to rewrite the expression as the common factor multiplied by a sum. This process is called *factoring*.

$$20 + 4x = 4(5) + 4(x) = 4(5 + x).$$

E

equivalent expressions Expressions that represent the same quantity. For example, $2 + 5$, $3 + 4$, and 7 are equivalent expressions. You can apply the Distributive Property to $2(x + 3)$ to write the equivalent expression $2x + 6$. You can apply the Commutative Property to $2x + 6$ to write the equivalent expression $6 + 2x$.

expanded form The form of an expression made up of sums or differences of terms rather than products of factors. The expressions $x^2 + 7x + 12$ and $x^2 + 2x$ are in expanded form.

F

factored form The form of an expression made up of products of factors rather than sums or differences of terms. The expressions $(x + 3)(x + 4)$ and $x(x - 2)$ are in factored form.

P

parabola The graph of a quadratic function. A parabola has a line of symmetry that passes through the maximum point if the graph opens downward or through the minimum point if the graph opens upward.

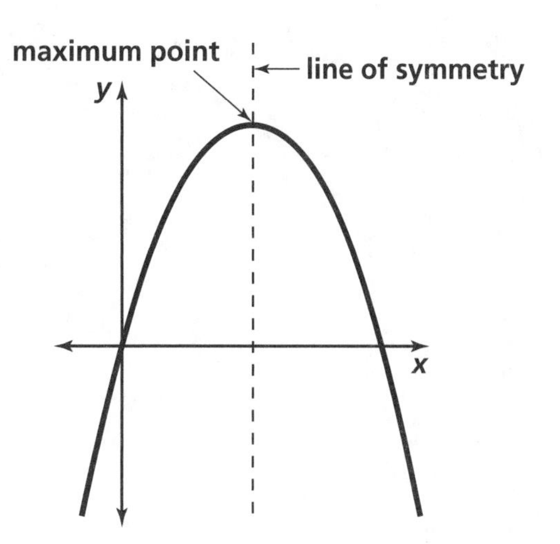

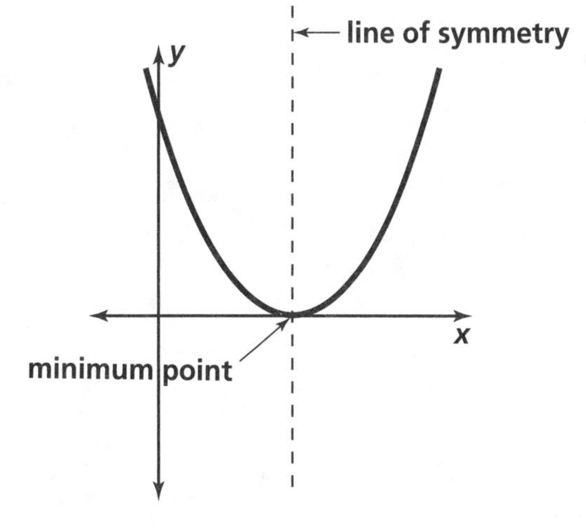

properties of equality The properties of equality state that if you add or subtract both sides of an equation by the same number, the two sides of the equation remain equal. If you multiply or divide both sides of an equation by the same non-zero number, the two sides of the equation remain equal.

GLOSSARY

R

roots The roots of an equation are the values of x that make y equal 0. For example, the roots of $y = x^2 + 5x$ are -5 and 0 because $(-5)^2 + 5(-5) = 0$ and $0^2 + 5(0) = 0$. The roots of $y = x^2 + 5x$ are the solutions to the equation $0 = x^2 + 5x$. The roots of an equation are the x-intercepts of its graph.

T

term An expression with numbers and/or variables multiplied together. In the expression $3x^2 - 2x + 10$, $3x^2$, $-2x$, and 10 are terms.

Index

Acknowledgments

Team Credits

The people who made up the **Connected Mathematics2** team—representing editorial, editorial services, design services, and production services—are listed below. Bold type denotes core team members.

Leora Adler, Judith Buice, Kerry Cashman, Patrick Culleton, Sheila DeFazio, Richard Heater, **Barbara Hollingdale, Jayne Holman,** Karen Holtzman, **Etta Jacobs,** Christine Lee, Carolyn Lock, Catherine Maglio, **Dotti Marshall,** Rich McMahon, Eve Melnechuk, Kristin Mingrone, Terri Mitchell, **Marsha Novak,** Irene Rubin, Donna Russo, Robin Samper, Siri Schwartzman, **Nancy Smith,** Emily Soltanoff, **Mark Tricca,** Paula Vergith, Roberta Warshaw, Helen Young

Additional Credits

Diana Bonfilio, Mairead Reddin, Michael Torocsik, nSight, Inc.

Technical Illustration

Seven Worldwide

Cover Design

9 Surf Studios